# Underwater

# Electroacoustic Measurements

Robert J. Bobber

*Naval Research Laboratory*
*Underwater Sound Reference Division*
*Orlando, Florida*

**July 1970**

D1379155

**Naval Research Laboratory**
**Washington, D.C.**

For sale by the Superintendent of Documents, U.S. Government Printing Office
Washington, D.C. 20402 - Price $3 (cloth)

# PREFACE

This book is essentially a compilation of the author's twenty years of experience, study, and observations as a member of the staff of the Navy Underwater Sound Reference Laboratory. This organization has specialized in underwater electroacoustic measurements since its establishment in 1941 as a part of the Columbia University Division of War Research. It became the Navy Underwater Sound Reference Laboratory in 1945 and the Underwater Sound Reference Division of the Naval Research Laboratory in 1966.

Hopefully, the book will provide a useful reference to the many naval and naval contractor personnel who work in sonar and other aspects of underwater electroacoustics, and to scientists, engineers, and technicians everywhere who use underwater sound transducers in marine science and technology.

The author is indebted to John M. Taylor, Jr. for his considerable help in reviewing and editing the whole manuscript, and to W. J. Trott, C. C. Sims, D. T. Hawley, I. D. Groves, Jr., G. A. Sabin, R. E. Ford, H. Dennis, W. L. Paine, and W. S. Cramer for reviewing selected chapters.

*Orlando, Florida*
*June 1969*                                                ROBERT J. BOBBER

# CONTENTS

vi

# Chapter I

# INTRODUCTION

## 1.0 Purpose

As man explores and uses the ocean depths, whether for military, commercial, or scientific purposes, he faces sensory and communication problems unlike those met in any other environment. The medium is hostile to man and equipment. It is essentially opaque to visible light, infrared, radio, radar—to all the familiar forms of electromagnetic radiation used for sensing and communicating in the atmosphere and in space. Because acoustic signals are, and probably will remain, the only feasible general method of transmitting information with waves through water at distances beyond a few yards, electroacoustic transducers are the only practicable means for sensing underwater sounds, and, in most cases, for producing them as controlled signals.

The electrical and acoustical measurements described in this book are those required to calibrate, test, or evaluate an underwater electroacoustic transducer and to enable one, indirectly, to produce or detect and measure an underwater acoustic signal, usually in terms of its acoustic pressure. These measurements will be referred to collectively as underwater electroacoustic measurements.

Applications in naval sonar systems for navigation, communication, and target location have provided the major need and impetus for the development of underwater electroacoustic measurements; however, applied sonics in liquids for such purposes as ultrasonic therapy and cleaning, delay lines, and flow meters, also have had a role in this development. More recently, the burgeoning interest in oceanography and marine sciences has given added importance to underwater acoustics and electroacoustics as scientific and engineering tools. As man himself penetrates deeper into the sea and seeks to free himself of encumbering electrical cables, electroacoustic instruments serve as his eyes, his ears, and his vocal apparatus.

Acoustics, particularly underwater acoustics, is not a very precise science. The second significant figure in a measurement usually is in doubt and the third, usually meaningless. Accuracies of ±1 dB (or about ±10% pressure amplitude) are quite acceptable in most circumstances. At least part of the reason for this is the instability of the medium and the unfavorable environment in which the electroacoustic instruments must operate. Except under the controlled conditions

1

that can be achieved only on a laboratory bench, water is not the simple, stable, homogeneous, quiet, and harmless medium that the layman imagines. The effects of temperature, hydrostatic pressure, dissolved salts and gases, marine life, pollutants, bubbles, weather, and boundary conditions are the bane of all who attempt scientific measurements in the ocean. Indeed, the physical chemistry of water itself is poorly understood.[1-3] Designing underwater instruments suitable for long-term immersion is as yet a young technology.

Water is much more dense and much less compliant than air. Its characteristic impedance is about 3,500 times that of air. These characteristics, plus the instability and hostility of an extended water medium, make the techniques for electroacoustic measurements underwater quite different from those used in air.

Other well-known books[4-15] and references[16] treat the science and technology of electroacoustic measurements, but only to a very limited extent or only for air acoustics. It is the author's purpose here to provide a comprehensive survey of the theory and practice of underwater electroacoustic measurements. The only previous literature in this specialized field is the well-known, but now obsolete, "red books" of World War II.[17-20]

## 1.2 A Little History

The history of the science and technology of calibrating underwater electroacoustic transducers begins about 1941. Before that time, interest and activity in this field was very sparse. A few scientists, mostly in foreign countries,[21-25] had experimented with methods of measuring sound pressure in fluids, but their methods were very complicated and of little practical use outside of a research laboratory. Calibration methods for air microphones had been developed, but these methods were not feasible for underwater measurements and were limited to audio frequencies. In 1941, on the eve of the United States participation in World War II, the U.S. Navy's capability for calibrating sonar transducers was negligible.

The Office of Scientific Research and Development, recognizing the paucity of research in this area, entered into a contract with the Bell Telephone Laboratories (BTL) in July 1941 and with the Columbia University Division of War Research (CUDWR) in March 1942 for the establishment of the Underwater Sound Reference Laboratories (USRL). BTL was to supply measurement instrumentation and systems; CUDWR was to operate the laboratories, do research on methods, and perform calibrations.

In 1940 and 1941, MacLean[26] and Cook[27] independently devised methods for calibrating electroacoustic transducers by using the reciprocity principle. Only electrical measurements and a few easily determined constants were required. The reciprocity calibration method proved to be a breakthrough that hastened the development of the science of calibrating sonar transducers. In the summer of 1942, only a few months after its establishment, the USRL began to study and test reciprocity calibration concepts, and found the method to be an accurate and reliable technique for testing and evaluating sonar transducers.

In the period 1942-45, development of sonar transducer calibration, test, and evaluation methods advanced very rapidly at the USRL[17] and at sonar development laboratories at Harvard[19] and the University of California.[20] The reciprocity calibration method was put on a firm theoretical and experimental basis. Practical procedures were worked out for making measurements in shallow lakes and tanks.

Standard hydrophones were developed by BTL using Rochelle salt and ammonium dihydrogen phosphate piezoelectric crystals. Hydrophones in which the interaction of electric currents and magnetic fields (magnetostriction) was utilized also were devised and built. BTL developed wide-frequency-band sound sources or projectors using piezoelectric crystals for the ultrasonic-frequency range, and modified moving-coil loudspeaker principles for the audio-frequency range.

The Massachusetts Institute of Technology's Underwater Sound Laboratory developed Rochelle salt hydrophones and a condenser hydrophone system in which an impedance bridge modulated-carrier principle was used. The Brush Development Company built several types of piezoelectric wide-range transducers. The Harvard Underwater Sound Laboratory exploited the principle of magnetostriction for many types of transducers. Natural piezoelectric crystals were used to a limited extent—tourmaline at the Naval Research Laboratory and quartz at BTL. Industrial organizations like the Submarine Signal Co., General Electric, Sangamo Electric, and the Radio Corporation of America made other contributions.

At the end of World War II in 1945, it was possible to calibrate a small hydrophone from 2 Hz to 2.2 MHz under ambient environmental conditions. Projectors or sound sources weighing up to a few hundred pounds could be calibrated from about 50 Hz to 140 kHz, with driving powers of 1½ kW available in the audio-frequency range. When pressure was a variable, the capabilities were limited to 2-100 Hz and 100 psi for small hydrophones only, and to 10-150 kHz and 300 psi for fairly small hydrophones and projectors (less than 100 lb). Standard hydrophones and projectors were adequate, but far from ideal. Stability with time, static pressure, and temperature in many cases was poor for "standard" purposes. Sound sources generally were cumbersome, and response curves were not smooth and flat as is desirable in calibration work. The measuring systems were not capable of pulsed-sound measurements. Good free-field, or unbounded medium, conditions were generally assumed but seldom obtained. Thus, in spite of great strides forward during World War II, the state of the art in 1945 was still relatively crude.

After World War II, the sharp drop in military-connected research and development affected underwater acoustics and sonar calibration work. Almost all private organizations, and particularly universities, which had been active in this field during the war withdrew wholly or partially from this activity. Responsibility for operating the university-managed laboratories was transferred to the U.S. Navy. The California group became the Navy Electronics Laboratory. The Harvard group became the Navy Underwater Sound Laboratory in New London, Connecticut, and the Navy-supported Ordnance Research Laboratory at Pennsylvania State University. The Columbia University Underwater Sound Reference Laboratories were transferred directly to the Navy.

In the early 1950s, research and development on measuring methods, transducers, and systems was resumed, mostly at the newly established naval laboratories or at Navy contract supported activities. Progress has been significant, as the many citations in this book will attest. There no doubt will be unintentional omissions from these citations. The author apologizes for them. Many omissions probably will involve European developments. *Acustica* has been the main reference for European work, but the author knows well that some work has been documented in other publications and has escaped his attention.

For those readers who wish more history about the broader subject of electroacoustics, Hunt's[6] book contains a very interesting chapter based largely on the chronology of patents; also, the Submarine Signal Division of the Raytheon Company has published a book, *Submarine Signal Log* (Submarine Signal Division, Raytheon Company, Portsmouth, R.I., 1963), that describes the pioneering years of sonar before and during World War II.

## 1.3 Scope of Measurements

The measurements described in this book serve a broad range of purposes and applications. At one end is the research investigation, for which thoroughness and accuracy are paramount and restrictions of time and complexity are secondary. At the other end is the quick and simple test measurement used in production or post-repair situations.

Electroacoustic measurements are of two general types. There is the passive measurement in which the acoustic signal is produced by some nonelectroacoustic means such as marine life, machinery vibration, explosions, mechanical or hydraulic oscillators, but the sensor is an electroacoustic hydrophone. Then, there is the active measurement where the sound is produced and controlled by an electroacoustic transducer.

It is the active measurement that is made in basic calibration, test, and evaluation work. Most of the methodology discussed in this book pertains to active measurements. In a typical case, a source and a receiver are coupled by a water medium. An electrical signal is fed into and measured at the input electrical terminals of the sound source. An electrical signal then is measured at the output of the receiver while the receiver is exposed to the acoustic radiation from the source. Variations on this particular set of measurements are the basis of most electroacoustic evaluation. There are, of course, very many ramifications and complications due to frequency, size, environment, purpose, and so forth;

and initially, various constants must be determined. In the final analysis, however, the measurements reduce to a determination of the electrical input and electrical output—or, in electrical engineering terms, the transfer impedance of the network.

In calibration measurements in particular, one often does not know, nor is he even concerned with, the acoustical pressures being used. The whole electro-acoustic-electro system is treated as an electrical two-port network. The acoustical part of the system is measured in terms of various dimensions, the acoustic impedance of the medium, the speed of sound in the medium, and so forth. These parameters usually are determined only once; they thereafter become constants in the calculations. In some techniques, measuring these constants is the most difficult part; in others, the measurement is simple, or handbook values are used.

The methods and theory of a wide variety of measurement techniques are discussed in Chapter II. Some of these are in common use; others have only highly specialized applications. Measurement practice in the widely used "free-field" technique is discussed separately and in detail in Chapter III. The "near-field" method, being relatively new and completely different in concept from the others, is described separately in Chapter IV. Standard hydrophones, reciprocal transducers, and wide-range sound sources are the key instruments needed in most practical measurements. The design of this specialized instrumentation is discussed in Chapter V. Acoustic baffles, windows, reflectors, anechoic coatings, and absorbers are closely associated with underwater electroacoustic measurements and transducers; evaluation measurements on them are discussed in Chapter VI.

## 1.4 Terminology

The American National Standards Institute, Inc. (formerly The American Standards Association) has published a standard terminology[28] written under the sponsorship of the Acoustical Society of America. This standard terminology is used in this book wherever it applies. Specific terms are defined herein where they are first discussed in detail. Acceptable terminology, however, is not static, and the reader will find that some terms, such as *Hertz, echo reduction,* and *near field* are not included in the standard. Terms like *coupler* and *insertion loss* are used in a broader sense than in the standard. Still other terms are used in an abbreviated form: *directivity pattern* instead of *directional response pattern,* for example. The standard consists of about 50 pages; the reader is referred to it for a comprehensive compilation of definitions.

Aside from definitions, the usage of some common terms needs some comment. In underwater acoustics, *transducer* usually means by implication *electroacoustic transducer.* Sometimes the meaning is even more restrictive in implying a reversible electroacoustic transducer. The latter meaning excludes small hydrophones with preamplifiers; this restriction is not standard, and it is not used in this book. *Transducer* is used here as a collective term for all kinds of electroacoustic transducers. A *hydrophone* is an underwater microphone or a transducer used to detect or receive sound underwater. Here, again, the use of the term sometimes is more restrictive in that it is limited to those transducers that can be used only as receivers. This meaning, too, is not standard, and no such limitation is implied throughout this book. A *projector* is a producer or transmitter of underwater sound. The terms *hydrophone* and *projector* are used here only to imply the purpose being served by a transducer at the moment and no assumptions should be made about its design, the transduction principle involved, or its other capabilities.

Both *receiving sensitivity* and *receiving response* are acceptable terms, although *sensitivity* is most commonly used. On the other hand, *transmitting response* is the only acceptable term. The reason for this inconsistency involves the notion that all types of instruments and devices respond in the sense that the output responds to the input, but only sensors or detectors have sensitivity.

### 1.5  Measurement Parameters

The end result of most measurements is the value of an electroacoustic parameter; that is, a ratio of an electrical variable to an acoustical one, or the inverse. Typically, the sensitivity (voltage/pressure) or the response (pressure/current or pressure/voltage) is the electroacoustic parameter computed from measured electrical data and various constants.

When the sensitivity (or response) is measured as a function of frequency, we obtain a frequency calibration of the transducer, which is by far the most common type of measurement.

The basic and widely used standard electroacoustic sensitivities or responses are defined as follows:

*Free-Field Voltage Sensitivity;* The free-field voltage sensitivity of an electroacoustic transducer used for sound reception is the ratio of the output open-circuit voltage to the free-field sound pressure in the undisturbed plane progressive wave. The frequency and angle of incidence must be specified.

*Transmitting Current (or Voltage) Response:* The transmitting current (or voltage) response of an electroacoustic transducer used for sound emission is the ratio of the sound pressure apparent at a distance of one meter in a specified direction from the effective acoustic center of the transducer to the signal current flowing into (or the voltage applied across) the electrical input terminals.

In underwater acoustics, sensitivity and response usually are measured and reported in decibels. In such cases, sensitivity and response *levels* are the technically correct terms; however, the use of decibels and levels is so common that level often is omitted in the interest of brevity, without risk of confusion or ambiguity.

When the relative sensitivity (or response) is measured as a function of direction or orientation, we call it a *directional response pattern,* or more simply a *beam pattern* or *directivity pattern.* The formal definition is:

The *directional response pattern* of a transducer used for sound emission or reception is a graphical description, usually in polar coordinates, of the response of the transducer as a function of the direction of the transmitted or incident sound waves in a specified plane and at a specified frequency.

A complete or three-dimensional pattern usually is described by a compilation of patterns in different planes through the acoustic axis of the transducer.

When response or sensitivity measurements are made as a function of signal level, we have the *linearity* or *dynamic range*. These terms are discussed and defined in Section 2.15.

Electrical impedance is an exception to the output/input category of measurements. It is still a quasi-electroacoustic parameter, however, because the electrical impedance is a function of and often quite sensitive to the acoustical characteristics of the medium into which the transducer is radiating sound. One is still measuring an electrical ratio (voltage/current), as in most other electroacoustic measurements, but, unlike the others, the phase between the two signals is important.

Phase in an absolute sense has little application in electroacoustic measurements aside from impedance, because it depends on an arbitrary choice of where the phase of the acoustic signal is measured. The wavelength of the signal in water often is smaller than the transducer, and the selection of the measuring point for the acoustic signal would have a large effect on an electroacoustic phase measurement.

Efficiency is a computed parameter, because direct measurements of electrical and acoustical power are not feasible. Other parameters like directivity factor and equivalent noise pressure also are computed from sensitivity (or response) and impedance measurements.

Other variables used in these measurements are environmental factors (hydrostatic pressure and temperature), the kind of signal (continuous wave, pulse, noise, impulse, etc.), the boundary conditions of the medium (free field, reverberant tank, baffled or unbaffled transducer, with or without a dome, etc.), and, of course, various internal changes or adjustments that can be made on particular transducers (elements connected in series or parallel, with or without a transformer, etc.).

Basically, there are three categories of electroacoustic parameters: (1) Sensitivity or response that is measured directly as a function of frequency, signal level or type, environmental factors, orientation, and so forth; (2) impedance; and (3) parameters computed from (1) and (2).

## 1.6 Decibels

The decibel system is widely used in underwater electroacoustic measurements. There are several reasons. One has roots in the tradition or history of acoustics, particularly psychological acoustics. The ear perceives approximately the same difference in loudness between 1 and 10 units as between 10 and 100 units. That is, the ear is a logarithmic detector. Consequently, a logarithmic scale or measuring system like the decibel scale is very useful. Human hearing and acoustic phenomena, in general, range over extremely wide values of signal amplitude—the order of $10^{12}$. For this reason, too, a logarithmic scale is convenient. Finally, in underwater electroacoustic measurements and in many other special areas of acoustics and communication engineering, the interest is in signal ratios rather than in absolute quantities. Decibels are a convenient measure of ratios.

The classic concept of a decibel is given by the equation

$$n = 10 \log_{10} \left[ \frac{P_1}{P_0} \right],\tag{1.1}$$

where $P_1/P_0$ is the ratio of two powers and $n$ is the number of decibels.

Parameters that are essentially equivalent to power (acoustic intensity $I$ or power per unit area, for example), are described similarly:

$$n = 10 \log_{10} \left[ \frac{I_1}{I_0} \right].\tag{1.2}$$

The convenience of the decibel system has led to its use in describing ratios of other parameters that are proportional to the square root of power: voltage, current, pressure, velocity, and so forth. Such use is valid and consistent with the classic concept, if these other parameters can be related to power. This relationship usually involves an impedance, sometimes specifically stated and at other times merely implied. In electroacoustics, the decibel system is carried a step further and used to specify output/input ratios like the sensitivity or response of a transducer. Then, the logarithm of a ratio of ratios actually is used, and the connection with power and impedance becomes somewhat tenuous.

Consider, first, however, the application of decibels to specify, by means of the relationship $P = e^2/R$, the ratio of two powers $P_1$ and $P_0$ separated in space or time,

$$n = 10 \log \left[ \frac{P_1}{P_0} \right] = 10 \log \left[ \frac{\dfrac{e_1^2}{R_1}}{\dfrac{e_0^2}{R_0}} \right]\tag{1.3}$$

If $R_1 = R_0$,

$$n = 20 \log \left[ \frac{e_1}{e_2} \right].\tag{1.4}$$

Equation (1.4) gives the ratio of two voltages in decibels when they share a common impedance. The ratio of two currents, sound pressures, and particle velocities would be given in the same way with some provision of common impedance.

Typical applications would be voltages at two points on the same uniform and effectively infinite transmission line, free-field sound pressures at two distances from the same projector, and currents in the same circuit at two different times.

The second application of decibels is to specify the amplitude (usually rms amplitude) of a parameter at a single point in time and space relative to a reference amplitude. In Eq. (1.4), for example, $e_0$ would be some standard or specified reference value and $e_1$ would be measured relative to $e_0$. Such usage is identified by the term level, as, for example, voltage level or pressure level. Here, it is understood that $e_1$ and $e_0$ are measured across the same impedance. When $e_0$ is one volt, the voltage level of $e_1$ in Eq. (1.4) is, by definition, given in dBV, which is read as "decibels referred to 1 volt."

Similarly, sound pressure $p$ is defined in terms of sound pressure level SPL:

$$ \text{SPL} = 20 \log \left[ \frac{p_1}{p_0} \right] , \qquad (1.5) $$

where $p_0$ is a reference pressure.

There is no universally accepted standard reference pressure. The pressure 0.0002 microbar is used in air acoustics and has been used in underwater noise acoustics. The pressure 1 microbar has been used in sonar work and underwater electroacoustic measurements other than noise since World War II. In 1968, one micronewton per square meter was selected as an American standard reference pressure level for acoustics in liquids. It has the advantages of being a power of ten, being small enough so that negative pressure levels are virtually eliminated, and fitting easily into the MKS system of units and the standard system of prefixes (milli, micro, etc.). The various reference pressures are shown schematically in Fig. 1.1.

The decibel system also is used to specify the output/input ratios of two-port networks and transducers. When used in this way, the system loses most of its connection with power ratios. It must, however, still be consistent with Eqs. (1.4) and (1.5). A voltage amplifier, for example, may have a numeric gain of 10, which means that

$$ 20 \log \frac{\text{output voltage}}{\text{input voltage}} = 20 \log 10 = 20 \, \text{dB}. \qquad (1.6) $$

The voltages do not have a common impedance; however, the impedance conditions at both the input and output are fixed. The input voltage, of course, is measured across the input impedance of the amplifier; the output voltage, across a specified load impedance.

Similarly, the free-field voltage sensitivity $M$ is given by

$$20 \log M = 20 \log \frac{\text{open-circuit output voltage}}{\text{free-field plane-wave pressure}}. \qquad (1.7)$$

Here, again, there is no common impedance, but the impedance conditions are fixed. The voltage is measured across an open-circuit or an essentially infinite impedance and the pressure is measured in a wave with a characteristic impedance of $\rho c$, where $\rho$ is the density of water and $c$ is the speed of sound. In Eq. (1.6), the units of voltage are immaterial as long as the same unit is used for both input and output. In Eq. (1.7), the voltage and pressure have nothing in common. It is necessary, therefore, that the voltage and pressure each have a reference value, or that a combination of Eqs. (1.4) and (1.5) be used instead of Eq. (1.7). Thus, we have a ratio of ratios,

$$20 \log M = 20 \log \frac{\dfrac{e_{oc}}{p_f}}{\left(\dfrac{e_{oc}}{p_f}\right)_0}, \qquad (1.8)$$

where $(e_{oc}/p_f)_0$ is a reference sensitivity level. The reference voltage always is one volt.

The reference free-field pressure in underwater acoustics has been standardized at one micronewton per square meter, but other levels in Fig. 1.1 may continue to appear, particularly in old measurement data. A free-field voltage sensitivity level, therefore, is given in dB referred to one volt per micronewton per square meter, or, abbreviated, dB re 1 $V/\mu N/m^2$.

A transmitting current response level similarly is given in dB re 1 $\mu N/m^2$ at one meter per ampere. Since sensitivity and response almost always are given in decibels, the term *level* ordinarily is not used. *Sensitivity* and *sensitivity level* are understood to be synonymous, as are *response* and *response level.*

The decibel system is not without its problems. Troubles arise largely from attempts to extend the system too far. Suppose, for example, that in a special case an (acoustical power output)/(voltage input) transmitting response is desired. Neither 10 nor 20 times the logarithm of $P/e$ would be consistent with Eqs. (1.1) and (1.4). One would have to use $10 \log P/e^2$ or not use decibels at all. The reference response level would have to be in watts per volt squared ($W/V^2$). As another illustration, application to a parameter like an impedance $Z$ is not recommended, because both $10 \log Z$ and $20 \log Z$ appear in different circumstances, as for example in $10 \log P = 10 \log i^2 R$ and $20 \log e/i = 20 \log R$. Finally, users of decibels sometimes forget that numbers of decibels represent ratios expressed in terms of exponents of ten, not the actual value of a quantity; consequently, decibels are not subject to the ordinary rules of arithmetic. Doubling a pressure amplitude does not double a pressure level; it increases it by 6 dB (actually, 6.02 dB = 20 log 2 = 20 × 0.301, because 2 = $10^{0.301}$).

Decibels should not be averaged unless one seeks a geometric mean or unless the difference between the arithmetic and geometric mean is negligible. Where the difference in levels in 4.0 dB or less, the average level (geometric mean) will differ from the level of the average signal (arithmetic mean) by only 0.2 dB or less. The error in averaging decibels always results in a level that is too low.

## 1.7 Units

The units used in underwater science and technology unfortunately are a confusing conglomeration of the English, cgs, and MKS systems. The mixture occurs because underwater acoustics is involved in the whole range of technical activity from basic science to production engineering. In addition, naval and nautical tradition influences the use and selection of units. It is not unusual to see fathoms and centimeters used in the same report or discussion. Scientists who diligently promote the usage of meters, liters, newtons, etc., still regularly use pounds per square inch for hydrostatic pressure. Hopefully, this matter will improve with time. Current common practice is used in this book.

Workers in electroacoustics have a particularly unusual situation, since they deal simultaneously with electrical and acoustical parameters. The practical or MKSA system is used for electrical measurements, while the cgs system has been used for acoustical parameters like pressure, velocity, density, etc. In the resulting hybrid system, for example, hydrophone sensitivity is expressed in volts per microbar. A worse example is the transmitting current response of a transducer, which usually is defined as the output pressure in microbars measured at one meter from the transducer for a one-ampere input. In some applications, however, the Navy prefers to measure the sound pressure at one yard instead of one meter, thereby introducing all three systems of units in one parameter.

There has been a gradual change from the cgs to the MKSA system in the scientific community. This is a sensible move that may be complete in another decade or so. Change probably will be much slower among those who are sensitive to tradition or to the cost of change.

The units used with some of the common parameters are given in the list that follows, along with some conversion factors.

|                        |                                        |
|------------------------|----------------------------------------|
| acoustic pressure      | microbars (dynes/centimeter$^2$)       |
|                        | newtons/meter$^2$                      |
|                        | (Note:  $10\,\mu$bar = 1 N/m$^2$)      |
|                        | micronewton/meter$^2$                  |
| hydrostatic pressure   | pounds/inch$^2$                        |
|                        | kilograms/meter$^2$                    |
|                        | (Note: 1 psi = 703 kg/m$^2$)           |

| | |
|---|---|
| velocity | centimeters/second<br>meters/second |
| volume velocity | centimeters$^3$/second<br>meters$^3$/second |
| voltage | volts |
| current | amperes |
| electrical power | watts |
| acoustical power | watts |
| acoustical intensity | watts/centimeter$^2$<br>watts/meter$^2$ |
| electrical impedance | ohms |
| acoustical impedance | acoustical ohms<br>(Note: The acoustical ohm is pressure/volume velocity in cgs units; the MKS acoustical ohm is pressure/volume velocity in MKS units.) |
| specific acoustic impedance | rayl or acoustical ohm/centimeter$^2$<br>MKS rayl or MKS acoustical ohm/meter$^2$<br>(Note: specific acoustic impedance often is referred to as the rho-c of the medium, because it is equal to the product of the density $\rho$ and speed of sound $c$.) |
| density | grams/centimeter$^3$<br>kilograms/meter$^3$<br>(Note: 1 g/cm$^3$ = $10^3$ kg/m$^3$) |
| speed | centimeters/second<br>meters/second |
| time | seconds |
| frequency | hertz (cycles per second) |
| bandwidth | hertz |
| temperature | degrees Celsius |
| efficiency | percent or numeric ratio |

Electroacoustic parameters almost always are described in terms of levels, and the unit is the decibel. In these cases, both the number and kind of units used in the reference level are important. Mention has been made of the various reference pressures in Section 1.3 and Fig. 1.1. Each can be substituted for pressure in the following reference units.

| | |
|---|---|
| free-field voltage sensitivity | volts/pressure unit |
| transmitting current response | (pressure at 1 meter)/amperes |
| transmitting voltage response | (pressure at 1 meter)/volts |

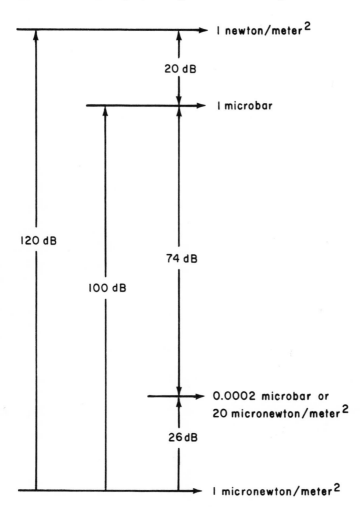

Fig. 1.1.  Reference pressure levels.

Since the disagreement about reference levels all pertains to the pressure and not to the voltage or current, the differences shown in Fig. 1.1 will apply also to the sensitivity and response levels.  A change from the microbar to the micronewton/meter$^2$ level, for example, will mean an even -100 dB change in sensitivity level, and a +100 dB change in transmitting response level.

## 1.8 Symbolism

Letter symbols as standardized by the USA Standards Institute[29] are used in this book. Some symbols, such as $M$ for microphone or receiving sensitivity and $S$ for speaker or transmitting response, are not defined in the standard but are used in other related standards.[16,28] Such implied standard symbols also are used here. Symbols are defined when they are introduced in the book. A compilation of symbol definitions is provided in the appendix; basic symbols and subscript symbols are listed separately.

The English and Greek alphabets are inadequate to provide a completely unambiguous set of symbols. Where one letter has more than one meaning, the context in which it is used will make clear which meaning is appropriate.

## 1.9 Analogs and Network Theory

Electromechanical and electroacoustical analogs are widely used analytical tools in electroacoustics. Anyone who seeks even a superficial understanding of electroacoustics for any purpose should be familiar with at least the elements of these analogies.

The direct or impedance analogy is the oldest and most used of the two types of analogies. It is used in this book. Olson[9] and others[5,7] describe it in detail. The basis of the impedance analogy is that the following characteristics are equivalent or analogous.

force : voltage

velocity : current

mechanical impedance : electrical impedance

The impedance analogy is most useful with transducers in which electrical coupling is used (piezoelectric or condenser).

The inverse or mobility analogy, developed by Firestone,[30,31] is based on the following analogous relationships:

force : current

velocity : voltage

mechanical admittance (mobility) : electrical impedance

The mobility analogy is most useful with transducers in which magnetic coupling is used (magnetostriction and moving coil).

When analogies are used to describe a pure mechanical or acoustical system, either analogy is applicable and the choice is arbitrary, but, as already mentioned, the impedance analogy is used most often in practice.

In addition to using analogies, it is convenient in acoustics and electroacoustics to draw heavily on electrical network theory. Thevenin's theorem, filter theory, the superposition theorem, impedance-matching concepts, transmission line equations, waveform analysis, and so forth, all are used directly in or adapted to use in acoustics. These subjects are found in such communication engineering references as Terman[32] and Everitt.[33]

# REFERENCES

1. N. E. Dorsey, *Properties of Ordinary Water-Substance* (Reinhold Publishing Corp., New York, 1940), pp. 161-177.
2. W. Drost-Hansen, "The Puzzle of Water," International Science and Technology, Oct. 1966, p. 86.
3. M. Glos, "Is Water What We Think It Is?" Scientific Research, Aug. 1967, p. 71.
4. L. L. Beranek, *Acoustic Measurements* (John Wiley & Sons, Inc., New York, 1949).
5. L. L. Beranek, *Acoustics* (McGraw-Hill Book Co., Inc., New York, 1954), Chap. XII.
6. F. V. Hunt, *Electroacoustics* (John Wiley & Sons, Inc., New York, 1954).
7. F. H. Fischer, *Grundzüge der Elektroakustik* (Fachverlag Schiele & Schön, Berlin, 1950), and an English translation by S. Ehrlich and F. Pordes, *Fundamentals of Electroacoustics* (Interscience Publishers, Inc., New York, 1955).
8. J. W. Horton, *Fundamentals of Sonar* (United States Naval Institute, Annapolis, Maryland, 1957), NAVSHIPS 92719.
9. H. F. Olson, *Acoustical Engineering* (D. Van Nostrand Co., Inc., Princeton, N. J., 1957), Chap. X.
10. E. G. Richardson, *Technical Aspects of Sound* (Elsevier Publishing Co., London, 1957), Vol. II, Chap. 4.
11. V. M. Albers, *Underwater Acoustics Handbook* (Pennsylvania State University Press, 1960), Part 4.
12. L. E. Kinsler and A. R. Frey, *Fundamentals of Acoustics* (John Wiley & Sons, Inc., New York, 1962), 2nd Ed., p. 327.
13. D. G. Tucker and B. K. Gazey, *Applied Underwater Acoustics* (Pergamon Press, London, 1966), p. 152.
14. E. Meyer and E. G. Neumann, *Physikalische und Technische Akustik* (Friedr. Vieweg & Sohn, Braunschweig, 1967).
15. R. J. Urick, *Principles of Underwater Sound for Engineers* (McGraw-Hill Book Co., Inc., New York, 1967).
16. "American Standard Procedures for Calibration of Electroacoustic Transducers, Particularly Those for Use in Water," Z24.24-1957, United States of America Standards Institute, New York, 1958.
17. Summary Technical Report of Division 6, NDRC, Vol. 10, "Basic Methods for the Calibration of Sonar Equipment," Washington, D.C., 1946.
18. Summary Technical Report of Division 6, NDRC, Vol. 11, "A Manual of Calibration Measurements of Sonar Equipment," Washington, D.C., 1946.
19. Summary Technical Report of Division 6, NDRC, Vol. 13, "Design and Construction of Magnetostriction Transducers," Washington, D.C., 1946.
20. Summary Technical Report of Division 6, NDRC, Vol. 12, "Design and Construction of Crystal Transducers," Washington, D.C., 1946.
21. Langevin, "The Employment of Ultrasonic Waves for Echo Sounding," International Hydrographic Bureau, Monaco, Special Papers No. 3, 1924; No. 4, 1926.
22. R. W. Boyle, Proc. Roy. Soc. Canada III, 1967 (1925).

23. Gerlach, Wissenschaftliche Veröffentlichungen aus dem Siemens-Konzern 3, 1939 (1923).
24. F. D. Smith, "The absolute measurement of sound intensity," Proc. Phys. Soc. (London) 41, 487 (1929).
25. E. Klein, "Absolute sound intensity in liquids by spherical torsion pendula," J. Acoust. Soc. Am. 9, 812 (1938).
26. W. R. MacLean, "Absolute measurement of sound without a primary standard," J. Acoust. Soc. Am. 12, 140 (1940).
27. R. K. Cook, "Absolute pressure calibration of microphones," J. Acoust. Soc. Am. 12, 415 (1941).
28. "American Standard Acoustical Terminology," S1.1-1960 (Revision of Z24.1-1951), American National Standards Institute, Inc., New York, 1960.
29. "American Standard Letter Symbols for Acoustics," Y10.11-1953, American National Standards Institute, Inc., New York, 1953.
30. F. A. Firestone, "A new analogy between mechanical and electrical systems," J. Acoust. Soc. Am. 4, 249 (1933).
31. F. A. Firestone, " 'Twixt earth and sky with rod and tube; the mobility and classical impedance analogies," J. Acoust. Soc. Am. 28, 1117 (1956).
32. F. E. Terman, *Radio Engineers Handbook* (McGraw-Hill Book Co., Inc., New York, 1943).
33. W. L. Everitt, *Communication Engineering* (McGraw-Hill Book Co., Inc., New York, 1937).

# Chapter II

# METHODS AND THEORY

## 2.1 Introduction

The most-often used electroacoustic parameter is the free-field voltage sensitivity of a hydrophone expressed as a function of frequency. It usually is determined by either the comparison method or the reciprocity method. The theory of these two common techniques will be discussed in this chapter and the practical details of calibrating standard hydrophones or sonar transducers in a free field or open water will be reserved for Chapter III because of their importance. Both the theory and practice of other methods that generally are more specialized and of restricted applications will be discussed completely in this chapter. The descriptions will be complete enough to acquaint the reader with the limitations as well as the applications; additional details are available in the references cited. The near-field method, being a unique and recent development, is treated separately in Chapter IV.

Of the methods to be described for calibrating a transducer, all except the techniques that require a calibrated standard transducer are considered to be primary methods. A primary method requires basic measurements of voltage, current, electrical and acoustical impedance, length, mass (or density), and time (or frequency). In practice, handbook values of density, sound speed, elasticity, and so forth are used rather than directly measured values of these parameters.

The secondary methods are those in which a transducer (usually a hydrophone) that has been calibrated by a primary method is used as a reference standard. The comparison calibration of a hydrophone is an example of a secondary method. Since a calibrated impedance bridge, voltmeter, oscillator, and so forth may be used in a primary method but a calibrated hydrophone may not, this distinction between primary and secondary methods perhaps is arbitrary; nevertheless, the distinction is made in underwater acoustics.

The methodology we are concerned with here provides means for measuring the magnitude, and sometimes the phase, of electrical voltage and current and acoustical pressure and particle velocity, or their ratios. The theory for the purely electrical measurements is well known, and the need for measuring particle velocity is small; consequently, it is the measurement of acoustical pressure or ratios involving acoustical pressure that is the major subject of this chapter.

17

## 2.2  Secondary Methods

Secondary methods for calibrating transducers, particularly hydrophones, require fewer measurements and provide fewer sources of error than do primary methods. Secondary methods, therefore, are more generally used for routine calibrations, although the accuracy of secondary calibrations never can be better than the accuracy of the primary calibration of the reference standard, if only one standard is used. Accuracy and reliability can be increased by averaging the results of measurements with two or three standards. This practice also detects failures or deterioration of the standards. Secondary calibrations usually involve standard hydrophones rather than standard projectors for reasons that will be given in the sections to follow.

### 2.2.1  Comparison calibration of hydrophones in a free field

The term "hydrophone calibration" implies a measurement of the free-field voltage sensitivity of a hydrophone. The free-field current sensitivity almost never is used, and is largely of only academic interest.

A free field is a homogeneous isotropic medium free from boundaries. A perfect free field, of course, never is achieved. Much of the cost and effort expended in underwater electroacoustic measurements is attributable to the need for establishing good approximations to free-field conditions, or somehow circumventing the need for a free field. Reflecting boundaries, temperature gradients, gas bubbles, marine life, and so forth, all contribute to imperfect free-field conditions. A free-field measurement is one in which an assumption of free-field conditions is a necessary part of the measurement theory, even though various practical means (pulsed sound, sound absorbers, data corrections for interference caused by reflections) are used to counteract the absence of a true free field. Natural bodies of water, artificial pools, and large tanks are used for free-field measurements.

A comparison calibration of a hydrophone is a simple measurement, and when properly made, it is reliable and accurate. This method consists of subjecting the unknown, or hydrophone being calibrated, and a calibrated reference or standard hydrophone to the same free-field pressure, and then comparing the electrical output voltages of the two hydrophones. The method also is known as the substitution method, because the unknown is substituted for the standard without otherwise changing the measurement conditions.

Assume that we have a free-field water medium. A sound field is established in it by spherical waves emanating from a projector. Theoretically, the characteristics of the projector are irrelevant. It is necessary only that it produce sound of the desired frequency and of sufficiently high signal level.

The standard hydrophone is immersed in the sound field. It must be far enough from the projector that it intercepts a segment of the spherical wave small enough (or having a radius of curvature large enough) that the segment is indistinguishable from a plane wave. Note that the definition of free-field voltage response in Section 1.5 specifies pressure in a plane wave. Any nearby housing for preamplifiers or other components must be included in the dimensions of the hydrophone because the presence of such housings may affect the sensitivity. The theory and practice of proximity requirements is discussed more fully in Section 3.4.

Unless the standard hydrophone is omnidirectional, it must be oriented so that its acoustic axis points toward the projector. The open-circuit output voltage $e_s$ of the standard hydrophone in such a position and orientation is measured. The standard hydrophone then is replaced by the unknown hydrophone, and the open-circuit output voltage $e_x$ of the unknown is measured. If the free-field voltage sensitivity of the standard is $M_s$, then the sensitivity of the unknown $M_x$ is found from

$$M_x = \frac{M_s e_x}{e_s},\qquad(2.1)$$

or, in decibels,

$$20 \log M_x = 20 \log M_s + 20 \log e_x - 20 \log e_s.\qquad(2.2)$$

In spite of the simplicity of the method, comparison calibrations are subject to error of four general types: (1) failure to measure the voltage under true open-circuit conditions, (2) instability of the standard, (3) absence of a true free field, and (4) absence of a sufficient signal-to-noise ratio.

The output voltage and the sensitivity of a hydrophone are measured at some specified pair of electrical terminals. If the hydrophone has no preamplifier, the specified terminals are at the end of the cable, and the cable may not be changed without jeopardizing the calibration. It is necessary also to adopt some standard electrical grounding condition like, for example, connecting both a cable electrical shield and one conductor to electrical ground at the cable end.

The voltmeter or other voltage-measuring system at the end of the hydrophone cable must have an input impedance very high in comparison with the hydrophone output impedance or the loading effect of the voltmeter must be measured. (See Section 3.6.) Hydrophones with small high-impedance piezoelectric generators and preamplifiers are calibrated either at the terminals connecting the piezoelectric generator output to the preamplifier input, or at the end of the cable. The former method requires a special calibration or coupling circuit (see Section 3.6) to measure the combined effect of the absence of open-circuit conditions and the preamplifier gain or loss. This "crystal output" type of calibration has been in vogue ever since the initial development of sonar calibration methods in World War II. Its philosophy was that the hydrophone calibration should be independent of the vagaries of preamplifiers; however, experience since World War II has shown that the electronic preamplifier (typically a cathode follower) usually is as stable as the electroacoustic element. With this experience and with the development of even more stable solid-state preamplifiers, end-of-cable calibrations now are acceptable and in common use. The problem of measuring an open-circuit voltage is common to all calibration techniques when a high-impedance hydrophone is being calibrated or being used.

Hydrophones are subject to many influences that affect the stability of their sensitivity. Hydrostatic pressure, temperature, rough handling, marine fouling, corrosion, and water leakage are some of the more obvious deleterious influences; others are more subtle, but no less important. Many hydrophones have small piezoelectric or piezoceramic generators with very high electrical impedances. The leakage resistance of such generators must remain very high—100 to 1000 megohms (see Section 3.6). The usual rubber materials that protect the generator elements from the water medium are not completely waterproof. Over a period of a year or so, minute amounts of water will diffuse into the generator, lower the leakage resistance, and cause a drop in sensitivity at low frequencies. Subtle chemical changes among the metals, oils, crystals, rubbers, plastics, and so forth, also will tend to pollute the generator environment and affect the hydrophone sensitivity. With the present state of the art, even a high-quality standard hydrophone should be recalibrated at least once a year. Sensitivities measured at some nominal temperature and hydrostatic pressure cannot be assumed to be valid at other temperatures and pressures.

The absence of a true free field is the most prevalent source of error or trouble. Reflections from the surface, bottom, walls, piling, rigging equipment, etc., and temperature gradients, gas bubbles, marine life, debris, water turbulence, etc., all disturb the free-field conditions. If the two hydrophones are influenced equally by a disturbance, the errors cancel. Often, this is not the case, however. For example, an omnidirectional hydrophone will be more influenced by interference from reflections than will be a directional hydrophone. The standard should be as much like the unknown hydrophone in size, shape, and design as is practical.

A variation of the comparison method is the practice of simultaneously immersing both the standard and the unknown hydrophone in the medium and in the same sound field. Since the two hydrophones cannot be in the same position, this technique requires some assurance that the sound pressure at the two locations is the same, or has some known relationship. If the hydrophones are placed close together, the presence of one may influence the sound pressure at the position of the other, and the free-field conditions will be affected. If the hydrophones are placed far apart, reflections from boundaries and the directivity of the projector may produce unequal pressures at the two locations. If the boundary and medium conditions are stable, the relationship between the sound pressures at the two locations can be measured. The disadvantages of this variation in the free-field comparison method usually outweigh the advantages, and the method is not used very much.

The signal-to-noise ratio is the ratio of the signal amplitude being measured to the unwanted but ever present electrical and acoustical noise. The noise must be low relative to the signal if the latter is to be measured accurately. It is this limitation that makes it impossible to calibrate hydrophones of very low sensitivity.

### 2.2.2 Standard projector calibration of a hydrophone

A hydrophone can be calibrated by reference to a standard projector rather than a standard hydrophone. If a projector is driven with a measured current $i_s$ and its transmitting current response $S_s$ is known, the free-field sound pressure at a point $d$ meters from the projector and on its acoustic axis is $i_s S_s / d$. If a hydrophone to be calibrated is placed at this point and its output open-circuit voltage is $e_x$ then the hydrophone free-field voltage sensitivity $M_x$ is

$$M_x = \frac{e_x d}{i_s S_s} \qquad (2.3)$$

The distance $d$ must be large enough so that proximity effects are negligible.

This kind of calibration measurement requires only one transducer besides the unknown and only one equipment arrangement; however, the calibration and use of standard projectors has serious drawbacks that are discussed in Section 2.2.4

### 2.2.3 Comparison calibration of hydrophones in small tanks

The technique of simultaneously subjecting a standard and an unknown hydrophone to the same sound pressure is most often used when the sound is produced in a small closed tank. If the largest dimension of a closed tank is much smaller than a wavelength of sound in water, the sound pressure is essentially the same everywhere in the tank. The tank must be *closed* in the sense that the water medium is entirely confined by high-impedance or rigid boundaries. Any water-air surface, air bubble, compliant wall, or other low-impedance boundary will result in high pressure gradients. As an illustration, consider two small sections of a standing-wave system as shown in Fig. 2.1. Where the wave impedance is high, or at the pressure antinode, the pressure amplitude is changing slowly with position; where the wave impedance is low, or at the pressure node, the pressure amplitude is changing rapidly with position.

The sound pressure acting on each hydrophone in a small closed tank will be essentially the same. This sound pressure is the actual applied pressure, however, and the relationship between this applied pressure and the corresponding free-field pressure must be known if a free-field voltage sensitivity calibration is desired. When a hydrophone is calibrated in terms of the applied pressure, the calibration is called a *pressure sensitivity*. To visualize the relationship between the free-field and pressure sensitivities, consider Fig. 2.2. A hydrophone in a free field is represented as a network with two electrical output terminals and two acoustic input terminals. The applied pressure $p_a$ appears across the input

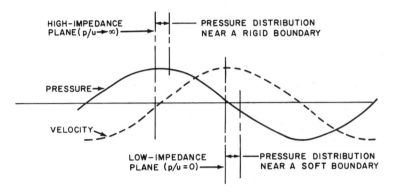

Fig. 2.1. Pressure and velocity distribution in a standing-wave system.

terminals. The input acoustical impedance is $Z_a$. The free-field plane progressive waves of pressure $p_f$ that impinge on the hydrophone are represented by the acoustical Thevenin generator. The generator pressure $p_b$ is the average pressure acting on the hydrophone diaphragm when the diaphragm is blocked, or when $Z_a \to \infty$. The generator impedance $Z_r$ is the acoustical impedance observed at the hydrophone terminals when looking into the acoustical generator. Then $Z_r$ is the radiation impedance observed at the hydrophone diaphragm when looking out into the water. The relationship between the blocked pressure and the free-field pressure is given by

$$\frac{p_b}{p_f} = D, \tag{2.4}$$

where $D$ is called a diffraction constant. The value of $D$ depends on the hydrophone size and the wavelength, and can vary from 0 to 2.[1,2] If $L$, the maximum dimension of the hydrophone, is small in comparison with the wavelength $\lambda$, however, then $D = 1$. (See Section 5.2 for more on diffraction.)

The blocked pressure and the applied pressure are related by

$$\frac{p_a}{p_b} = \frac{Z_a}{(Z_a + Z_r)}. \tag{2.5}$$

If $Z_a \gg Z_r$, then $p_a/p_b \simeq 1$. Consequently, if $L \ll \lambda$ and $Z_a \gg Z_r$, then $p_f = p_a$, and the free-field and the pressure sensitivities are equal.

As a general rule, pressure sensitivities are measured and used only when they are the same as the free-field sensitivity. In any case, a valid free-field sensitivity calibration in a small tank is obtained only when $L \ll \lambda$ and $Z_a \gg Z_r$ for all hydrophones used. These criteria apply for both comparison calibrations and primary calibrations that will be discussed later. An exception would be the

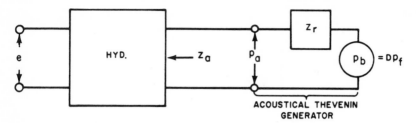

Fig. 2.2. Electrical analog of a hydrophone in a free field, with the free-field sound pressure represented as an acoustical generator according to Thevenin's Theorem; $p_a$ is the applied pressure, $p_b$ is the Thevenin blocked pressure, $p_f$ is the free-field pressure, $Z_r$ is the hydrophone radiation impedance, $D$ is the diffraction constant, $Z_a$ is the hydrophone acoustical impedance, and $e$ is the voltage.

special case where the unknown and the standard hydrophone in a comparison calibration had identical $Z_a$, $Z_r$, and $D$.

Since our hydrophone must fit into a tank that is much smaller than a wavelength, the requirement $L \ll \lambda$ is automatically fulfilled, and $Z_r$ must be small. Virtually all conventional hydrophones, except moving-coil types, meet the $Z_a \gg Z_r$ requirement, *except near a resonance.*

In summary, then, it is feasible to calibrate small, hard, nonresonant hydrophones in small closed tanks.

Figure 2.3 is a schematic diagram of a typical closed tank system. Figure 2.4 is an electrical analog circuit of the system. It is assumed that the particle velocity in the medium is negligible except near the projector diaphragm. Consequently, near the diaphragm, the acoustic impedance is the inertia of the mass of a small volume of the medium near the diaphragm. Away from the diaphragm, the acoustic impedance is mainly the compliance of a relatively large volume of the medium. The impedances of the tank walls or boundaries and of the hydrophones are in parallel with the medium compliance, but assumed to be high. The calibration formula is the same here as for the free-field calibration case, Eq. (2.1) or (2.2).

In this method, the medium need not be water. Other liquids may be used—usually to obtain a longer wavelength or to change the electrical conductance of the medium. Air or other gases also can be used, but only at the sacrifice of a lower maximum usable frequency. A wavelength in air is about one-fifth the wavelength in water at the same frequency. The assumption of a tank size much smaller than a wavelength becomes invalid in air at a frequency equal to one-fifth the limiting frequency in water. Since the compliance $C$ of the medium in Figs. 2.3 and 2.4 becomes high when the medium is air, $p$ will be low unless the velocity $u$ is made correspondingly large. The velocity can be made large by using air loudspeakers as projectors. Since using air as the acoustic medium

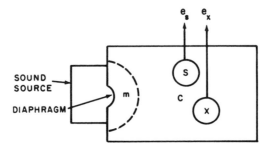

Fig. 2.3. Typical small closed-tank system; S is the standard hydrophone and X is the unknown hydrophone, $e_s$ and $e_x$ are output voltages, $m$ is the mass of the fluid medium near the diaphragm, and $C$ is the compliance of the fluid medium away from the diaphragm.

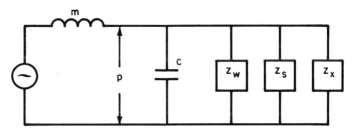

Fig. 2.4. Electrical analog of the system in Fig. 2.3; $Z_w$, $Z_s$, and $Z_x$ are the impedances of the walls, the standard hydrophone, and the unknown hydrophone; $p$ is the pressure in that part of the tank away from the diaphragm.

results in a low impedance everywhere in the tank rather than at local points of low impedance, the pressure uniformity is not disturbed by a low-impedance hydrophone. The use of air does allow the pressure sensitivity of a low-impedance hydrophone to be measured, but such calibrations have little application in underwater acoustics.

In one variation of this technique, the tank is open and very small. It is so small and so designed that all of the water is represented by $m$ in Figs. 2.3 and 2.4, $Z_w$ and $1/\omega C$ are zero, and the hydrophones are placed in the moving mass of the water. Further details about this rather special technique are given in Section 2.5.2.

### 2.2.4 Calibration of projectors

A projector calibration is a measurement of its transmitting current or voltage response. The current response, being reciprocally related to the free-field voltage sensitivity, is preferred in calibration work. The voltage response is used in sonar engineering and other practical situations where voltage is a more common and more easily measured parameter or more constant with frequency than current. Neither transmitting response is recommended for use in precision calibration work because, among other reasons, such application requires exceptionally good free-field conditions. A transmitting response is referred to the pressure produced at a meter away from the projector in a free field. In practice, measurements may be made with even longer distances. The pressure and the response are dependent on both the transducer and the medium into which the transducer radiates sound energy. In calibrating or using a standard projector, there is less cancellation of interference errors than there is in the comparison calibration of a hydrophone because, in the hydrophone calibration, only the ratio (or difference in dB) of two voltages is measured.

Typically, the plot of response versus frequency for a projector is less constant than the sensitivity versus frequency curve for a hydrophone. Projectors generally are larger than standard hydrophones and thus are more subject to diffraction effects, and they have more spurious resonances. Some projectors are nonlinear and unstable at or near a resonance frequency. All these factors weigh against the use of *standard* projectors.

Projectors can be very stable at off-resonance frequencies—more stable than small hydrophones, because the electrical impedance is lower and less sensitive to changing leakage resistance and stray capacitance. Being large, they also are directional. For the frequencies at which projectors are stable and directional, they can be calibrated and used as hydrophones. Most standard hydrophones are small only because small hydrophones are versatile; that is, they are omnidirectional and their sensitivities are constant over a wide range of frequencies (see Section 5.2).

Projectors usually are calibrated only when they are being evaluated as a part of a sonar, oceanographic, or other underwater electroacoustic system. The calibration measurements are made by placing the projector in a free field and electrically driving it with an arbitrary nominal current $i_x$ or voltage $e_x$. A standard hydrophone with free-field voltage sensitivity $M_s$ is placed at a distance of $d$ meters from the projector and on the acoustic axis of the projector. The open-circuit output voltage of the hydrophone $e_s$ is measured. The transmitting current response $S_x$ or voltage response $S_x'$ is, then,

$$S_x = \frac{e_s d}{M_s i_x}, \tag{2.6}$$

$$S_x' = \frac{e_s d}{M_s e_x}. \tag{2.7}$$

Note that Eq. (2.6) is a rearrangement of Eq. (2.3) with the roles and the subscripts of the standard and the unknown interchanged.

An alternate method of measuring $S$ is a projector comparison calibration that is analogous to the hydrophone comparison calibration. That is, a standard projector transmits sound that is measured by an uncalibrated hydrophone. The standard projector then is replaced by the unknown, and the current (or voltage) driving the unknown is adjusted until the hydrophone output voltage is the same as that for the standard projector. Then,

$$S_x = \frac{S_s i_s}{i_x}, \qquad (2.8)$$

$$S_x' = \frac{S_s' e_s}{e_x}, \qquad (2.9)$$

where $S_x$ and $S_s$ are the transmitting current responses and $S_x'$ and $S_s'$ are the transmitting voltage responses of the unknown and the standard; $i_x$ and $i_s$ are the respective driving currents; and $e_x$ and $e_s$, the respective driving voltages.

As in hydrophone comparison methods, errors due to reflection interference may tend to cancel out in projector comparisons; however, projectors are more often dissimilar in size, shape, and directivity patterns than are hydrophones. This advantage in the projector comparison method, therefore, is limited to the exceptional case where the standard and unknown are of the same or similar design.

All transmitting responses are defined in terms of the radiated pressure at one meter from the acoustic center of the projector. This definition does not mean that the measurements are made with one meter separating the projector and hydrophone. If a projector is large, the one-meter point may be in the near field or Fresnel zone of the transducer. It may even be inside the projector itself, as, for example, in a cylindrical projector of 2-m radius! Then, the actual measurements are made at some distance larger than one meter where the diverging waves are spherical and the inverse square law applies—that is, where the energy density or the square of the pressure in the wave is diminishing in proportion to the inverse square of the distance. The sound pressure then is inversely proportional to distance. Values of pressure measured at $d$ meters are converted to values at one meter by multiplying them by $d$. For example, a transmitting response measured at 4 meters should be multiplied by 4, or, in the decibel system, 20 log 4, or 12 dB should be added.

Most electroacoustic projectors are reciprocal, except perhaps at a high-Q resonance frequency. The transmitting current response can be obtained, therefore, by calibrating the transducer as a hydrophone and computing the transmitting response $S$ from the reciprocity relation $S = M/J$, where $M$ is the free-field voltage sensitivity and $J$ is the reciprocity parameter (see Section 3.15.2). The reciprocity of the projector should be verified by the procedure described in Section 2.3.

## 2.3 Reciprocity Methods

The reciprocity principle as applied to electroacoustics was introduced by Schottky[3] in 1926 and Ballantine[4] in 1929. MacLean[5] and Cook[6] first used it for calibration purposes in 1940 and 1941. The Underwater Sound Reference Laboratory of Columbia University Division of War Research (and later of the Navy) developed the method for sonar calibration.[7]

The reciprocity principle is used in a family of calibration methods. When the term *reciprocity calibration* is used without qualification in underwater acoustics, it usually pertains to the most widely used of the many reciprocity methods. This method will be called *conventional reciprocity*. A more descriptive name that would distinguish it from other variations of the method would be *three-transducer spherical-wave reciprocity*.

All reciprocity methods depend on one electroacoustic transducer being reciprocal; that is, the ratio of its receiving sensitivity $M$ to its transmitting response $S$ must be equal to a constant $J$ called the reciprocity parameter. This parameter depends on the acoustic medium, the frequency, and the boundary conditions, but is independent of the type or construction details of the transducer.

To be reciprocal, a transducer must be linear, passive, and reversible. Not all linear, passive, and reversible transducers are reciprocal,[8] however; an example is a transducer that contains both piezoelectric and magnetostrictive elements.[9] Although most conventional transducers (i.e., piezoelectric, piezoceramic, magnetostrictive, moving-coil, etc.) are reciprocal at nominal signal levels, a reliable reciprocity calibration requires some assurance that the presumed reciprocal transducer is indeed reciprocal. There is, unfortunately, no known absolute method for determining this, but there are methods for ascertaining that the probability of a transducer's being reciprocal is very high.

A method that is easy to use in connection with a reciprocity calibration is referred to simply as a reciprocity check. Consider two reversible transducers $T_1$ and $T_2$ placed in any arbitrary positions in the same medium. Drive $T_1$ with a current $i_1$ and measure the open-circuit voltage output $e_2$ of $T_2$. Without changing the positions of the transducers or the boundary conditions, reverse the signal direction; that is, drive $T_2$ with a current $i_2$ and measure the output $e_1$ of $T_1$. Now, if the system comprised of the two transducers and the water medium and its boundaries is reciprocal, then $e_2/i_1 = e_1/i_2$. It does not necessarily follow that the system and its individual parts are reciprocal if $e_2/i_1 = e_1/i_2$, but this is a safe assumption in practice, if $T_1$ and $T_2$ are dissimilar transducers. Using dissimilar transducers avoids the possibility that both are nonreciprocal but $e_2/i_1$ and $e_1/i_2$ are coincidentally equal as would be the case, for example, if both transducers were identically nonlinear. As we shall see, these reciprocity check measurements are easily combined with the necessary measurements in a conventional reciprocity calibration.

In a second method, a hydrophone is calibrated by a reciprocity technique and then by any of the several other independent methods described in this

chapter.  If the results are the same, the agreement is evidence that all the assumptions of both methods are valid.  Among these is the assumption of a
reciprocal transducer.  It should not be forgotten, however, that the agreement
is evidence—not proof!  Both methods could be wrong, and the errors could
coincidentally be equal.

Among the various reciprocity methods to be discussed, the two-transducer
and self-reciprocity methods are special cases of conventional reciprocity.  The
remaining variations all pertain to special boundary conditions.  Among the
latter, the definitions of $M$, $S$, or both, differ from the definitions for free-field
conditions.  Since $S$, more than $M$, depends on the medium and medium boundaries, it usually is $S$ that is different.  It can be shown that the reciprocity parameter $J$ in each case is the ratio of the volume velocity emanating from the
reciprocal transducer to the resulting sound pressure used in the definition of
$S$,[10] as for example, the pressure at a point on the axis at one meter.  The parameter thus is a transfer acoustical admittance of the medium and medium
boundaries.

### 2.3.1  Conventional reciprocity

A conventional reciprocity calibration requires three transducers of which one
serves only as a projector P, one is a reciprocal transducer T and serves as both a
projector and a hydrophone, and one serves only as a hydrophone H.  Any one
of the three transducers can be the unknown or the one being calibrated; however, the calibration formula usually is derived for the free-field voltage sensitivity
$M_H$ of the hydrophone.  The measurements are made in free-field far-field conditions so that only spherical waves emanating from the projector impinge on the
hydrophone.

The arrangements and measurements made are shown schematically in Fig. 2.5.
Only the first three shown, or (a), (b), and (c) in Fig. 2.5, are necessary for the
calibration.

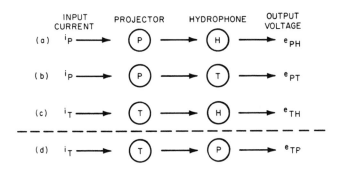

Fig. 2.5.  Diagram of the three measurements (a), (b), and (c) for a
reciprocity calibration; and a fourth measurement (d) for a reciprocity
check of the reversible transducer T.

The free-field voltage sensitivity $M_H$ of the hydrophone is obtained from the first three measurements as follows. The free-field sound pressure $p_P$ produced by P at the position of H or T, $d_1$ centimeters from P, is $i_P S_P d_0 / d_1$, where $S_P$ is the transmitting current response of P, and $d_0$ is the reference distance in centimeters at which the transmitted pressure is specified in the definition of $S_P$ (usually 100 cm). Then,

$$e_{PH} = M_H p_P = \frac{M_H i_P S_P d_0}{d_1},$$  (2.10)

and

$$e_{PT} = M_T p_P = \frac{M_T i_P S_P d_0}{d_1},$$  (2.11)

where $M_T$ is the free-field voltage sensitivity of T. From Eqs. (2.10) and (2.11),

$$\frac{e_{PH}}{e_{PT}} = \frac{M_H}{M_T}.$$  (2.12)

If T is a reciprocal transducer,

$$\frac{M_T}{S_T} = J,$$  (2.13)

and, from Eqs. (2.12) and (2.13),

$$M_H = \frac{J S_T e_{PH}}{e_{PT}}.$$  (2.14)

The free-field sound pressure $p_T$ produced by T at the position of H, $d_1$ centimeters from T, is $i_T S_T d_0 / d_1$, where $S_T$ is the transmitting current response of T. Then

$$e_{TH} = M_H p_T = \frac{M_H i_T S_T d_0}{d_1},$$  (2.15)

and from Eqs. (2.14) and (2.15),

$$M_H = \left( \frac{e_{TH} e_{PH}}{e_{PT} i_T} \frac{d_1}{d_0} J \right)^{\frac{1}{2}}.$$  (2.16)

The reciprocity parameter $J$ is derived in the literature;[5,11] it is equal to $(2d_0/\rho f)10^{-7}$, where $\rho$ is the density of the medium in grams per cubic centimeter and $f$ is the frequency in hertz. The factor $10^{-7}$ arises from the use of a mixed system of units, since the dimension of $J$ is volt-amperes/microbar$^2$. The voltage and current are measured in MKS volts and amperes. The distance, density, and pressure are measured in cgs units. The ratio $d_1/d_0$ does not usually appear in Eq. (2.16) because either the voltages are corrected to what they would be if $d_1 = 100$ cm and $d_1/d_0 = 1$, or $(d_1/d_0)$ $(2d_0/\rho f)$ is combined. That is, $J$ is defined as $2d_1/\rho f$ instead of $2d_0/\rho f$. When voltage corrections are used, it must be remembered that the voltage is proportional to the sound pressure, not the intensity. In a spherically divergent wave, the voltage therefore is proportional to the distance, not the distance squared. Assuming that either $d_1 = d_0$ or that $J = 2d_1/\rho f$, Eq. (2.16) becomes

$$M_H = \left( \frac{e_{PH} e_{TH}}{e_{PT} i_T} J \right)^{\frac{1}{2}}.$$
(2.17)

Now, taking H as a calibrated standard, P and T can be calibrated by secondary calibration methods. If the projector P also is a reciprocal transducer and the additional measurement (d) in Fig. 2.5 is made, then measurements (b) and (d) constitute the reciprocity check described in Section 2.3. That is, both P and T are assumed reciprocal if $e_{PT}/i_P = e_{TP}/i_T$. From measurements (a), (c), and (d),

$$M_H = \left( \frac{e_{TH} e_{PH}}{e_{TP} i_P} J \right)^{\frac{1}{2}}.$$
(2.18)

The numerators of Eqs. (2.17) and (2.18) are identical and the denominators are equal. The addition of a fourth measurement to the necessary three provides both a reciprocity check and some redundancy that increases the reliability of the measurements.

All of the reciprocity measurements are subject to the same errors described for free-field measurements in Sections 2.2.1 and 2.2.3. However, the square root in Eq. (2.18) reduces the magnitude of some errors.

It can be seen from Eq. (2.17) that the electrical standard in a reciprocity calibration is an $e/i$ ratio or an impedance. The current $i_T$ can be measured as the voltage drop $e_T$ across a standard impedance—usually a resistance $R$. Then, Eq. (2.17) becomes

$$M_H = \left( \frac{e_{PH} e_{TH}}{e_{PT} e_T} \frac{J}{R} \right)^{\frac{1}{2}}.$$
(2.19)

Since the four voltages appear as a dimensionless ratio, they can be measured by an uncalibrated voltmeter. Because the voltages may vary widely in magnitude, however, the voltmeter must be linear, or a calibrated attenuator must be used to compare them.

### 2.3.2 Two-transducer reciprocity

If two transducers have identical sensitivity and are used as the hydrophone and reciprocal transducer in a conventional reciprocity calibration, $e_{PT}$ and $e_{PH}$ in Fig. 2.5 become the same and Eq. (2.17) reduces to

$$M_H = \left( \frac{e_{TH}}{i_T} J \right)^{\frac{1}{2}}. \qquad (2.20)$$

It appears, then, that only two transducers and one measurement—that is, (c) in Fig. 2.5—are necessary for a calibration. This is not really true, because there is no way of verifying that two transducers have the same sensitivity without resorting to a third transducer and two more measurements. For example, the two transducers could be compared by subjecting each to the same sound pressure produced by a third transducer; however, this is equivalent to measurements (a) and (b) in Fig. 2.5. Thus, the two-transducer reciprocity method is a special case of the conventional method in which two of the three measurements perhaps have been made at some earlier time and place. The two-transducer technique usually is used as a quick method of verifying or monitoring a prior calibration; it is not a true primary calibration.

### 2.3.3 Self-reciprocity

The two-transducer reciprocity method can be a true primary method if the same transducer is used as both the hydrophone and the reciprocal transducer. This can be done by reflecting the transmitted signal back to the transducer so that it receives its own signal. This self-reciprocity arrangement is shown schematically in Fig. 2.6. The image of the transducer can be thought of as the second transducer. Theoretically, the reflection must be perfect so that the transmitting current response of the image is identical to that of the real transducer. In Carstensen's original self-reciprocity technique,[12] a connected transmitting and receiving electronic system was used to drive the transducer with a current $i_T$ and measure the received open-circuit voltage $e_{TH}$. Pulsed signals were used, and $e_{TH}$ and $i_T$ were measured separately. The free-field voltage sensitivity $M_H$ is given by Eq. (2.20). Sabin improved this technique by measuring the ratio $e_{TH}/i_T$ as an impedance.[13] The transducer can be represented according to Thevenin's Theorem by the circuit in Fig. 2.7. The total impedance $Z_T$ of this circuit, when it is being driven by the current $i_T$ and before the reflected signal $e_{TH}$ is received, is the free-field impedance $Z_f$. When the transducer is being driven both electrically by $i_T$ and acoustically by the received reflected signal $e_{TH}$, the total impedance $Z_T$ is given by

$$Z_T = Z_f + \frac{e_{TH}}{i_T}. \qquad (2.21)$$

Thus, the ratio $e_{TH}/i_T$ is obtained as the difference $\Delta Z$ between two impedance measurements

$$\frac{e_{TH}}{i_T} = Z_T - Z_f = \Delta Z, \qquad (2.22)$$

and the free-field voltage sensitivity becomes

$$M_H = (\Delta Z J)^{\frac{1}{2}}. \qquad (2.23)$$

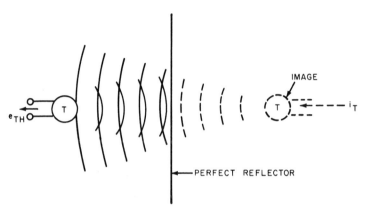

Fig. 2.6. Arrangement for a self-reciprocity calibration.

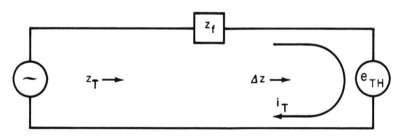

Fig. 2.7. Schematic diagram of a transducer being driven both electrically with current $i_T$ and acoustically with received open-circuit voltage $e_{TH}$.

To make such measurements, it is necessary to drive the transducer by placing it in the "unknown" arm of an impedance bridge and to use pulsed sound. The relationship among $Z_T$, $Z_f$, and $\Delta Z$ is shown in Fig. 2.8. The phase of $\Delta Z$ or $e_{TH}/i_T$ is variable and arbitrary because it depends on the distance traveled by the sound pulse or twice the distance from the transducer to the reflector, which also is the distance used in $J$. It is possible, therefore, to arrange for $\Delta Z$ to be a simple change in resistance only (or reactance only), and reduce the calibration to a single turn of one knob on an impedance bridge. The signal from the reflected pulse has much the same effect on the transducer impedance as does a standing wave in the medium. The impedance method is feasible only when $\Delta Z$ is large enough to measure as the difference $Z_T - Z_f$. In practice, this is true in the frequency range near resonance where the motional impedance can be separated from the blocked impedance.

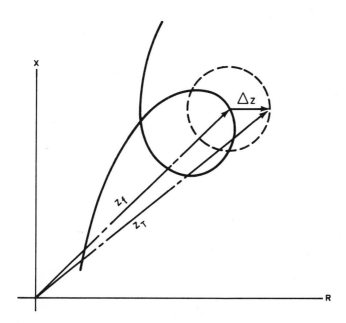

Fig. 2.8. Diagram of impedances in Fig. 2.7.

In the impedance version of this technique, the reflector must be a smooth plane and the reflector-to-transducer distance must be very stable because the phase of the impedance is sensitive to small changes in the geometry. In the pulsed-sound version, phase is not involved, and the geometry is not so critical. In addition, with pulsed sound, numerous redundant measurements can be made more easily and averaged. Patterson[14] has reported a self-reciprocity calibration with the ocean surface as the reflector, and the transducer suspended at a 1200-ft depth. The ocean surface waves were 1 ft high. The signal wavelength was 3.3 ft (1.78 kHz). Sixty-eight pulses or separate measurements were made. Although no direct comparison was made with a separate independent technique, it was estimated that a field calibration accuracy of ±2 dB could be obtained with this ocean self-reciprocity method.

### 2.3.4 Cylindrical-wave reciprocity

Cylindrical-wave reciprocity is a reciprocity calibration measurement made under the special conditions that only cylindrical waves are propagated between the projector and hydrophone. This condition exists between two parallel long-line or thin-cylinder transducers as shown in Fig. 2.9. The distance separating the two lines must be small enough so the hydrophone is in the near field of the projector where the sound energy is propagated with two-dimensional spreading. The sound pressure on the line hydrophone will vary from point to point, but the pressure averaged along the line will be inversely proportional to the distance $d$. The cylindrical-wave region exists for values of $\lambda/2 < d < L^2/\lambda$, where $L$ is the length of the line. The same three-transducer arrangements and measurements as used in conventional reciprocity shown in Figs. 2.5 and Eq. (2.17) are used, but the reciprocity parameter is different. The cylindrical wave reciprocity parameter was derived by Bobber and Sabin:[15]

$$J_c = \frac{2Ld^{\frac{1}{2}}\lambda^{\frac{1}{2}}}{\rho c} 10^{-7}. \tag{2.24}$$

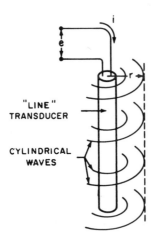

"LINE" TRANSDUCER

CYLINDRICAL WAVES

Fig. 2.9. Cylindrical-wave electroacoustic system.

The receiving sensitivity that is measured is $M = e_{oc}/\overline{p}_c$, where $\overline{p}_c$ now is the sound pressure averaged along the line of the hydrophone. Since the effect of this average pressure on a true line hydrophone—that is, a cylindrical hydrophone of negligible diameter—is indistinguishable from the effect of a plane wave of the same pressure, the measured receiving sensitivity is the free-field voltage sensitivity. The transmitting response is $\overline{p}_c/i$, which differs, of course, from the free-field transmitting current response.

Cylindrical-wave reciprocity is a specialized technique of limited practical application. It has found use in the Trott near-field calibration method described in Chapter IV. It also can be combined with the self-reciprocity technique, in which case the calibration formula becomes

$$M_H = (\Delta Z J_c)^{1/2}. \tag{2.25}$$

### 2.3.5 Plane-wave reciprocity

Plane-wave reciprocity is a reciprocity calibration measurement made under the special condition that only plane progressive waves are propagated between the projector and hydrophone. This condition exists, for example, between two large piston transducers as shown in Fig. 2.10. The distance separating the two transducers must be small enough so that the hydrophone is in the near field of the projector. In the near field of a large piston radiator, the sound is propagated in a nondivergent or collimated beam. Although the sound pressure varies from point to point, the average sound pressure in any plane parallel to the radiating piston face is uniform; therefore, the sound energy in the near field is, in effect, propagated as plane progressive waves. This effective plane-wave region extends for a distance $d = r^2/\lambda$ from the projector, where $r$ is the radius of the piston radiator and $\lambda$ is the wavelength. For piston shapes other than round, $r$ can be taken as half the shortest width dimension. The distance $d$ cannot be shorter than a few wavelengths, because pulsed sound is used to avoid standing waves.

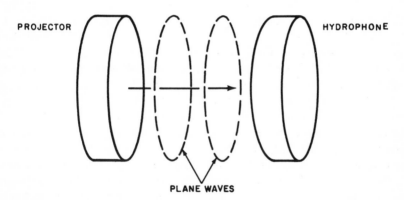

**PROJECTOR**      **HYDROPHONE**

**PLANE WAVES**

Fig. 2.10. Plane waves between two closely spaced parallel piston transducers.

Figure 2.10 could represent also the condition in a rigid-walled tube. The transducers would fill the tube cross section, and true plane waves would propagate between transducers.

Again, the three-transducer arrangement shown in Fig. 2.5 for conventional reciprocity and Eq. (2.17) are used for plane-wave reciprocity calibration. The reciprocity parameter is different, however; it is given by Simmons and Urick[16] as

$$J_p = \frac{2A}{\rho c} 10^{-7} \qquad (2.26)$$

where $A$ is the area of the piston, beam, or tube cross section in square centimeters; $\rho$ is the density of the medium in grams per cubic centimeter; and $c$ is the speed of sound in centimeters per second. The measured receiving sensitivity is $M = e_{oc}/\bar{p}_p$, where $\bar{p}_p$ is the average plane-wave pressure. Since the average pressure is indistinguishable from a uniform plane-wave pressure, the receiving sensitivity $M$ will be the same as the free-field voltage sensitivity. The transmitting response is $\bar{p}_p/i$, which, again, is different from the free-field transmitting current response.

Plane-wave reciprocity, like cylindrical-wave reciprocity, is a specialized method. In its original form as developed by Simmons and Urick, it is useful only with large ultrasonic transducers. In a modified form, it is used in a tube at audio frequencies. Tube reciprocity is described in the next section.

Plane-wave reciprocity, like cylindrical-wave reciprocity, is used in the Trott near-field techniques and can be combined with self reciprocity where

$$M_H = (\Delta Z J_p)^{1/2}. \qquad (2.27)$$

### 2.3.6  Tube reciprocity

Tube reciprocity requires the use of the three transducers labeled P, T, and H in Fig. 2.11: P is the projector, T is the reciprocal transducer, and H is the hydrophone. The second projector P' is used as an active impedance to control the reflections from the left-hand end, thereby controlling the wave conditions in the tube. The conventional three measurements of Fig. 2.5 and Eq. (2.17) are used to calibrate the hydrophone. The two measurements P → T and P → H are obtained with the arrangement in Fig. 2.11a. Sound emanates from P and travels in plane progressive waves past H and impinges on T. With proper control of the magnitude and phase of the signal to P' with respect to the signal to P, the waves impinging on T are not reflected; all the sound energy is absorbed by T or passes on to be absorbed by P'. The measurement T → H is made with the arrangement shown in Fig. 2.11b. Sound now emanates from T. Plane progressive waves travel in both directions and are absorbed by P and P'. In this case, P and P' act as the characteristic impedance of the acoustic transmission line.

Beatty gives the reciprocity parameter for this method as $J = 2A/\rho c$ where $A$ is the cross section of the tube.[17,18] Although the parameter $J$ is the same as that for the plane-wave reciprocity method, there are several important theoretical and practical differences between Simmons and Urick's plane-wave reciprocity and Beatty's tube reciprocity. In the tube, the transducers are not in the near field of each other. The transducers may be very small, and the reciprocal transducer T and hydrophone H must be smaller than the cross section of the tube. Thus, when T is transmitting, there is a region near the transducer where

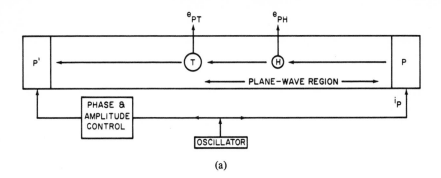

(a)

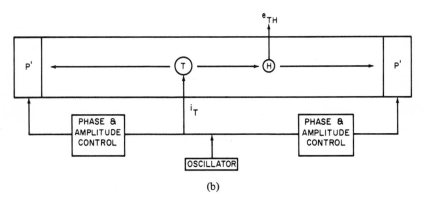

(b)

Fig. 2.11. Two arrangements for measurements in tube reciprocity calibration.

the sound energy diverges from the transducer before it propagates as plane progressive waves. In practice, the same is true for the projector P. Continuous-
wave rather than pulsed sound is used in the tube. The high-frequency limit for
the tube method is set by the tube diameter. When the diameter is greater than
about one third of a wavelength, the sound pressure no longer is uniform in a
cross-section plane.

The receiving sensitivity $M_H$ of the hydrophone measured in the tube is the
same as the free-field voltage sensitivity. The receiving sensitivity $M_T$ of the
reciprocal transducer is the same as the free-field voltage sensitivity, if the transducer is not resonant. If it is resonant, a frequency adjustment or correction
$f = f'(1 - \Delta f)$ must be used. The term $\Delta f$ is the difference between the resonance
frequency in the tube and in a free field. The measured frequency is $f'$, and the
adjusted frequency is $f$.

The tube reciprocity method is useful for calibrating resonant transducers in
high-pressure vessels. The Underwater Sound Reference Division of the Naval
Research Laboratory (USRD-NRL) has a tube 50 ft long and 15 in. in diameter

for hydrostatic pressures to 8500 psig and frequencies from 40 to 1500 Hz, and a tube 8 ft long, 8 in. in diameter, for hydrostatic pressures to 10,000 psi and frequencies from 10 to 4000 Hz.

### 2.3.7 Coupler reciprocity

The term coupler as used in acoustics refers to a small chamber that is used to couple or connect a projector (or loudspeaker) and a hydrophone together acoustically. The chamber is small in comparison with a wavelength of sound in the medium in the chamber, and the chamber boundaries have a high acoustical impedance. The sound pressure is then essentially the same everywhere in the chamber, and the sound pressure produced by the projector is the same as that acting on the hydrophone.

A coupler chamber is similar to the small tanks discussed in Section 2.2.3 for comparison calibrations. It differs in one important respect, however: Whereas the pressure in the tank in Fig. 2.3 is the same everywhere except near the sound source, no such exception is allowed in the coupler. The acoustic mass $m$ in Figs. 2.3 and 2.4 must be eliminated so that the pressure acting on the hydrophone is the same as the generator pressure. This is accomplished by making the chamber extremely small—so small that the transducers usually are inserted only partially into the chamber; that is, the transducer diaphragms form part of the chamber wall or chamber boundaries.

Figure 2.12 is a schematic diagram of a coupler containing three transducers. As in the other reciprocity methods, P is a projector, T is a reciprocal transducer, and H is a hydrophone. The same three conventional measurements of Fig. 2.5 and Eq. (2.17) are used. The reciprocity parameter in this case is $J = 2\pi f C$, where $f$ is the frequency and $C$ is the acoustical compliance of the medium and medium boundaries when T is transmitting. The electrical analog of the acoustical system is the circuit shown in Fig. 2.13. It is assumed that the transducers, chamber cavity, chamber walls, and so forth in Fig. 2.13 are all stiffness or compliance controlled—that is, all resonances are at frequencies above the applicable range.

Coupler reciprocity is feasible only for the calibration of small, hard hydrophones at low frequencies where the free-field voltage sensitivity and pressure sensitivity are the same. It is most useful for calibrating special hydrophones at very high static pressures. The hydrophones must be special in the sense that the coupler and the hydrophone must be designed to be compatible with each other in terms of size, shape, and means for bringing the electrical signals through the chamber wall.

Since the chamber volume of a coupler and the compliance $C$ are low, the projector needs to provide only a small volume velocity to produce measurable sound pressure; therefore, small piezoelectric or piezoceramic motors can be used at low frequencies. In practice, P, T, and H frequently are alike and the basic design is that of a small omnidirectional hydrophone.

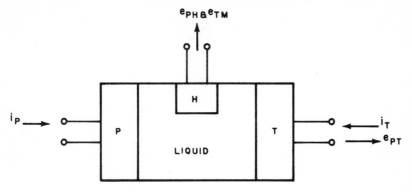

Fig. 2.12. Diagram of a reciprocity coupler chamber; P is the projector, H is the hydrophone, and T is the reciprocal transducer.

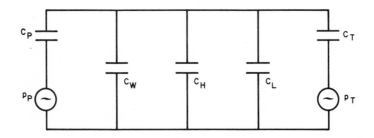

Fig. 2.13. Electrical analog of the system in Fig. 2.12; $C_p$, $C_w$, $C_H$, $C_L$, and $C_T$ are the acoustical compliances of the projector, walls, hydrophone, liquid, and reciprocal transducer, respectively, $p_p$ and $p_T$ are the blocked pressures of P and T, respectively.

Figure 2.14 shows a coupler used at the USRD-NRL to calibrate a primary standard hydrophone in the hydrostatic pressure range 0-16,000 psi and the frequency range 20-3000 Hz.[19]

The chamber walls and transducers in this system are very rigid. The compliance $C$, attributed entirely to the chamber fluid, is computed from

$$C = \frac{V}{\rho c^2} = \beta V, \tag{2.28}$$

where $V$ is the volume of the fluid in cubic centimeters, $\rho$ is the fluid density in grams per $cm^2$, $c$ is the speed of sound in the fluid in cm/sec, and $\beta$ is the adiabatic compressibility in fractional volume change per microbar. The fluid in a coupler need not be water. Castor oil or silicone oil is used in the USRD-NRL

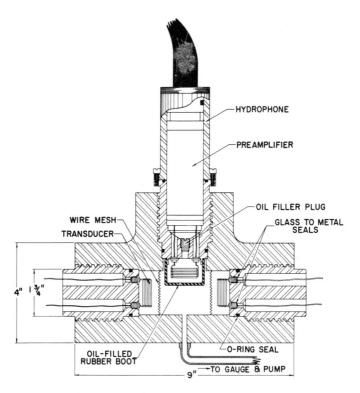

Fig. 2.14. System for reciprocity coupler calibration.

system because the piezoelectric or piezoceramic projector and reciprocal transducer elements then can be directly exposed to the medium.

A steel chemical-reaction vessel 5 in. in diameter and 20 in. long designed for
15,000 psi is used in a coupler system at the Canadian Naval Research Establishment (CNRE).[20] A chamber of this size allows some choice in the transducers
used and calibrated, but at a sacrifice in frequency bandwidth. The high-frequency
limit of the CNRE system is about 400 Hz. The compliance $C$ of the CNRE
chamber is measured rather than computed. A precisely measured volume of
fluid $\Delta V$ is forced into the chamber to raise the hydrostatic pressure by the
amount $\Delta p$. Then, $C = \Delta V/\Delta p$. The pressure change $\Delta p$ is measured by a pressure balance commercially available from the American Instrument Company,
Silver Spring, Md. This is a static or isothermal measurement rather than the
adiabatic or dynamic measurement that is needed. This difference introduces a
small error.

In a Russian version of this technique,[21] the compliance is measured by
inserting a small tube into the chamber and determining the Helmholtz resonance
for two conditions of water mass in the tube.

The most troublesome problem in a coupler reciprocity system is the complete removal of air bubbles. Since the acoustical impedance of the parallel combination of the medium, chamber walls, the transducers is very high, a small bubble will raise the total compliance, reduce the pressure, and increase the pressure gradient. In terms of the electrical analog of Fig. 2.13, a bubble will short circuit the whole system. Sometimes the bubble problem is so persistent that measurements at atmospheric pressure cannot be made. A small hydrostatic pressure, such as 50 psi, is needed to force the air bubbles into the liquid as dissolved air.

The electrical impedances of the transducers usually are very high, which causes problems with electrical cross talk—that is, the transmission of electromagnetic signals between transducers, by-passing the acoustic link. The wire mesh screens in Fig. 2.14 are used to reduce cross talk.

The high-frequency limit of practical coupler systems is set by either the size of the chamber or the resonance of some part of the system. The low-frequency limit, 20 Hz in both the USRD-NRL and CNRE systems, usually is set by the problem of driving a small high-impedance piezoelectric element electrically at infrasonic frequencies.

The coupler reciprocity method is simple in theory. It is a reliable and practicable method for calibrating a hydrophone at low audio frequencies and high hydrostatic pressures. It is not a versatile method in that not just any hydrophone can be calibrated in a coupler system. For this reason, the method is used only for the primary calibration of one or a few types of hydrophones.

### 2.3.8 Diffuse-sound reciprocity

Diffuse-sound reciprocity has been used primarily in air acoustics by Diestel.[22] It demonstrates the versatility of the reciprocity method, however, and no discussion of reciprocity calibrations would be complete without it. Diffuse sound is sound with completely random direction. The diffuse sound sensitivity of a hydrophone is the ratio of the rms open-circuit voltage output to the rms pressure of the diffuse sound field before insertion of the hydrophone. Such a sensitivity is useful in ambient noise measurements, for example. If a hydrophone is omnidirectional, its diffuse-sound and plane-wave sensitivities are the same. If the hydrophone is not omnidirectional, the two sensitivities are different and are related by the directivity factor $R_\theta$; that is,

$$M_{df} = R_\theta M_f, \qquad (2.29)$$

where the subscripts $df$ and $f$ refer to diffuse field and free field, respectively. The value of $M_{df}$ can be computed if both $R_\theta$ and $M_f$ are known. The directivity factor is difficult to measure accurately, however, except for the simple cases where the three-dimensional directivity pattern is symmetrical about one direction. The sensitivity $M_{df}$ can be measured directly by the diffuse-sound reciprocity calibration method.

Suppose we have a reverberation tank or room with good diffusion charac-teristics—that is, with many asymmetrical reflecting boundaries so that the steady-state sound level is the same everywhere except near the sound source. Place the usual projector P, reciprocal transducer T, and hydrophone H in the tank. Let the projector transmit sound into the tank at a steady rate. The sound pressure in the tank will rise until the sound power lost into the tank walls equals the sound power delivered into the tank by the projector. In this steady-state condition, the sound field at any point in the tank can be considered to be composed of two parts: (1) the sound pressure $p_f$ received directly from the projector, and (2) the diffuse-sound pressure $p_{df}$ received from a large number of image sources outside the tank. The direct-sound pressure is the free-field pressure—that is, it is the pressure that would exist at the point if all the reflecting boundaries were removed and the projector-emitted power were unchanged. The direct-sound pressure is spreading in spherical waves, and thus the amplitude is a function of position in the tank. The diffuse-sound pressure is the phasor sum of the pressure from many randomly spaced image sources and therefore is inde-pendent of position.

The three transducers must be placed so the receiving transducers (T and H) receive essentially only the diffuse-sound pressure $p_{df}$ from the transmitting transducers (P and T); that is, $p_{df} \gg p_f$. The direct or free-field pressure $p_f$ can be made small by making the tank large so as to allow wide separation of the transducers. The diffuse pressure $p_{df}$ can be made large by keeping the wall absorption low or reverberation time high.

With P, T, and H properly placed, the same measurements of Fig. 2.5 and the same formula or Eq. (2.17) are used to find $M_{df}$. As in the other variations of the reciprocity method, only the reciprocity parameter changes. The diffuse-sound reciprocity parameter $J_{df}$ is given by Diestel[22] as

$$J_{df} = \left(\frac{2.1}{\rho f}\right)\left(\frac{V}{ct}\right)^{1/2} 10^{-7}, \qquad (2.30)$$

where $\rho$ is the density of the water, $f$ is frequency, $V$ is the volume of the tank, $c$ is the speed of sound, and $t$ is the Sabine reverberation time or the time in seconds required for the diffuse-sound level to decrease 60 dB after the sound source is stopped.

At some distance $h$ from the source, the diffuse sound and the direct sound will be the same. Diestel shows that Eq. (2.30) can be put into the form

$$J_{df} = \frac{2h}{\rho f} 10^{-7}, \qquad (2.31)$$

if the reciprocal transducer is omnidirectional. Then, $J_{df}$ is similar to the spherical wave parameter $J = (2d/\rho f)10^{-7}$, as would be expected, since the diffuse-sound pressure is the same as the free-field or direct-sound pressure at the distance $h$ centimeters from the source.

The major problem in this kind of calibration is obtaining a good diffuse-sound field. Transducer positions near walls must be avoided. A narrow band of white noise or a warbled tone usually is used to produce a more uniform diffuse-sound field. In air acoustics, large rooms are needed. Diestel's room was approximately 15 x 20 x 25 ft. A tank or other reverberant body of water would have to be extremely large to be useful for underwater diffuse-sound calibration measurements.

### 2.3.9 General and in-situ reciprocity

It can be shown that a reciprocity calibration theoretically can be performed under any boundary conditions of the medium.[10] It is necessary only that the bounded medium itself obey the acoustical reciprocity theorem. That is, it must be linear, passive, and reversible. As can be seen from the various reciprocity parameters, $J$ is dependent on the characteristics of the medium, the medium boundaries, and some dimensions. The dimensions appear to be, and usually are, transducer dimensions. This, however, is not required by theory. In the tube reciprocity, for example, the area $A$ has no relation to the transducer dimensions; it is the area over which both the transmitted and received pressures of the reciprocal transducer are measured. For the general case, the reciprocity parameter is dependent on the manner in which $M$ and $S$ are defined. Visualize a transducer T of arbitrary shape in a medium with arbitrary boundary conditions, as shown in Fig. 2.15. Let the transmitting response $S$ be defined as the average pressure produced over the area $A_s$ per unit input current. That is,

$$S = \frac{\frac{1}{A_s} \int_{A_s} p \, dA}{i}. \tag{2.32}$$

Let the receiving sensitivity $M$ be defined as the open-circuit output voltage per unit pressure averaged over the area $A_m$. That is,

$$M = \frac{e_{oc}}{\frac{1}{A_m} \int_{A_m} p \, dA}. \tag{2.33}$$

It can be shown that for this general case,[10]

$$J = \frac{u(A_s)}{p(A_m)}, \tag{2.34}$$

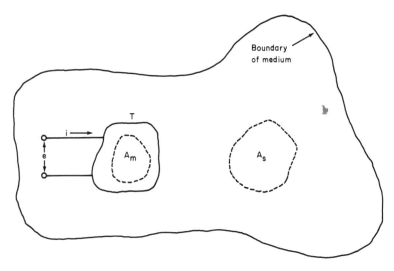

Fig. 2.15. Transducer T of arbitrary shape in a medium with an arbitrary boundary; $A_s$ is the area over which the transmitted pressure is measured, $A_m$ is the area over which the received pressure is measured, $e$ is voltage, and $i$ is current.

where $u(A_s)$ is a volume velocity emanating from $A_s$ and $p(A_m)$ is the resulting average pressure over the area $A_m$. In the spherical-wave case, $A_s$ and $A_m$ are vanishingly small spheres, or for practical purposes, points. In the cylindrical-wave case, $A_s$ and $A_m$ are lines (cylinders with infinitesimally small diameters). In the plane-wave and tube cases, $A_s$ and $A_m$ are areas (actually two parallel plane areas separated by only an infinitesimal distance). In the general case, $J$ is an acoustical transfer admittance between the two areas $A_s$ and $A_m$ specified in $M$ and $S$ of the reciprocal transducer. Since the medium is reciprocal, the transfer impedance must be the same in both directions. Thus, $J$ can be defined also as $u(A_m)/p(A_s)$, as was done in Section 2.3.

Sometimes $J$ cannot be computed because the boundary conditions are unknown or too complicated. Then one can use Eq. (2.17) in a backward sense. That is, if a calibrated hydrophone is used and $M$ is known, $J$ can be the unknown. Suppose, for example, it is necessary to monitor the calibration of a transducer in a remote position on the bottom of the ocean. The usual trio of transducers for a reciprocity calibration are fixed to some framework and lowered to the ocean bottom. The usual reciprocity measurements depicted in Fig. 2.5 are made through long cables. The receiving sensitivity $M$ of the hydrophone already is known. Therefore, Eq. (2.17) can be used to compute $J$. This *in situ* $J$ is valid so long as the boundary conditions do not change. In a stable environment, the boundary conditions may remain unchanged for a longer period of time than does the hydrophone calibration. Thus, reciprocity calibrations can be repeated at intervals of time, and the calibration depends on the *in-situ J* rather than on the original hydrophone sensitivity *M*.

## 2.4 Two-Projector Null Method

The two-projector null method (TPNM)[23] derives its name from the use of two projectors and a technique whereby a known electromechanical force is balanced against an unknown sound pressure to produce a null, or zero motion of a diaphragm. A TPNM system is shown in Fig. 2.16 and the electrical analog of the acoustical system is shown in Fig. 2.17. The two projectors are driven electrically by the same oscillator with a provision for controlling the relative phase and amplitude of the two signals. The diaphragm of the null projector then is acted upon by two forces: (1) the electromechanical force *F* of the null projector, and (2) the force resulting from the acoustical pressure *p*, produced in the medium by the source projector, acting on the null projector diaphragm area *A*. With the phase and amplitude control, these two forces can be made equal in magnitude and opposite in phase. The balancing-to-a-null procedure in the electrical analog reduces the velocity *u* to zero, thereby making *p* and *F/A* the same. The diaphragm motion detector then indicates a null condition. The two forces are equal:

$$pA = F. \tag{2.35}$$

A moving-coil transducer is most suitable for the null projector. For such a transducer,

$$F = BLi, \tag{2.36}$$

where *B* is the magnetic flux density, *L* is the coil length, and *i* is the current. Then,

$$p = \frac{BLi}{A}. \tag{2.37}$$

The expression $BL/A$ is a constant, independent of frequency, and stable with time. It can be measured statically by balancing a small measurable change in the hydrostatic pressure $\Delta p_{dc}$ with a direct current $i_{dc}$ through the null projector. Then,

$$\frac{BL}{A} = \frac{\Delta p_{dc}}{i_{dc}}. \tag{2.38}$$

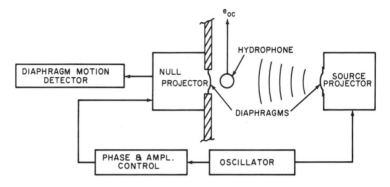

Fig. 2.16. Two-projector null method calibration system.

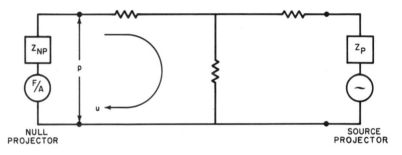

Fig. 2.17. Electrical analog of acoustical system in Fig. 2.16.

The pressure change is easy to obtain. If the water level over the null projector is altered by $h$ centimeters, then $\Delta p_{dc} = \rho g h$, where $g$ is the acceleration due to gravity in cm/sec$^2$ and $\rho$ is the density of water in g/cm$^3$.

If a hydrophone is placed near the null projector diaphragm, the hydrophone sensitivity $M$ is given by

$$M = \frac{e_{oc}}{\left(\dfrac{BLi}{A}\right)} = \left(\frac{e_{oc}}{i}\right)\left(\frac{i_{dc}}{\rho g h}\right). \tag{2.39}$$

Neither the transducer impedance $Z_{NP}$ nor any of the other system impedances need be known.

Although the method is most useful at low frequencies and in small chambers, it can be used under many other boundary conditions, including free field. It is necessary only that the hydrophone be near enough to the null projector diaphragm that it is subject to the same sound pressure as the diaphragm. The method is applicable only to nonresonant hydrophones, because the hydrophone radiation impedance in the null projector system will differ from that in a free field. This difference can be neglected at off-resonance frequencies. As a practical matter, the hydrophone also must be hard because a soft boundary will result in pressure gradients, and the pressure at the null projector diaphragm then may differ from that at the hydrophone position.

Various schemes can be used for the diaphragm motion detector. Usually, the metal diaphragm is a part of some electrical system, and the motion produces changes in the system. For example, the diaphragm can be one plate of a capacitor, or be part of a magnetic circuit. The detector does not need to be calibrated. The null projector diaphragm will have a resonance below or at the low end of the TPNM system frequency range and therefore will be mass controlled. The displacement will be inversely proportional to the square of the frequency; the velocity will be inversely proportional to frequency; the acceleration will be constant with frequency. An acceleration detector, therefore, would be preferred to a displacement detector; however, the static measurement of $BL/A$ can be made only with a displacement-monitoring device. For this reason, the Underwater Sound Reference Division of NRL, where the TPN method originated in 1955, uses a commercial displacement detector manufactured by the Bently Scientific Company. The maximum frequency of the USRD-NRL system, 1000 Hz, is determined by the sensitivity of the displacement detector. A combination detection system, consisting of a displacement detector for static and infrasonic frequency measurements and a velocity or acceleration detector for audio frequencies, could be used. Other problems with resonances and short wavelengths restrict the use of the method at frequencies above 1000 Hz. The method has no low-frequency limit; USRD-NRL uses it from 0.3 to 1000 Hz.

The main advantages of the method are freedom from any acoustical impedance measurement and absence of any restriction on tank size. The main disadvantage pertains to practice rather than theory. If hydrostatic pressure is a variable in the calibration, the relatively fragile null projector diaphragm must be pressure compensated; that is, the air pressure inside the transducer must be equal to the hydrostatic pressure in the tank within about ±2 psi. The pressure compensation system along with normal filling, circulation, and vacuum equipment (to aid in eliminating air bubbles) all result in considerable plumbing.

## 2.5 Impedance Methods

The impedance method is a class of absolute calibration methods in which the acoustic pressure is found from some characteristic of a sound source (pressure, velocity, or displacement) and the acoustic impedances of the medium and medium boundaries. The general case is represented by the electrical analog in Fig. 2.18. With sufficient knowledge about the parameters $p_f$, $U$, $Z_s$, and $Z_m$, the sound pressure $p$ in the medium can be determined. As with the similar cases of comparison calibrations in small tanks (Section 2.2.3) and coupler reciprocity

(Section 2.3.7), only the pressure sensitivity of small, hard hydrophones can be measured, and this only at low frequencies. The volume of the medium is small; that is, the maximum dimension must be a small fraction of a wavelength in the medium. The hydrophone sensitivity $M = e_{oc}/p$ is found from a direct measurement of $e_{oc}$ and the indirect measurement of $p$.

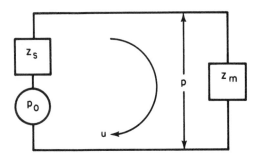

Fig. 2.18. Electrical analog of acoustical system used in impedance calibration methods.

There are two general types of impedance methods corresponding to the two types of acoustic reactance. In the first method, the medium is compliance $(1/j\omega C)$ or stiffness $(s/j\omega)$ controlled. The terms compliance and stiffness both are used in acoustics. Stiffness is a term carried over from mechanical engineering. Compliance is more useful in acoustics, and will be used here because it is directly related to electrical capacitance in electroacoustic analogs, whereas stiffness is inversely related to capacitance. In compliance-controlled systems, the medium is assumed to act as a massless spring and the sound pressure is a result of compression and extension of this spring. In the second method, the medium is mass $(j\omega m)$ controlled. The medium is assumed to act as a nonelastic mass, and the sound pressure is a result of the inertia of this mass. Both methods are low-frequency approximations, but can be extended upward in frequency if the system can be described by wave equations. Closed chambers are used for compliance-controlled systems, and open chambers for inertial systems. The compliance-controlled systems have been called pistonphones ever since E. C. Wente[24] first devised this technique in 1917.

### 2.5.1 Pistonphone methods

The pistonphone is one of the oldest absolute calibration techniques. In its original form, it was used only for calibrating microphones. In several modified forms, it has been used to calibrate hydrophones. It consists of a small gas-filled chamber and a piston sound source, as depicted in Fig. 2.19. The piston in the original version[24,25] is driven by an electric motor, and in later versions[26,27,28] by a moving-coil transducer. Its displacement amplitude is measured by an optical system. The main requirements of a suitable driver are the capability of vibrating with large displacements and a convenient means of measuring the displacement. The volume displacement $X$ is found from the linear displacement and the piston area. Then,

$$p = UZ_m = (j\omega X)Z_m,$$ (2.40)

where $U$ is the volume velocity and $Z_m$ is the impedance of the medium in Fig. 2.18. It is assumed that resonances in the medium and boundaries are at frequencies higher than the frequency range of the system. That is, we are dealing with a purely elastic impedance, and $Z_m$ is a compliance $1/j\omega C$. The impedance $Z_m$ actually is the compliance of the parallel combination of the medium $C_m$, the chamber wall, and the microphone. The latter two compliances usually are much smaller than $C_m$, so that $Z_m \simeq 1/j\omega C_m$. Then,

$$p = j\omega X \frac{1}{j\omega C_m} = \frac{X}{C_m}.$$ (2.41)

From the gas laws, $C_m = V/\gamma p_0$, where $V$ is the volume, $p_0$ is the static pressure, and $\gamma$ is the ratio of specific heats for the gas. Some small corrections must be made to $C_m$, depending on the heat conduction of the chamber walls. The reader is referred to the references[24-28] for further details.

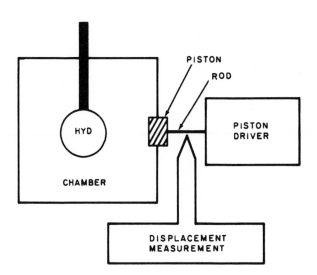

Fig. 2.19. Pistonphone calibration.

The air pistonphone can be used to calibrate hydrophones, but for this purpose, the method has one major drawback. The air chamber must be small, or, alternatively, the upper frequency limit must be low. The upper frequency limit of chambers only a few inches in the largest dimension is about 200 Hz. A water-air pistonphone has been used to circumvent, in part, this drawback. A water-air pistonphone is shown in Fig. 2.20. A larger chamber is used, but it is filled mostly with water. Since the wavelength in water at a given frequency is about 5 times that in air, a dimension in water can be five times the same dimension in air without affecting the "small in comparison with a wavelength" criterion for the chamber. Thus, a large hydrophone can be accommodated. At the same time, Eqs. (2.40) and (2.41) are unaffected. The compliance of the water is very much lower than the compliance of the air, so that the water compliance, like the wall compliance, can be neglected. The sound pressure still is approximately uniform throughout the fluid mediums and is the same in the water as in the air. The electrical analog of the water-air pistonphone is shown in Fig. 2.21.

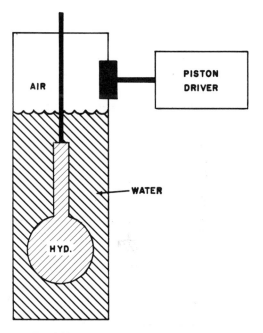

Fig. 2.20. Water-air pistonphone calibrator.

A further modification is the water pistonphone in which the air is eliminated and a pressure source is used. The electrical analog is shown in Fig. 2.22. The compliance $C_m$ of the medium, consisting of the parallel combination of the wall, water, and hydrophone, must be measured with some kind of static technique (see, for example, references 20 and 21). The sound source must have a known mechanical impedance $Z_s$ and its blocked pressure $p_b$ must be measurable. A

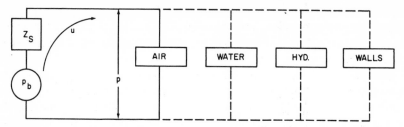

Fig. 2.21. Electrical analog of water-air pistonphone. Dashed lines indicate that the impedance of the water, hydrophone, and chamber walls all are high enough to be neglected in the parallel circuit.

moving-coil transducer sound source meets all requirements. The blocked pressure is given by

$$p_b = \frac{BLi}{A},$$ (2.42)

where $B$ is the magnetic flux density, $L$ is the coil length, $i$ is the current, and $A$ is the diaphragm area. The impedance $Z_s$ consists of the diaphragm mass and compliance of the spring suspension of the diaphragm. These are measured only once and thereafter are assumed to be constant. Then, from Fig. 2.22,

$$p = \frac{\dfrac{1}{j\omega C_m}}{Z_s + \dfrac{1}{j\omega C_m}} \frac{BLi}{A}.$$ (2.43)

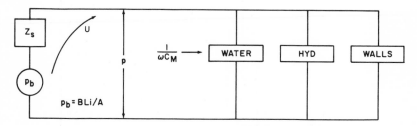

Fig. 2.22. Electrical analog of water pistonphone.

The impedance $1/j\omega C_m$ always will be high; therefore, air bubbles, soft gaskets, thin-walled pipes, and other low impedances can have large effects on $C_m$ and $p$, and must be avoided or acoustically isolated from the medium. If the diaphragm does not move like a true piston, the area $A$ must be determined as an "effective" area. A water pistonphone has the advantages of higher acoustic pressures, higher upper frequency limits, and larger hydrophone size than an air pistonphone. A water pistonphone was used at the USRD-NRL for about ten years. The chamber was 10 inches in diameter and 24 inches long. The upper frequency limit was 200 Hz.

The value of $C_m$ depends on the compliance and size of the hydrophone and hydrophone cable, and on the vagaries of the water medium. It must be measured for every calibration. The need to repeat this measurement is the main disadvantage of the method, and it was because of this that the USRD-NRL water pistonphone was superseded by the Two-Projector Null Method.

A final variation of the pistonphone method is called a pressurephone.[29]  In Fig. 2.22, if $1/\omega C_m \gg Z_s$, Eq. (2.43) reduces to

$$p = p_b = \frac{BLi}{A},\qquad(2.44)$$

and impedance measurements are eliminated. The value of $C_m$ can be made very low by using a very small chamber. This reduces the versatility of the system, however, and the pressurephone therefore is most useful for the absolute calibration of specially designed standard hydrophones only. Figure 2.23 is a schematic diagram of the USRD pressurephone. The frequency range of the pressurephone is much larger than that of other pistonphones, because the chamber is so small. The frequency range of the USRD pressurephone is 10 to 3000 Hz.

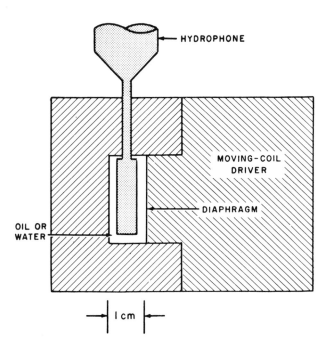

Fig. 2.23. Pressurephone calibrator.

## 2.5.2 Inertial methods

The two known systems for applying inertial methods are the Sims Calibrator[30] and the Schloss and Strasberg shaker.[31]  Both of these devices contain tubular chambers that are short acoustic transmission lines and therefore are amenable to wave analysis.  This method therefore will be discussed in general terms, and then the low-frequency approximations will be obtained as special cases.

Suppose we have a rigid-walled tube as shown in Fig. 2.24.  The diameter is much smaller than a wavelength of sound in water, but the length $L$ is unrestricted.  The column of water is set into vertical oscillation by motion at the bottom.  The bottom in the Sims Calibrator is the diaphragm of a moving-coil transducer.  The whole tube in the Schloss and Strasberg technique is vibrated by a vibration generator or mechanical shaker.  The cylindrical walls also vibrate vertically in the latter case, but this vibration contributes nothing to the sound pressure.  Given the boundary conditions that the sound pressure at the water-air surface is zero and at the bottom is $p_L$, it can be shown that the sound pressure $p_d$ at any depth $d$ is given by

$$p_d = p_L \frac{\sin kd}{\sin kL},\qquad(2.45)$$

where $k$ is the wavenumber $2\pi/\lambda = \omega/c$.  If the vibration velocity of the bottom is $\dot{x}$ and $Z_L$ is the load or specific acoustic radiation impedance on the bottom, then

$$p_L = \dot{x}Z_L.\qquad(2.46)$$

From transmission line theory, $Z_L = j\rho c \tan kL$, where $\rho$ is the density of water and $c$ is the speed of sound in water.  The speed $c$ in a tube is the same as the speed in a free field only if the tube walls are truly rigid.  In practice, the walls have a finite impedance and $c$ is less in the tube than it is in a free field.  Then

$$p_L = j\dot{x}\rho c \tan kL \qquad(2.47)$$

and

$$p_d = \frac{(j\dot{x}\rho c \tan kL)(\sin kd)}{(\sin kL)},\qquad(2.48)$$

or

$$|p_d| = \frac{\ddot{x}\rho c}{\omega}\frac{\sin kd}{\cos kL}.\qquad(2.49)$$

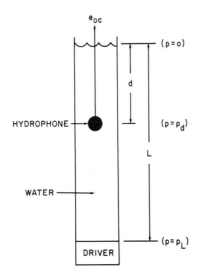

Fig. 2.24. System for inertial impedance calibration methods.

Equation (2.49) is rigorous for any length $L$, if there is no energy loss in the tube. With the usual low-frequency approximation $kd \ll 1$ and $kL \ll 1$, Eq. (2.49) reduces to

$$|p_d| = \frac{\ddot{x}\rho c k d}{\omega} = (\rho d)\ddot{x}. \qquad (2.50)$$

Equation (2.50), a form of Newton's second law of motion, shows that the pressure is a function of the inertia of the water mass above the depth $d$. The receiving sensitivity $M$ of a small hydrophone placed at the depth $d$ then is

$$M = \frac{e_{oc}}{p_d} = \frac{e_{oc}\omega \cos kL}{\ddot{x}\rho c \sin kd} \simeq \frac{e_{oc}}{(\rho d)\ddot{x}}. \qquad (2.51)$$

Scholss and Strasberg give a cross-section criterion: The radius $r$ of a spherical hydrophone is limited by $x \ll r \ll d$. That is, the hydrophone radius must be much larger than the driving amplitude $x$ and much smaller than the depth. A small line hydrophone inserted along the tube axis can be calibrated, provided that the pressure $p_d$ is linear over the length of the hydrophone and $d$ is measured from the midpoint. The effects of the greater sound pressure at depths below $d$ and the lesser sound pressure at depths above $d$ will produce an average pressure equal to the midpoint pressure.

In both versions of this technique, the hydrophone is supported from a point that does not vibrate. The hydrophone, therefore, also is subjected to an oscillating pressure due to the periodic change in depth. This pressure is very small in comparison with the inertial pressure except at very low frequencies (less than 10 Hz).

Schloss and Strasberg measure $\ddot{x}$ directly with a calibrated accelerometer. The current driving the moving-coil transducer in the Sims calibrator technique is measured and the force factor $BL$ and mechanical impedance $Z$ of the transducer must be known. Then the blocked pressure at the diaphragm, which forms the bottom of the tube, is given by

$$p_b = \frac{BLi}{A_s},$$

where $B$ is the flux density, $L$ is the coil length, $i$ is the current, and $A_s$ is the source diaphragm area. The system can be depicted as in the analog, Fig. 2.25a, At frequencies above the transducer resonance and below the tube resonance, the approximation shown in Fig. 2.25b can be used. Here, $p_d$ is the pressure measured across only that part of the water mass load between the depth $d$ and the surface ($d = 0$). All parameters in Fig. 2.25 are constants except $i$ and $d$. Therefore, once the system is calibrated, $p_d$ becomes a function of $i$:

$$p_d = \left[ \frac{\dfrac{BL}{A_s} \dfrac{d}{L} \dfrac{m_w}{A^2}}{\dfrac{m_s}{A_s^2} + \dfrac{m_w}{A^2}} \right] i, \tag{2.52}$$

where $m_w$ and $m_s$ are the masses of the water column and the source transducer, respectively.

If the diaphragm area $A_s$ and the tube cross section area $A$ are not the same, there will be a short divergent region near the diaphragm. The hydrophone must not be positioned in this region.

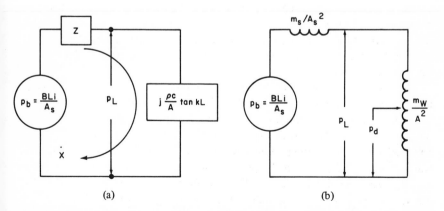

(a)                                        (b)

Fig. 2.25.  Electrical analogs of Sims inertial impedance calibration system (a) for any length $L$, (b) for $L \ll \lambda$, and for frequencies above driver transducer resonance.

The two versions of the inertial method differ only in practice, and the choice between them depends on cost and convenience in a particular application. Commercially available shakers and calibrated accelerometers are readily available, so that the Schloss and Strasberg apparatus can be assembled easily. The Sims calibrator is a specially designed apparatus, and the development and calibration require some knowledge of transducer design; however, the Sims calibrator, once built and calibrated, is compact, portable, and easy to use. The Sims apparatus can be calibrated easily, if a calibrated hydrophone already is available. Either apparatus can be used for comparison calibrations, in which case the two methods become almost identical. The Sims calibrator has been used in many places as a simple and rapid means for the comparison calibration of large numbers of small hydrophones. Schloss and Strasberg report calibration data in the 10 to 700 Hz range, and Sims in the 100 to 3000 Hz range.

## 2.6  Static Methods

Static methods are those in which dynamic calibrations are based on static measurements and static impedances. The methods are limited to very low audio and infrasonic frequencies at which a sound pressure can be treated as a rapidly changing hydrostatic pressure.

### 2.6.1  Capacitor hydrophone

A capacitor hydrophone calibration system is shown in Fig. 2.26. The hydrophone consists of a capacitor in which one plate has a spring suspension and the other plate is immobile. The suspended plate or diaphragm is acted upon by both the hydrostatic pressure and the sound pressure in the water, which action changes the distance between the plates and thus the capacitance. The capacitor constitutes one arm of an impedance bridge. A carrier frequency at a constant input voltage is supplied to the bridge. The output voltage $e_o$ will be a function of the hydrophone capacitance $C_H$ as shown in Fig. 2.27. If $C_H$ oscillates under the influence of the sound pressure, and if the bridge is slightly unbalanced when the sound pressure is zero, $e_o$ will be modulated by the sound pressure signal frequency, and the demodulated voltage $e_{oo}$ will be approximately proportional to the sound pressure.

The system is calibrated by keeping $e_1$ constant, varying the static pressure, and observing the voltage $e_o$. The ratio $e_o/e_{oo}$ can be obtained with an electrical calibration of the demodulator. The bridge must be unbalanced to avoid frequency doubling. That is, in Fig. 2.27 at the value of $C_H$ where the bridge is balanced or $e_o$ is zero, either an increase of a decrease in $C_H$ due to a sound wave will increase $e_o$. Thus, both the positive and negative halves of a pressure wave would produce a full wave in $e_o$. The operating point in the curve in Fig. 2.27 can be moved away from the null or balanced bridge point by a bridge adjustment—that is, by changing the value of any of the four bridge impedances. It usually is most convenient to adjust $C_s$.

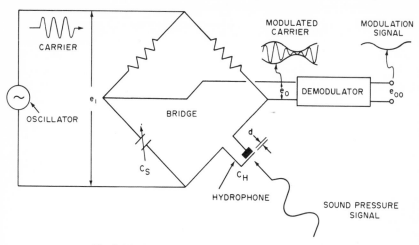

Fig. 2.26. Capacitor hydrophone calibration system.

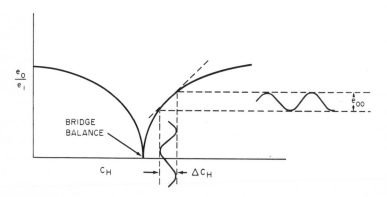

Fig. 2.27. Bridge voltage output as a function of hydrophone capacitance.

The sensitivity of the system depends on the ratio $\Delta e_o/\Delta C_H$. From Fig. 2.27, it can be seen that the magnitude and linearity of this sensitivity depend on the shape of the curve, which in turn depends on the bridge design. A second factor affecting both the sensitivity and linearity of the system is the distance $d$ between the capacitor plates. The capacitance $C_H$ is inversely proportional to $d$, and the sensitivity of the system will depend also on the ratio $\Delta C_H/\Delta d$ or the shape of the curve in Fig. 2.28. The sensitivity is highest for close spacing or small values of $d$. The nonlinearity, or change in slope, also is greatest for small values of $d$, however, so a design compromise becomes necessary. A third factor in the sensitivity is the mechanical compliance of the diaphragm, or the change in $d$ per unit sound pressure.

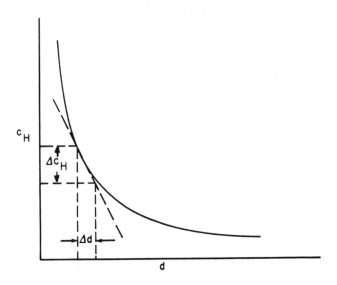

Fig. 2.28. Hydrophone capacitance as a function of plate separation.

Since the system is sensitive to static as well as dynamic pressures, the sensitivity will be a function of water depth. To eliminate static pressure sensitivity, a static pressure compensation system that will equalize the static water pressure on the outside with the static air pressure on the inside of the suspended plate or diaphragm becomes necessary. The compensation system must include an acoustic low-pass filter so that static, but not dynamic, pressures are compensated. Provision is made to eliminate the compensation temporarily during the system calibration. The static calibration is valid only for those frequencies at which the diaphragm is stiffness or compliance controlled and dynamic or inertial effects can be neglected. Thus, the high-frequency limit is about one octave below the resonance frequency of the diaphragm.

The one main advantage of a capacitor hydrophone system is very high sensitivity. Unlike more conventional hydrophones, whose sensitivity depends mainly on a piezoelectric, magnetostrictive, or magnetic material, the capacitor hydrophone sensitivity depends largely on the mechanical design of the diaphragm and the electrical design of the bridge. The softer the diaphragm suspension and the sharper the bridge null in Fig. 2.27, the more sensitive the hydrophone will be. One of the original versions[32] of this type of hydrophone had an over-all system voltage sensitivity of −45 dB re 1 V/μbar. This is about 40 dB higher than a typical good piezoelectric hydrophone with a cathode-follower preamplifier, and about 20 dB better than a good noise-measuring hydrophone with 20 dB of gain in the preamplifier.

The disadvantages of the system are the complexity, the inherent non-linearity, and the limited frequency range. The high-frequency limit of the original version already mentioned was only 75 Hz.

In other versions of this technique, the bridge is replaced by an electronic circuit in which the amplitude or frequency of a carrier signal is sensitive to small changes in a capacitance.

### 2.6.2 Electronic hydrophone

Several manufacturers make electronic vacuum tubes in which one of the electrodes (usually the anode) is mechanically linked to an external pin (RCA 5734, for example).[33] When the pin vibrates, the transconductance of the tube oscillates. Such a hydrophone is shown schematically in Fig. 2.29. The output voltage $e$ is proportional to the displacement $x$ of the diaphragm-pin mechanical link. At frequencies below the first resonance in the mechanical system, the displacement will be proportional to the sound pressure $p$. The over-all system proportionality constant, or the calibration ratio $e/p$, can be measured statically.

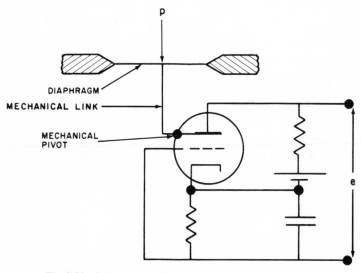

Fig. 2.29. Schematic drawing of an electronic hydrophone.

Like the capacitor hydrophone, the electronic hydrophone can be made very sensitive but it has a very limited frequency range.[34] It also has a high self-noise level.

### 2.6.3 Variable-depth techniques

If the depth of a hydrophone is varied periodically with simple harmonic motion, the oscillating hydrostatic pressure will be indistinguishable from a sound pressure at very low frequencies. If $x$ is the amplitude of vertical motion, the oscillating pressure is given by

$$p = x\rho g. \tag{2.53}$$

where $\rho$ is the water density and $g$ is the acceleration due to gravity. Then, if the hydrophone output voltage is $e_{oc}$, the sensitivity $M$ is

$$M = \frac{e_{oc}}{x\rho g} . \tag{2.54}$$

The amplitudes $e_{oc}$ and $x$ can have any standard form—that is, rms, peak, or peak-to-peak—but the same form must be used for both $e_{oc}$ and $x$.

The depth can be varied either by moving the hydrophone or moving the water-air surface. Both methods have been used. In the moving hydrophone version, the mechanical oscillator, called a dunking machine, consists of a variable-speed electric motor and a "scotch yoke" or other mechanical link for converting rotary motion to linear simple harmonic motion. Figure 2.30 is a diagram of the scotch yoke used by the Navy Underwater Sound Reference Laboratory (NUSRL).[35]   The pin attached to the rotating disk slides in the groove of the yoke. The yoke and supporting rod are constrained to move only in a vertical direction. Then, as the disk rotates, the yoke and rod move up and down sinusoidally. The peak amplitude $x$ is equal to the radius of the pin position.

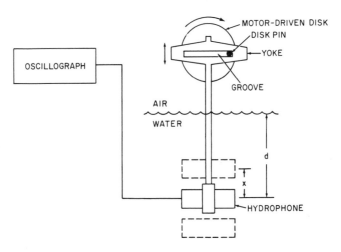

Fig. 2.30. Dunking machine calibration system.

The system contains several sources of dynamic pressure other than the variable head of water. These include (1) the hydrodynamic laminar flow around the hydrophone, (2) inertial effects of the medium, (3) inertial effects within the hydrophone, and (4) turbulence. The hydrodynamic pressures are a function of the hydrophone shape, and it is difficult to generalize on the effect. For simple cylindrical shapes, the hydrodynamic pressures are harmonically related to the fundamental frequency and therefore can be eliminated by filters. Inertial effects of the medium can be eliminated or minimized by properly orienting the hydrophone. For example, the diaphragm or active face of the hydrophone should be in a vertical plane so the water next to the diaphragm is not displaced by the hydrophone motion. Inertial effects of the hydrophone elements also can be minimized by orientation. However, the optimum orientation for the two inertial effects may not be the same. In an oil-filled hydrophone, the inertial effects used in the Schloss and Strasberg shaker and described in Section 2.5.2 will be present and cannot be eliminated. Turbulence is the most unpredictable of the extraneous sources of dynamic pressure. All fixtures in the water should be streamlined as much as possible. If small tanks are used, the motion of the hydrophone may also excite a "slosh" resonance. This resonance of the 55-gallon drum used at the Navy Underwater Sound Reference Laboratory was at 1.8 Hz, but it had no significant effect on the calibration pressure.

These various sources of error severely limit the useable upper frequency of a dunking machine. There is no low-frequency limit. The NUSRL dunking machine provided accurate calibrations in the range 0.3 to 4 Hz. Within the frequency range where the extraneous sources of pressure can be neglected, the dunking machine is a simple, straightforward calibrating system.

The alternate method, in which the hydrophone is stationary and the water-air surface is moved, can take two forms. The whole tank, or at least the whole water volume, can be moved, as was done in the inertial techniques described in Section 2.5.2, or only a small part of the system can be moved as in the Golenkov technique[36] shown in Fig. 2.31. The dynamic pressure that is due to variable depth, inherent in the inertial techniques, does not become large in comparison with the dynamic inertial pressures until very low frequencies are used. From Eqs. (2.50) and (2.53), it can be shown that the two pressures become equal when $\omega^2 = g/d$. For a depth of 10 cm, this frequency is 1.6 Hz.

In the Golenkov technique, only the small upper chamber oscillates. It is driven vertically by a mechanical oscillator similar to that described for the dunking machine. The variable head of water then acts on the stationary hydrophone in the lower chamber. The connecting tubing must, of course, be compliant. This technique eliminates turbulence, and to some extent the inertial pressures. It also allows large oscillation amplitudes. The two chambers and connecting tube have resonances similar to those in a Helmholtz resonator, however, and the useful upper frequency limit for this technique is lower than that for the dunking machine. Golenkov reports the high-frequency limit as about 1 Hz.

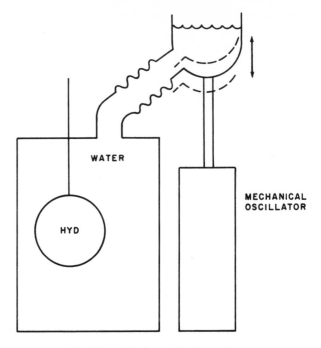

Fig. 2.31. Golenkov calibration system.

### 2.7 Impulse Method

The impulse method is used for the rapid calibration of small piezoelectric hydrophones in the frequency range below the first resonance. The method consists of subjecting the hydrophone to an impulse or sudden change in static pressure $\Delta p$ and measuring the initial voltage $e_0$ or the electric charge $Q$ produced by the piezoelectric crystal or ceramic element. Then the receiving sensitivity $M$ is found from

$$M = \frac{e_0}{\Delta p} = \frac{\dfrac{Q}{C}}{\Delta p}, \tag{2.55}$$

where $C$ is the electrical capacitance of the hydrophone.

After a pressure impulse, the charge leaks rapidly through the shunt resistance $R$ across the crystal electrodes, and the voltage rapidly drops from its initial value. Therefore, the voltage $e_0$ must be measured quickly. Alternatively, the charge $Q$ can be measured as it discharges through a ballistic galvanometer. Either measurement must be made in a time short in comparison with the time constant $RC$ of the system. In the voltage measurement, $R$ and $C$ include the input of the voltmeter as well as the crystal shunt resistance and capacitance. An instrument such as an electrometer that has an extremely high input impedance should be used. Typical voltage-versus-time curves for each type of measurement are shown in Fig. 2.32. The ballistic galvanometer measures the total charge over the whole period of discharge, whereas the electrometer must measure the initial voltage $e_0$ at the beginning of the discharge. Thus, although both $e_0$ and $Q$ must be measured in a time $t \ll RC$, $Q$ is measured over a longer period than $e_0$ and is less susceptible to error caused by slow measurement.

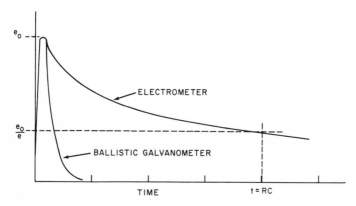

Fig. 2.32. Voltage impulse output of a hydrophone measured with an electrometer and a ballistic galvanometer.

The pressure impulse $\Delta p$ must be applied rapidly. The required speed is most easily achieved by the quick release of a static pressure rather than by a quick application. Figure 2.33 shows a simple arrangement for doing this. The hydrophone is subjected to a static pressure from the dead weight of the mass $m$. After the charge due to the pressure leaks off, the crystal electrodes contain no net charge. The mass $m$ then is snatched or quickly removed, thereby suddenly reducing the pressure. Thus, $\Delta p$ actually is a negative change. An alternative technique used by the Atlantic Research Corporation, manufacturers of commercial hydrophones, is illustrated by the dashed-line part of Fig. 2.33. Here, the quick-opening value releases the pressure in about 0.01 second. The weight snatching is the faster of the two methods. When $e_0$ is being measured, it is important that $\Delta p$ reach its maximum value before any charge has leaked off the crystal electrodes. Inertial impedances such as the valve orifice that slow the change in pressure should be minimized.

The calibration obtained with Eq. (2.55) is valid in the frequency range where (1) the hydrophone is electrically equivalent to a perfect capacitor, (2) the hydrophone is mechanically equivalent to a perfect spring, and (3) the hydrophone dimensions are small in comparison with a wavelength of sound in both water and

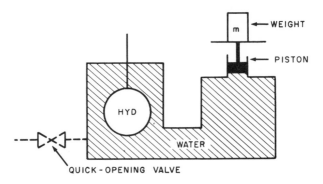

Fig. 2.33. Impulse calibration system for releasing the static pressure either by snatching the weight $m$ off the piston or by opening a valve.

the piezoelectric material. Requirement (1) sets the low-frequency limit at which the assumption $R \gg 1/\omega C$ no longer is valid and the sensitivity rolls off as shown in Fig. 2.34. Requirements (2) and (3) set the high-frequency limit at which the hydrophone is near a resonance or is too large.

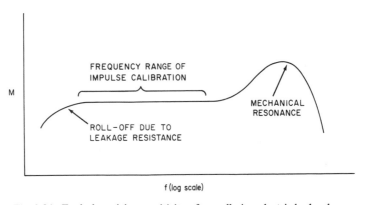

Fig. 2.34. Typical receiving sensitivity of a small piezoelectric hydrophone.

The calibration method is quasi-static in that, in the absence of any crystal leakage resistance, the measurement could be made under completely static conditions; Eq. (2.55) is essentially a static relationship. The measurement problems arise from the need to make static measurements before the effect of the leakage resistance $R$ sets in.

Since sound pressures usually are small (the order of 1000 $\mu$bar or 0.001 atm), the dead weight in Fig. 2.33 also should be small. Otherwise, nonlinearity may affect the calibration.

Variations of this technique are used to measure the piezoelectric constants of crystals and ceramics.

## 2.8 Radiation Pressure Techniques

A second-order effect called radiation pressure can be used for calibration purposes under special conditions. Radiation pressure is a small static pressure present in any acoustic wave. In a plane progressive wave of intensity $I$, average energy density $E$, rms sound pressure $p$, speed $c$, in a medium of density $\rho$, the radiation pressure $p_r$ is given by[37]

$$p_r = E = \frac{I}{c} = \frac{p^2}{\rho c^2} . \tag{2.56}$$

In sound fields that are equivalent to the superposition of two or more plane progressive waves, the radiation pressure is equal to the average total energy density.

When a sound beam impinges on a boundary, the reflection or absorption at the boundary results in sound energy density that is different on the two sides of the boundary. Therefore, a radiation pressure differential or net force acts on the boundary. For example, suppose a sound beam of energy density $E$ impinges normally on a perfectly absorbing plane boundary. Then, $p_r = E$ on one side, and $p_r = 0$ on the other side. The net force on the boundary then is $EA$, where $A$ is the boundary area. If the boundary is a perfect reflector instead of a perfect absorber, the energy density on the front or reflecting side averaged over both space and time will be doubled so that the net force becomes $2EA$. If the medium itself absorbs some of the energy in a sound beam, the energy density and radiation pressure will decrease as the distance from the sound source is increased. The resulting differential radiation pressure will produce streaming or a flow of the medium away from the source, unless the beam is confined to a tube where circulating flow cannot take place.

Radiation pressure is used for calibration purposes by measuring the static radiation pressure on reflecting or absorbing boundaries and calculating the sound pressure from Eq. (2.56). The difference between the sound pressure and the radiation pressure is very large. For example, in water an rms sound pressure of 150,000 $\mu$bar is needed to produce a radiation pressure of 1 $\mu$bar—a 103.5 dB difference. Consequently, a very sensitive mechanical balance or spring system must be used to measure the forces produced by radiation pressure. Thus, the technique is feasible only for very high intensity sound.

The radiation pressure technique is most applicable for high-frequency high-intensity applications such as are found in cavitation studies and medical or industrial ultrasonics. Usually, the plane waves are the collimated near-field zone of a piston source many wavelengths in diameter. Such near-field plane waves are not truly plane, because the pressure in a near-field plane varies from point to point; however, when average pressures over a plane are used, the results are equivalent to true plane waves.

One version of a commercial instrument[38] based on the radiation pressure principle is shown schematically and simplified in Fig. 2.35. The reflecting boundary is slanted from the incident sound to avoid standing waves or the reaction of the reflected sound on the source. The reflector thus is equivalent to a plane absorber, insofar as the vertical forces are concerned, and the downward force $F$ is given by

$$F = p_rA = EA, \tag{2.57}$$

where $A$ is the area, normal to the beam, that intercepts the beam. The average plane-wave rms sound pressure $p$ then is

$$p = (E\rho)^{\frac{1}{2}}c = \left(\frac{F\rho}{A}\right)^{\frac{1}{2}}c. \tag{2.58}$$

The force $F$ is measured by the balance in Fig. 2.35, although the scale may be calibrated in terms of pressure or intensity. The instrument itself is calibrated by placing known weights on the reflector.

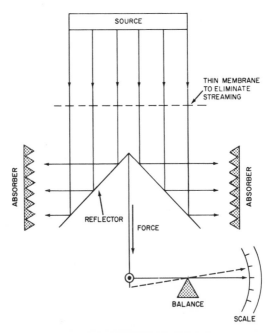

Fig. 2.35. Radiation pressure meter.

An instrument like that shown in Fig. 2.35 calibrates the source in the sense that the near-field average pressure or intensity is measured. These are the parameters of interest in cavitation and ultrasonic engineering application, and there is no intent to extrapolate the measurements to free-field far-field conditions. The instrument shown in Fig. 2.35 is used in the 50 kHz to 5 MHz frequency range.

Another version of the radiation pressure technique is shown in Fig. 2.36.[39] Here, the receiving sensitivity of a piezoelectric plate is measured. The plate also serves as an almost perfect reflector. Since the source is not being evaluated here, the presence of standing waves does not affect the measurement. Insofar as the effect on the hydrophone is concerned, there always is sound pressure doubling. That is, there is a standing-wave condition in the medium next to the plate if it is a near-perfect reflector—regardless of whether there is a complete entrapment of the waves between the source and hydrophone. The standing-wave condition actually helps to obtain high energy densities without a high-energy steady-state output from the source. The standing waves store acoustic energy; consequently, higher energy densities can be obtained, for a constant energy output of the source, than in a single plane progressive wave.

The standing waves are equivalent to two plane progressive waves traveling in opposite directions. The energy density average over both space and time then is double that of a single plane progressive wave. Note that although the sound

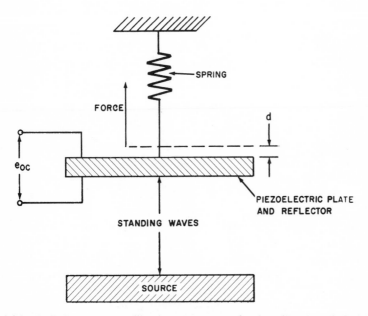

Fig. 2.36. Radiation pressure calibration arrangement for the calibration of piezoelectric plate hydrophone.

pressure also is doubled at the reflecting surface, the intensity is not quadrupled. A quarter-wave away from the reflector, the sound pressure always is near zero, and the space-averaging accounts for the factor $1/2$. The force on the hydrophone reflector thus is

$$F = p_r A = 2EA, \tag{2.59}$$

and the sound pressure in the plane progressive wave is given by

$$p = (E\rho)^{1/2} c = \left(\frac{F\rho}{2A}\right)^{1/2} c. \tag{2.60}$$

The force is measured by observing the upward displacement $d$ of the reflector caused by the radiation pressure, and computing the force from $F = kd$, where $k$ is the spring constant. The open-circuit voltage output $e_{oc}$ of the hydrophone is measured simultaneously with the force, so that the receiving sensitivity $M$ becomes

$$M = \left(\frac{e_{oc}}{c}\right)\left(\frac{2A}{F\rho}\right)^{1/2}. \tag{2.61}$$

In this case, $M$ is the free-field voltage sensitivity, even though the hydrophone neither is used in nor calibrated in a free field. This technique has been used in the frequency range 300 to 5000 kHz.

Another version of a radiation pressure calibration technique involves amplitude modulation of a high-frequency (about 1000 kHz) sound beam with a low-frequency (about 1 kHz) signal. The radiation pressure oscillates at the low frequency, resulting in a pseudo sound pressure. In this way a low-frequency pressure can be obtained in a narrow beam that normally is characteristic of only high-frequency radiation. This is an interesting technique that is periodically suggested in the literature. Experiments at the Navy Underwater Sound Reference Laboratory have shown that the technique has many difficulties, most of which evolve from the large difference (100 dB or more) between the high-frequency or carrier signals and the low-frequency modulation or radiation pressure signals. As the carrier signal amplitude is increased, cavitation usually occurs in the high-intensity sound beam before a measurable low-frequency signal can be obtained. The sensitivity of the hydrophone and the receiving electronic circuits must be more than 100 dB higher at the modulation frequency than at the carrier frequency. Since the radiation pressure is proportional to the square of the sound pressure, the radiation pressure signal and the modulation signal have different wave shapes. The diffraction effects of a true low-frequency sound wave are not duplicated by the modulated radiation pressure except for the case of a piston in an infinite baffle. These difficulties have precluded the practical use of this technique.

## 2.9 Measurements in Air

If the acoustical impedance of a transducer itself is high enough so that its radiation impedance can be neglected, and if it also is small enough so that diffraction effects also can be neglected, then its receiving sensitivity will be the same in water as it is in air. For example, ordinary piezoelectric hydrophones containing electroacoustical elements having dimensions of about an inch or less fit these restrictions. Consequently, air acoustical methods can be used to calibrate these hydrophones at audio frequencies. One such method, the air piston-phone, already has been described. The reciprocity method also is used in microphone calibration.

The electrostatic actuator method is one primary method of air acoustics that is not adaptable directly to underwater acoustics; however, it can be used for an air calibration of a hydrophone if the hydrophone has a flat metal diaphragm. The electrostatic actuator is a device consisting of a metal grid or plate that is placed close to the metal diaphragm to form a parallel plate electrical condenser. The electrically induced forces between the two plates provide the calibration pressure. Beranek[28] describes this method in detail. Pyett at the British Admiralty Underwater Weapons Establishment has used the electrostatic actuator at frequencies as high as 60 kHz for an unusual application wherein the pressure sensitivity rather than the free-field sensitivity was needed to measure water flow noise. The calibration was made with a helium medium between the parallel plates.

## 2.10 Velocity or Pressure-Gradient Sensitivity

The electrical output of some hydrophones is proportional to the particle velocity or pressure gradient in the sound field. The terms "velocity" and "pressure gradient" often are used interchangeably for such hydrophones, although some distinctions can be drawn between the two terms (see Section 5.12). The hydrophones are designed so a part of the hydrophone oscillates in the medium under the influence of the sound pressure gradient, or with motion similar to that of particle velocity. The main characteristic and advantage of a velocity or pressure-gradient hydrophone is the directivity pattern. The pattern is shown in Fig. 2.37. It is called the "figure-eight," "cosine," or "dipole" pattern and is independent of frequency. The pressure at any angle $\theta$ relative to the axial pressure is equal to $\cos \theta$.

Velocity and pressure-gradient hydrophones may be, and usually are, calibrated in terms of pressure rather than velocity (pressure gradient is never used as a reference). Since the relationship between pressure and velocity depends on the wave and boundary conditions, however, these conditions must be known, be standard, or fit the definition of the sensitivity.

Plane progressive waves are specified in the definition of free-field voltage sensitivity, and the relationship between the pressure $p$ and velocity $u$ in such

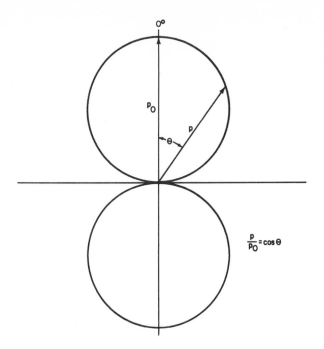

Fig. 2.37. Directivity pattern of a velocity or pressure-gradient hydrophone.

waves is given by the wave or characteristic impedance $p/u = \rho c$. Thus, the sensitivity of a velocity hydrophone expressed in terms of pressure differs from the sensitivity expressed in terms of velocity by the constant factor $\rho c$

A velocity hydrophone can be calibrated by direct comparison with a standard pressure hydrophone only if essentially plane waves impinge on both hydrophones. Otherwise, corrections that account for the difference between the quotient $p/u$ and the value of $\rho c$ must be applied to the measurements.

Waves in a free field never are perfectly plane, and the extent to which slightly spherical waves can be assumed to be plane is important when dealing with velocity hydrophones calibrated in terms of pressure.

The criteria for plane waves can be obtained from the expressions for the pressure $p$, the particle velocity $u$, and the magnitude of the wave impedance $|p/u|$ in a wave emanating from a point source:

$$p \quad = \left(\frac{A}{r}\right) \exp j(\omega t - kr), \tag{2.62}$$

$$u \quad = \left(\frac{A}{r\rho c}\right)\left[1 - j\frac{\lambda}{2\pi r}\right] \exp j(\omega t - kr), \tag{2.63}$$

$$\left|\frac{p}{u}\right|^2 = (\rho c)^2 \left[1 + \left(\frac{\lambda}{2\pi r}\right)^2\right], \tag{2.64}$$

where $r$ is the distance from the source and $A$ is a constant. From these equations and Fig. 2.38, it can be seen that for small values of $r/\lambda$, the velocity is augmented, and the plane wave relation $p/u = \rho c$ is not valid. A correction factor, $10 \log (1 + \lambda^2/(2\pi r)^2)$, must be subtracted from the measured sensitivity when a velocity hydrophone is calibrated with a standard pressure hydrophone. That is, the augmentation that occurs in spherical waves must be eliminated from the results. The magnitude of the correction is shown in Fig. 2.38. It can be seen from the figure that the correction is less than 0.5 dB when $r/\lambda = 0.5$. Therefore, as a rule of thumb, the source-to-hydrophone distance should be greater than a half wavelength if the velocity augmenting factor is to be negligible.

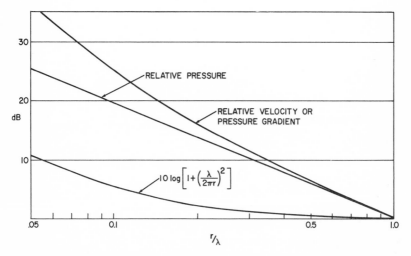

Fig. 2.38. Velocity or pressure-gradient augmentation is a spherical wave.

The pressure gradient is related to the particle velocity by $\partial p/\partial r = j\omega\rho u$ for both spherical and plane waves; consequently, the augmenting factor for velocity applies also to the pressure gradient.

When the sensitivity referred to actual particle velocity is required, the simplest technique is to calibrate the velocity or pressure-gradient hydrophone in terms of a measured free-field sound pressure $p$, and then compute the particle velocity from the pressure with Eqs. (2.62), (2.63), and (2.64).

If free-field conditions are not available, a standing-wave tube like that shown in Fig. 2.39 can be used. Since a water-air boundary is a near-zero impedance boundary, essentially complete reflection will take place. A standing-wave system then can be established and the following relations hold:

$$p \propto \sin kd, \tag{2.65}$$

$$u \propto \cos kd \tag{2.66}$$

$$|p/u| = \rho c \tan kd. \tag{2.67}$$

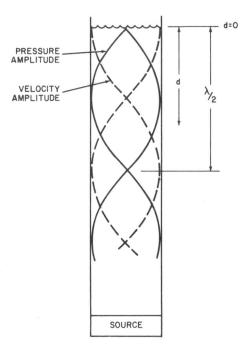

Fig. 2.39. Pressure and velocity distribution in a standing-wave tube.

If the pressure is measured at a point a distance $d$ from the water-air surface, Eqs. (2.65) and (2.66) can be used to compute the pressure and velocity at any other point. It must be assumed here that the hydrophones have a negligible effect on the standing-wave pattern. Also, the wavelength or the speed of sound which is used in the wave number $2\pi/\lambda = \omega/c$ in the tube probably will differ from that in a free field; therefore, the half-wavelength or pressure-node-to-node distance should be measured.

Another version of the standing-wave tube, developed by Bauer,[40] is shown in Fig. 2.40a. Here, the whole rigid tube section is vibrated *en masse*. The fluid medium inside then moves as a short section of a standing-wave system with the velocity and pressure amplitude distribution shown in Fig. 2.40b. If $u_e$, the velocity of both ends of the tube (and of every other point on the tube), is measured with an accelerometer, both the velocity $u_d$ and the pressure $p_d$ at any point $d$ can be computed from

$$u_d = u_e \frac{\cos kd}{\cos \tfrac{1}{2}kL}, \qquad (2.68)$$

$$p_d = ju_e \rho c \frac{\sin kd}{\sin \tfrac{1}{2}kL}, \qquad (2.69)$$

where $L$ is the tube length, $d$ is the distance of any point from the midpoint of $L$, and $\rho c$ is the characteristic impedance of the medium. The velocity $u_0$ at the midpoint of the tube can be found by letting $d = 0$ in Eq. (2.68):

$$u_0 = \frac{u_d}{\cos \tfrac{1}{2}kL}. \qquad (2.70)$$

The velocity $u_0$ also can be determined by pressure measurements and other combinations of Eqs. (2.68) and (2.69). Thus, if a velocity hydrophone is placed at the midpoint of the tube and its voltage output $e_{oc}$ is measured, the free-field voltage sensitivity $M$ is given by

$$M = \frac{e_{oc}}{\rho c u_0}. \qquad (2.71)$$

The Bauer vibrator is adaptable to measurements in a closed pressure vessel and also permits the velocity to be determined in any arbitrary direction. The open tube of Fig. 2.39 is limited, of course, to velocity in the vertical direction.

## 2.11 Directivity Patterns

The measurement of the directivity characteristics of a transducer involves little calibration theory in comparison with that required for measuring response or sensitivity. The directivity pattern, factor, and index all are relative and dimensionless parameters. They also are free-field, far-field parameters, and for patterns, there is no feasible alternative to free-field measurements. There is an alternative to the far-field requirement, however; conventional patterns can be measured under the free-field, near-field conditions described in Chapter IV. Measurement problems consist largely of obtaining free-field conditions and arranging the mechanics for rotating transducers in various planes.

Some of the theory underlying the definition and meaning of the directivity characteristics and mathematical solutions for some common special cases are presented here. One technique for measuring the directivity factor under conditions other than free field also is discussed.

The directivity pattern of a transducer shows how the sensitivity of the transducer varies as a function of direction. It usually is normalized; that is, it is a plot

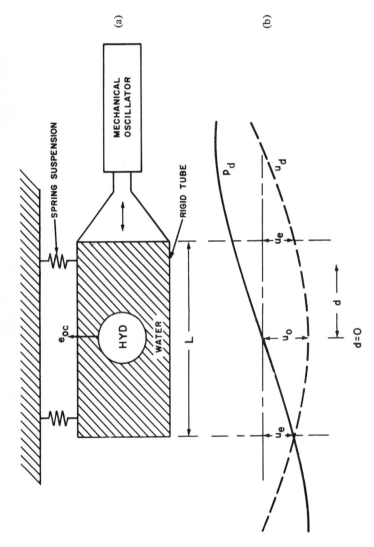

Fig. 2.40. (a) A Bauer vibrator, and (b) the pressure and velocity distribution within the tube.

of the sensitivity in any direction relative to the sensitivity in a given reference direction—usually an axial direction. Thus, the pattern level on the axis of a typical transducer will be 1, or 0 dB, and the levels in other directions will be some fraction less than 1 or some number of dB below zero or "dB down." In some unusual cases, the axis is not the direction of maximum sensitivity. Then, the normalized pattern level in the direction of maximum sensitivity will be greater than 1 or some number of dB above zero. Occasionally, a series of patterns will be measured on one transducer at the same frequency—usually after some electrical or mechanical adjustment. In such cases, only the first or "control" pattern may be normalized. Succeeding patterns then may be measured without adjusting the measuring system to allow direct comparison with the first pattern.

If a transducer is reciprocal, its transmitting and receiving patterns are the same even though they have different physical meanings. The transmitting pattern is essentially a diagram of how much sound emanates from a transducer simultaneously in different directions. The receiving pattern is a measure of the average pressure acting on a transducer diaphragm as a function of the direction of an impinging plane wave. The transmitting pattern is used almost exclusively for analytical purposes, perhaps because it's easier to visualize. However, the summations or integrals that must be solved to obtain a mathematical expression for the pattern are the same for either case.

The complete directivity pattern is a three-dimensional model. In practice, however, two-dimensional polar diagrams usually are used to represent the pattern in some plane that includes the acoustic axis. The complete pattern is deduced or visualized from a collection of many two-dimensional patterns. Often, the complete pattern has an axis of symmetry so that one two-dimensional pattern in a plane of such an axis gives a picture of the complete pattern.

The transmitting pattern is a representation of far-field or Fraunhofer diffraction phenomena. That is, the radiated sound pressure is observed or measured at an "effectively infinite" distance from the transducer. The distance is "effectively infinite" if the signal attenuation due to spherical spreading of the wave is essentially the same for signals emanating from all points of the transducer, or the sound rays from all points on the transducer to the observation point can be assumed to be parallel. Thus, for a uniform radiator, the wave interference that gives rise to directivity patterns, or Fraunhofer diffraction, is due entirely to phase differences among contributions from different parts of the transducer. In the near field, the Fresnel diffraction, or interference, is due to both phase and amplitude differences.

Practical criteria for "effectively infinite" measurement distances are presented in Section 3.4. In general, however, the distance should be large in comparison with the largest dimension of the transducer in the plane of rotation.

In addition to sufficient far-field conditions, good free-field conditions also must prevail. Pattern measurements usually require better free-field conditions than response measurements do, because longer measurement distances are required and because the "difference" between a high signal level (on the axis) and low signal levels (on the minor lobes) is being measured. To illustrate, a reflection, noise, or other unwanted interference may be 26 dB below the signal level for response in the axial direction and therefore introduce only a small error of ±0.5 dB in the axial response. This same unwanted signal would produce a large error (+3.5 to −6 dB) on the height of a minor lobe 20 dB below the major lobe.

### 2.11.1  Uniform radiators

The mathematical expressions for $p(\theta)$, the normalized directivity pattern, of some common uniform radiators are given below.

a. Plane, uniform, baffled circular piston:

$$p(\theta) = \frac{2J_1\left\{\left(\frac{\pi x}{\lambda}\right)\sin\theta\right\}}{\left(\frac{\pi x}{\lambda}\right)\sin\theta}. \tag{2.72}$$

b. Plane, uniform, baffled rectangular piston, in a plane parallel to an edge; or a uniform continuous line:

$$p(\theta) = \frac{\sin\left\{\left(\frac{\pi x}{\lambda}\right)\sin\theta\right\}}{\left(\frac{\pi x}{\lambda}\right)\sin\theta}. \tag{2.73}$$

c. A plane, baffled, uniform square, in the plane of the diagonal (or a straight "tapered" or "shaded" line, where the source strength is maximum at the center and decreases linearly to zero at each end):

$$p(\theta) = \frac{\sin^2\left\{\left(\frac{\pi x}{2\lambda}\right)\sin\theta\right\}}{\left\{\left(\frac{\pi x}{2\lambda}\right)\sin\theta\right\}^2}. \tag{2.74}$$

d. $N$, uniform, equally spaced points in a straight line:

$$p(\theta) = \frac{\sin\left\{\left(\frac{\pi N d}{\lambda}\right)\sin\theta\right\}}{N\sin\left\{\left(\frac{\pi d}{\lambda}\right)\sin\theta\right\}}. \tag{2.75}$$

In these expressions, $J_1$ is the first-order Bessel function; $x$ is the circular piston diameter (Case a), length of line or edge of rectangle (Case b), or diagonal length

(Case c); $d$ is the separation distance of points in a line; and $\theta$ is the angle between the axis or normal direction and the direction of observation—that is, the variable in all the expressions.

Graphs of these expressions are shown in Fig. 2.41 for Cases (a), (b), and (c). By using the normalizing parameter $(x/\lambda) \sin \theta$ for the abscissa, the patterns in the figures are made applicable to any transducer size and any frequency. Mathematical expressions and graphs for radiators of other configurations are given in the literature.[41-46]

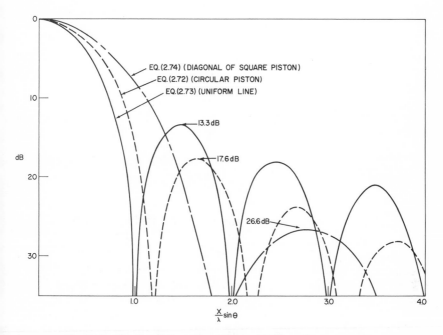

Fig. 2.41. The directivity pattern $20 \log p(\theta)$ of continuous sources.

The line of $N$ points is not included in Fig. 2.41 because it differs basically from a continuous source. The most striking characteristic of the pattern of a line of point sources is the high side lobes. If the point spacing is one wavelength or greater, the $(N-1)$, $2(N-1)$, $3(N-1)$, etc., minor lobes will be of the same height as the major lobe. The height of the other minor lobes will depend on $N$. If the number of points per unit length increases, the spacing $d$ decreases and the approximation $\sin \left\{(\pi d/\lambda) \sin \theta\right\} \simeq (\pi d/\lambda) \sin \theta$ can be made in the denominator of Eq. (2.75). Then, Eqs. (2.75) and (2.73) become the same, with $Nd$ becoming equivalent to $x$, and the line of points approximates a continuous line. Figure 2.42 shows the patterns for a 6-point line.

Some radiators combine the characteristics of both continuous and discrete sources. For example, a large planar array often consists of many individual

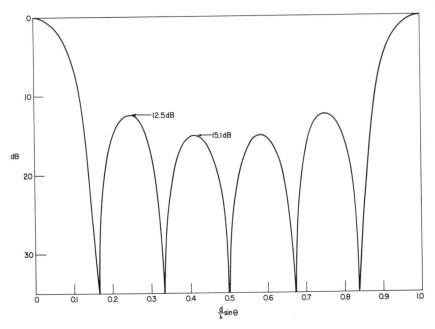

Fig. 2.42. The directivity pattern $20 \log p(\theta)$ of a line of six point sources.

elements, each of which constitutes a small radiator that has a directivity pattern that is not omnidirectional. That is, the elements are not point sources. Spaces exist between the elements so that even when the elements vibrate with uniform phase and amplitude, the array does not radiate as a continuous uniform piston. A similar situation exists with a segmented line radiator. In such cases, an understanding of Bridge's Product Theorem is helpful. This theorem states that *for the case of a number of radiators of the same frequency and of identical pattern and orientation in space, but possibly of different amplitude and phases of motion, when the reaction of one radiator on the other is neglected, the pattern produced by the aggregate of the radiators is the pattern produced by an aggregate of point sources having the same distribution in space, amplitude, and phase as the actual radiators, multipled by the pattern of a single radiator.*

This means, for example, that if the pattern level is expected to be 0.5, or −6 dB, in a particular direction $\theta$ when the elements of an array are assumed to be points, and the pattern of an individual element is expected to be 0.9, or −1 dB, at the same angle $\theta$, then the array or aggregate pattern level at $\theta$ should be 0.45, or −7 dB.

The qualification in the theorem as to the reaction of one radiator on the other becomes important when the element spacing is small (generally a small fraction of a wavelength) and the transducer mechanical impedance is low.

### 2.11.2 Nonuniform radiators

If the displacement or velocity of every point of the diaphragm, or radiating area of a transducer, does not vibrate with the same amplitude and phase when the transducer is used as a projector, the transducer is referred to as a nonuniform radiator. Some transducer diaphragms, for example, bend rather than move as a rigid piston. Bending and other types of nonuniform vibration usually are used to obtain resonance at low frequencies. In such cases, the transducers are essentially omnidirectional, and the nonuniformity has negligible effect on the directivity pattern.

Another more important type of nonuniformity is exemplified by the shaded transducer. Here, nonuniformity is introduced in an otherwise uniform radiator to change the directivity pattern. The usual purpose is to reduce the level of the minor lobes. Typically, the transducer will consist of a plane array of elements that are mechanically identical so that, for example, all elements resonate at the same frequency. The outside or peripheral elements, however, will be driven at a lower electrical signal level than are the inside elements. Variations in phasing and spacing, as well as amplitude, also have been used for controlling the pattern.

Equation (2.73) applies to a shaded line (also called a tapered line)—that is, a line in which the vibration amplitude is a maximum at the center and decreases linearly to zero at each end. If we compare the graphs of Eqs. (2.73) and (2.74) in Fig. 2.41, we see that this shading substantially reduces the minor lobe level, but also broadens the major lobe. Unfortunately, these two effects are inseparable.

Pattern control is an extensive subject covered elsewhere in the literature.[41-45] It is used extensively in sonar transducers. Insofar as measurements are concerned, it is helpful to know whether a transducer is a uniform or nonuniform radiator. Such knowledge not only aids in detecting mistakes or malfunctioning equipment, but also affects measurement conditions, such as the minimum acceptable distance between a projector and hydrophone.

### 2.11.3 Beam widths and minor lobe level

Patterns usually are characterized by the beam width and by the relative level of the highest (usually the first) minor lobe. The beam width is the angle included between the directions, on each side of the main lobe or beam, in which the level of the sound pressure is at some fixed level relative to the axial sound pressure. There is no standard fixed level; −3 dB, −6 dB, and −10 dB, all, commonly are used. The level must be specified, therefore, and the beam width is described as, for example, the "6-dB-down beam width." Note that the beam width is the total angle between two directions—one on each side of the axis. Where a pattern is symmetrical about the axis, the half-beam width sometimes is used. The half-beam width is the angle included between the axis and the direction of the specified pressure level. Beam width is a function of both the radiator configuration (circular piston, line, line-of-points, etc.) and the ratio $x/\lambda$ of size to wavelength.

The 6-dB-down beam widths $\Delta\theta$ for the three patterns in Fig. 2.43 are given by:

$$\text{Circular piston:} \qquad \Delta\theta = 2 \arcsin\left(\frac{0.70\lambda}{x}\right) \qquad (2.76)$$

$$\text{Uniform line:} \qquad \Delta\theta = 2 \arcsin\left(\frac{0.60\lambda}{x}\right) \qquad (2.77)$$

$$\text{Diagonal of square:} \quad \Delta\theta = 2 \arcsin\left(\frac{0.88\lambda}{x}\right). \qquad (2.78)$$

Equation (2.75) is approximately the same as Eq. (2.73), when $\sin\theta$ is small as well as when $d$ is small. Thus, near the axis, the pattern of a line of points is essentially the same as the pattern of a line for which $x = Nd$. Equation (2.77)

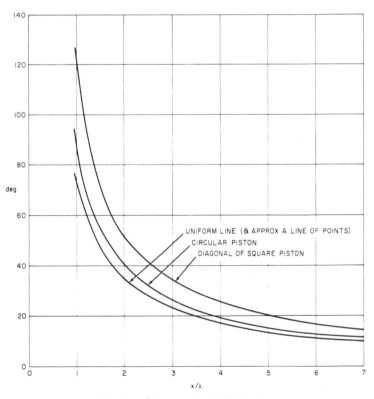

Fig. 2.43. Beamwidths (6-dB-down).

can be used for a line of points whenever the line of points approximates a continuous line ($d \ll \lambda$), or when the region of interest is near the axis ($\sin \theta \ll 1$).

The level of the minor lobes of continuous sources is a function of the configuration, but is independent of the size/wavelength ratio. The level of the minor lobes shown in Fig. 2.41 applies to all sources with the stated configurations. The minor lobe level in Fig. 2.42 applies only to a 6-point source. Kraus[41] gives similar patterns for cases of $N$ equal to 1 through 24.

## 2.12 Directivity Factor and Index

The directivity factor or index is a measure of the sharpness of the sound beam or major lobe of the directivity pattern. It is the ratio of $I_0$, the intensity (or $p_0^2$, the rms pressure squared), in a reference direction—usually the axis—to the intensity $\bar{I}$ (or $\bar{p}^2$, the rms pressure squared) averaged over all directions. In its numeric form, this ratio is the directivity factor $R_\theta$, and in the decibel form, it is the directivity index $D_i$. Thus,

$$R_\theta = \frac{I_0}{\bar{I}} = \frac{p_0^2}{\bar{p}^2}, \qquad (2.79)$$

$$D_i = 10 \log\left(\frac{I_0}{\bar{I}}\right) = 10 \log\left(\frac{p_0^2}{\bar{p}^2}\right). \qquad (2.80)$$

Note that $\bar{p}^2$ is the average of the pressure squared, not the square of the average pressure.

If $p_0$ is measured at distance $r$, then $\bar{p}^2$ is the pressure squared integrated over a spherical surface $S$ of radius $r$, divided by the area $S$. Then,

$$R_\theta = \frac{p_0^2}{\bar{p}^2} = \frac{p_0^2}{\frac{\int_S p^2 dS}{4\pi r^2}} = \frac{p_0^2 4\pi r^2}{\int_S p^2 dS}. \qquad (2.81)$$

It is the measurements and computations involving the integral $\int_S p^2 dS$ that constitute the major task in finding $R_\theta$ or $D_i$.

## 2.12.1 Theory

The theoretical $D_i$ of some idealized radiator configurations have been determined by Stenzel[44] and Molloy.[47] The $D_i$ of a circular piston in an infinite rigid baffle is given by

$$D_i = 10 \log\left(\frac{(kr)^2}{1 - \frac{J_1(2kr)}{kr}}\right), \qquad (2.82)$$

where $r$ is the radius and $k$ is the wave number. For large values of $kr$, the Bessel function $J_1(2kr)$ becomes negligible and $D_i \simeq 10 \log (kr)^2$. Since $(kr)^2 = 4\pi(\pi r^2)/\lambda^2$, the $D_i$ of large pistons can be approximated by

$$D_i = 10 \log\left(\frac{4\pi(\text{Area})}{\lambda^2}\right). \tag{2.83}$$

Figure 2.44, a plot of Eqs. (2.82) and (2.83), shows that Eq. (2.83) is a good approximation for $2a/\lambda > 1/2$.

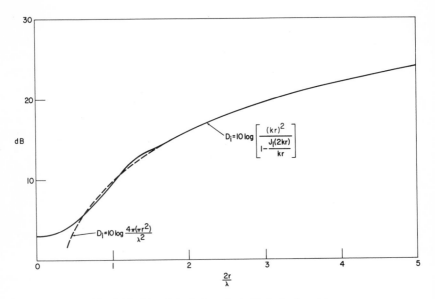

Fig. 2.44. Directivity index of a baffled circular piston.

For a uniform line,

$$D_i = 10 \log\left[ kL\left(\pi - \frac{2}{kL} - \frac{2 \sin kL}{kL} + \frac{4 \cos kL}{(kL)^3} - \cdots\right)\right], \tag{2.84}$$

where $L$ is the length of the line. For a long line, $L > \lambda$, and Eq. (2.84) approaches

$$D_i = 10 \log\left(\frac{2L}{\lambda}\right). \tag{2.85}$$

A rectangular piston in an infinite rigid baffle is a much more complicated case than a circular piston, but from the work of Stenzel[44] and Molloy,[47] it can be shown that Eq. (2.83) applies also to a large rectangular piston with about the same degree of approximation as for a circular piston. As a rule of thumb, Eq. (2.83) applies to both circular and rectangular pistons, if the minimum dimension is greater than a half wavelength and, for the case of the rectangle, if the length/width ratio is greater than 2. At the low limit of this approximation, where the minimum dimension is a half to one wavelength, the approximation error is about ±0.5 dB. In most practical cases, however, where $D_i$ is an important factor, the transducers are large or have narrow beams. Then, Eq. (2.83) becomes a very good approximation with negligible error. Moreover, since Eq. (2.83) applies to both circular and rectangular pistons, one would assume that it applies to other shapes that approximate either a circle or a rectangle.

It can be shown[2,48] that the directivity factor for plane pistons in infinite rigid baffles is inversely proportional to the radiation resistance. The acoustical radiation resistance of pistons of any shape approaches $\rho c/A$ as the size/wavelength ratio becomes large. It follows, then, that Eq. (2.83) applies to large pistons of any shape if the minimum dimension is greater than a half wavelength.

In all the foregoing, it has been assumed that the pistons are in an infinite rigid baffle because such a boundary condition makes the mathematics manageable. In practice, such baffles are not used, of course. In planar transducers whose smallest dimension is greater than a half wavelength, the type of baffle has a negligible effect on the directivity pattern, and theory and practice are in good agreement.

Analyses of the $D_i$ of horn transducers, pistons in a spherical baffle, rings, lines of points, shaded lines, and stretched membranes (or bending modes) are available in references 44 and 47.

### 2.12.2 Measurement

Three different approaches are used to determine the $R_\theta$ or $D_i$ of a specific transducer.

*Case 1.* Some transducers are good approximations, insofar as the directivity pattern is concerned, of perfect uniform, circular, square, or rectangular pistons, or of perfect uniform lines. When this is true, the $R_\theta$ or $D_i$ is well known from expressions such as Eqs. (2.82) through (2.85), and various slide rules,[49] graphs, and similar aids are available for obtaining the $D_i$ easily. Figures 2.45 and 2.46 are two such graphs.[50] Whether the pattern is a good approximation to one of the ideal cases must be ascertained by pattern measurements and comparison with Figs. 2.41, 2.42, and 2.43. About 90% of the energy radiated by ideal pistons and lines is in the main lobe, and about 95% is in the main lobe and first minor lobe. Thus, a transducer can be assumed to be radiating as its ideal mathematical model if the measured and theoretical patterns are the same, within measurement accuracy, on the major lobe and first minor lobe. This rule of thumb is valid if none of the minor lobes are unusually high. A strong minor lobe at 180° or to the rear in piston transducers is a particularly common type of undesirable and unintentional radiation.

84 METHODS AND THEORY

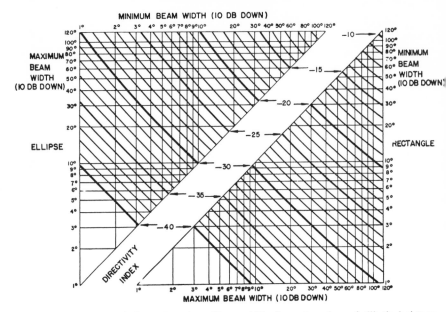

Fig. 2.45. Directivity index as function of beamwidths for rectangular and elliptical pistons. Maximum beamwidths are measured in the plane through the acoustic axis parallel to the short side of the rectangle or including the minor axis of the ellipse. Minimum beamwidths are measured in the plane through the acoustic axis parallel to the long side of the rectangle or including the major axis of the ellipse. (From Reference 50.)

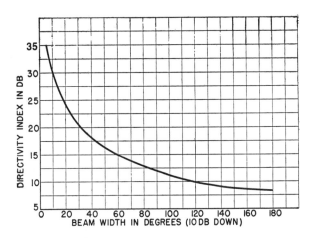

Fig. 2.46. Directivity index as a function of the beamwidth for a circular baffled piston. (From Reference 50.)

*Case 2.* Some transducers, like circular pistons, cylinders, or lines, may radiate with a nonideal pattern, but still have an axis of circular symmetry. That is, the pattern is the same in all planes through the axis of symmetry. This fact should be verified by actual measurement of several patterns. The integration over a complete spherical surface is obtained by taking the elemental area $dS$ as shown in Fig. 2.47 and integrating

$$\int_S dS = \int_0^\pi 2\pi r^2 \sin \theta \, d\theta, \tag{2.86}$$

where $\theta$ is the angle between the reference direction or axis and the direction of measurement. If we let $p(\theta)$ be the pressure as a function of $\theta$, we obtain $R_\theta$ from Eqs. (2.81) and (2.86):

$$R_\theta = \frac{2}{\displaystyle\int_0^\pi \left(\frac{p(\theta)}{p_0}\right)^2 \sin \theta \, d\theta}. \tag{2.87}$$

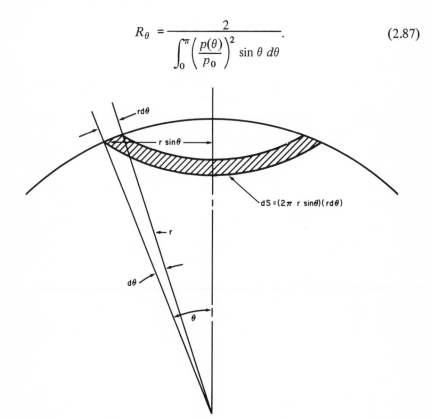

Fig. 2.47. Elemental area segment $dS$ used to integrate over a spherical surface.

If, as we have assumed, the transducer pattern is nonideal, the function $p(\theta)$ is unknown, and the integral must be evaluated graphically or numerically. Several kinds of aids are used for graphical integration. For example, either of the two charts in Figs. 2.48 or 2.49 can be used.[51] The ordinate scale is

$[p(\theta)/p_0]^2$, with the scale marked for easy transposition from the usual decibel scale on pattern plots. The abscissa scale is the angle $\theta$ with the spacing adjusted so that the area represented by the product $[p(\theta)/p_0]^2\theta$ is proportional to the area of the spherical surface from 0 to $\theta$, or proportional to $\int_0^\theta \sin\theta\, d\theta$. After the pattern is transposed to Fig. 2.48 or 2.49, the area under the curve is measured with a planimeter. If there is radiation in the rear hemisphere, the pattern there must be plotted separately. Then the $R_\theta$ is given by

$$R_\theta = \frac{2(\text{area of front + rear charts})}{(\text{area under front + rear curves})}. \tag{2.88}$$

Even if there is no radiation toward the rear and the denominator of Eq. (2.88) constitutes the area under only one curve, the numerator still must be the area of the two charts. For narrow-beam patterns, Fig. 2.49 is more accurate than Fig. 2.48; however, the numerator of Eq. (2.88) still must include the whole area corresponding to $0 \leqslant \theta \leqslant 180°$. Consequently, the area found from the whole chart in Fig. 2.49 should be taken as 7.46 times its size as shown, or the numerator of Eq. (2.88) should contain 7.46 as an additional coefficient.

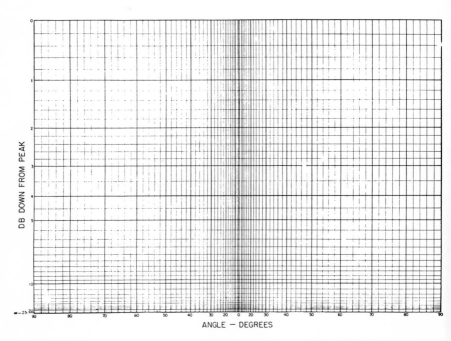

Fig. 2.48. Chart for determining radiation directivity. (From Reference 51.)

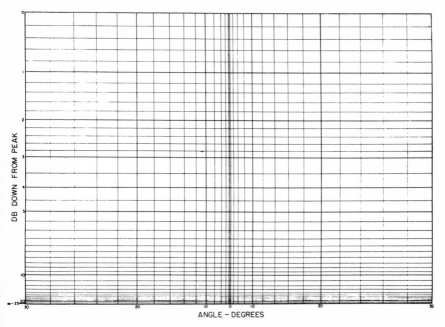

Fig. 2.49. Chart for determining radiation directivity. (From Reference 51.)

Another graphical aid, shown in Fig. 2.50,[50] is used to obtain the integral of Eq. (2.87) by a summation approximation. That is, the summation

$$\sum_{i=0}^{n} \left(\frac{p(\theta_i)}{p_0}\right)^2 (\sin \theta_i)\Delta\theta$$

is substituted for the integral. Fig. 2.50 is used in the form of a transparent overlay on the measured polar pattern. The peak axial response (or $20 \log p_0$) is made to coincide with the polar angle zero, and the radial level at the top of the paper as illustrated by the dashed-line pattern. Then to find $[p(\theta_i)/p_0]^2 \sin \theta_i$ for any angle $\theta_i$, one proceeds along the radial line corresponding to $\theta_i$ until the intersection with the directivity pattern line is reached. The point of intersection then is read on the bow-shaped coordinates. For example, at $\theta_i = 20°$ or $i = 4$ in Fig. 2.50, the point of intersection is at 0.009 in the bow-shaped coordinates. Thus, $[p(20°)/p_0]^2 \sin 20° = 0.009$. This reading is made at regular angular intervals—say every 5° from 0 to 180°. Then 37 measurements are made. The regular angular interval $\Delta\theta$ must be expressed in radians, so $\Delta\theta = \pi/36$. If $A_i$ is the value of $[p(\theta_i)/p_0]^2 \sin \theta_i$, or the number read from the bow-shaped coordinates on Fig. 2.50, Eq. (2.87) is approximated by

$$R_\theta = \frac{2}{\Delta\theta \sum\limits_{i=0}^{n} A_i},$$  (2.89)

or, in the example just given,

$$R_\theta = \frac{2}{\left(\dfrac{\pi}{36}\right)\sum\limits_{i=0}^{36} A_i}.$$  (2.90)

The pattern should be measured so that the pattern level at zero degrees or in the reference direction is either at the top of the chart, or at the discrete levels 10, 20, 30, etc., dB below the top. The radial scale is 10 dB per major division (usually 10 dB per inch). When the pattern level at zero degrees is at −10 dB, all the bow-shaped coordinate scale numbers must be multiplied by 0.1. When the pattern level at zero degrees is at −20 dB, the scale numbers must be multiplied by 0.01, and so forth. Note that at $\theta = 0$, $A_0$ always is zero, because $\sin 0° = 0$.

The angle $\theta = 0$ corresponds to the axis of symmetry, whether it is in the direction of maximum response, the acoustic axis, or in general the reference direction. If the axis of symmetry is not the reference direction, the $D_i$ is computed with $\theta = 0$ taken as the axis of symmetry, and then a correction is added. The correction in decibels is the pattern level in the direction of the axis of symmetry subtracted from the level in the reference directions. The pattern of a uniform line or thin cylinder is the most common example of this. The pattern has a toroid or "doughnut" shape. The axis of symmetry coincides with the line or cylinder axis, but the reference direction usually is normal to the line. Thus, the intensity in the direction of the line or axis of symmetry is very low—less than the average intensity. This results in a fractional $R_\theta$ or negative $D_i$. When the large difference between the high response normal to the line and low response parallel to the line is added to the $D_i$, the $D_i$ becomes positive.

Electronic analog systems have been built by the Navy Electronics Laboratory and by Scientific-Atlanta, Inc., to perform the integration $\int \{p(\theta)/p_0\}^2 \sin\theta \, d\theta$. The Underwater Sound Reference Division of the Naval Research Laboratory has used a small digital computer to perform the integration numerically.

*Case 3.* When a radiation pattern does not conform closely to an ideal one, as in Case 1, nor have an axis of circular symmetry, as in Case 2, the integration task becomes formidable. If a transducer does not have circular symmetry, but is symmetrical in the sense that the right and left halves, or top and bottom halves, are mirror images of each other, an averaging process can be used. Then, the patterns in several planes through the axis of symmetry are measured and each treated as in Case 2. The average $R_\theta$ then is computed. (Do not average

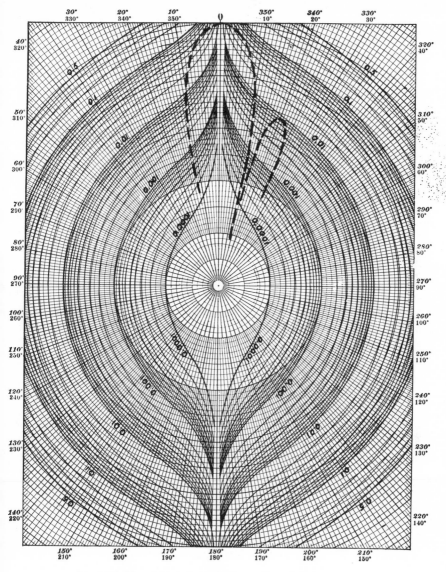

Fig. 2.50. Directivity index calculator. (From Reference 50.)

$D_i$ or decibels!) When there is no symmetry at all, a long tedious three-dimensional graphical integration is necessary, but seldom attempted.

One alternative to graphical or electronic integration is a diffuse sound technique that is equivalent to acoustical integration. A diffuse sound field is one in which the time average of the mean-square sound pressure is everywhere the same and the flow of energy in all directions is equally probable. The diffuse sound sensitivity of a hydrophone is the ratio of the time-averaged voltage output to the diffuse sound pressure. The diffuse sound sensitivity thus is the free-field voltage sensitivity of the hydrophone averaged over all directions. It follows then that the ratio of the free-field voltage sensitivity to the diffuse sound sensitivity is the $R_\theta$, or the difference is the $D_i$, when the sensitivity is given as 20 log $M$. This technique, theoretically, is very simple; however, there is little mention of it in the literature and it has been used to only a limited extent.[52] The expense of building a large enough reverberation tank in which a satisfactory diffuse sound field can be established is a major drawback.

## 2.13 Impedance

The impedance of an electroacoustic transducer usually is understood to mean the electrical impedance measured at its electrical terminals. When some other meaning is intended, the term is qualified. For example, one would say that a soft transducer has a "low acoustical impedance." Along with sensitivity or response and patterns, the electrical impedance is a common and standard parameter in the calibration and evaluation of electroacoustic transducers. The impedance serves three purposes: (1) It provides information for impedance matching between the transducer and the electronic transmitting or receiving equipment. (2) It is used in the computation of transducer efficiency and driving voltage from current responses (or vice versa). (3) It is an analytical tool for studying the performance of a transducer.

Impedances usually are measured with wide-frequency-range impedance bridges, and, theoretically, the measurement does not differ from the measurement of the impedance of a resistor, condenser, or coil. In practice, however, there are several important considerations that must be recognized. The transducer must have its proper acoustic load—usually a free field. An underwater transducer must be immersed in water, and the effect of reflections from boundaries must be negligible. A simple test for boundary interference is to measure the impedance in several locations or orientations. Electrical ground conditions usually are important and often bothersome. The impedance may depend on which of the two terminals is grounded, or on whether any terminal is grounded. When one terminal is grounded, the measurement is referred to as unbalanced. If both terminals are ungrounded and have the same potential with respect to ground, the measurement is referred to as balanced. The cable shield in unbalanced measurements may be connected to ground or be "floating"—that is, not connected to anything. Grounding conditions in fresh water differ from those in salt water. If a cable is long—say 100 feet or more—the manner in which it is coiled or strung out, or whether or not it is in the water, may affect the impedance. These effects are caused by stray inductance and capacitance, and are most pronounced at ultrasonic frequencies. All these effects occur in sensitivity measurements as well as in impedance measurements. The general rule is that all grounding and connection conditions should be, to the greatest possible extent, the same in the measurement of impedance and sensitivity as in the actual use of the transducer.

Conversion of series impedance to parallel impedance or admittance, or vice versa, is given by the following formulas:

$$R_s = \frac{R_p}{\left(\frac{R_p}{X_p}\right)^2 + 1} = \frac{\frac{1}{G}}{\left(\frac{B}{G}\right)^2 + 1}, \tag{2.91}$$

$$X_s = \frac{X_p}{\left(\frac{X_p}{R_p}\right)^2 + 1} = \frac{\frac{-1}{B}}{\left(\frac{G}{B}\right)^2 + 1}, \tag{2.92}$$

$$R_p = \frac{1}{G} = \frac{R_s^2 + X_s^2}{R_s}, \tag{2.93}$$

$$X_p = -\frac{1}{B} = \frac{R_s^2 + X_s^2}{X_s}, \tag{2.94}$$

where $R$ is resistance, $X$ is reactance, $G$ is conductance, $B$ is susceptance, and the subscripts $s$ and $p$ indicate series or parallel. The three ways of describing the inpedance are as follows:

$$Z = R_s + jX_s = \frac{1}{G + jB} = \frac{1}{\left(\frac{1}{R_p}\right) + \left(\frac{1}{jX_p}\right)}. \tag{2.95}$$

A fundamental understanding of the nature of the impedance of an electro-acoustic transducer is needed in connection with its application as an analytical tool. Although it is measured electrically, the impedance is a function of the mechanical and acoustical (or radiation) characteristics of the transducer. The mechanical mass, stiffness or compliance, and resistance, all appear as electrical impedances through the electromechanical coupling characteristic of the transducer—that is, through the piezoelectric effect, magnetostrictive effect, the emf induced in a wire cutting a magnetic flux, and so forth. The characteristics of the medium also appear as electrical impedances because of the medium's effect on the vibrating parts. Consequently, the impedance of a transducer can be divided into several parts. The purely electrical part is the part that would be measured if the transducer could be prevented from vibrating; it is called the blocked impedance $Z_b$.

The difference between the impedance when the transducer is vibrating and the blocked impedance is called motional impedance $Z_M$ because it is due to the vibratory motion. The motional impedance is an electrical impedance measured in electrical ohms, even though it arises from mechanical motion. The motional impedance $Z_M$ has two parts: (1) the part corresponding to the mechanical impedance $Z_m$ of the vibrating part of the transducer, and (2) the part corresponding to the radiation or acoustical impedance $Z_r$ of the medium reacting on the diaphragm.

Blocked and motional admittances also can be defined in the same manner as the two kinds of impedances are defined.

The relationship between the motional impedance or admittance and $Z_m$ and $Z_r$ is complex and depends on the type of electromechanical coupling used. That is, it depends on whether the transducer has electrical coupling (piezoelectric, condenser) or magnetic coupling (magnetostrictive, moving-coil, etc.). Just as the measured electrical impedance can be a function of the mechanical motion, the mechanical impedances can be a function of the electrical current. The mechanical impedance of a transducer is the quotient force/velocity at some designated point (or mechanical terminals). This mechanical impedance is not the same when the electrical terminals are open-circuited as it is when they are short-circuited. Consequently, one speaks of open-circuit mechanical impedance $Z_{ocm}$ and short-circuit mechanical impedance $Z_{scm}$. It can be shown that the electrical analog of a transducer is the circuit in Fig. 2.51. The factor $\phi_e$ is the electromechanical coupling factor or proportionality constant between mechanical force and electrical voltage in the transducer. Similarly, $\phi_m$ is the proportionality constant between the force and electrical current. Figure 2.51a is most useful for transducers with electrical coupling, and Fig. 2.51b for transducers with magnetic coupling.

For analytical purposes, the various impedance components in Fig. 2.51a can be obtained most easily from a measurement of the admittance of the circuit, Let $Z = 1/Y$, $Z_b = 1/Y_b$, and $Y_M$ be the motional admittance. Then

$$Y = Y_b + Y_M = Y_b + \frac{\phi_e^2}{Z_{scm} + Z_r}, \qquad (2.96)$$

Similarly, the components in Fig. 2.51b can be obtained most easily from an impedance measurement:

$$Z = Z_b + Z_M = Z_b + \frac{\phi_m^2}{Z_{ocm} + Z_r}. \qquad (2.97)$$

Figure 2.52 is a graphical illustration of Eq. (2.96) for a piezoelectric transducer. Figure 2.52a is a plot of the data obtainable directly from a bridge. Figure 2.52b is a plot of the same data combined into one locus of $G + jB$ as a function of frequency. The blocked and motional admittance is obtained by

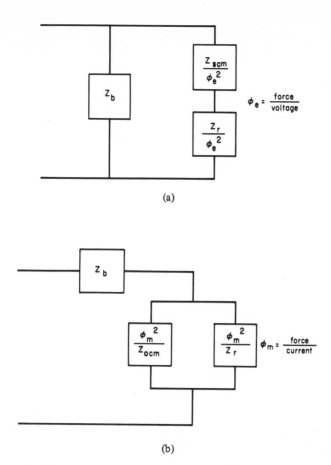

(a)

(b)

Fig. 2.51. Electrical analogs of electroacoustic transducers.

interpolation as shown with the dashed lines in Fig. 2.52a. When plotted alone, $G_b$ is a constant, $Y_b$ is a straight vertical line, and $Y_M$ is a circle, as shown in Figs. 2.52b and 2.52c.

Figure 2.52 also could be used to represent Eq. (2.97) for a magnetic transducer by substituting $R$ and $jX$ for $G$ and $jB$. Piezoelectric transducers conform rather closely to the idealized case represented in Fig. 2.52, however, but magnetic transducers do not. A typical plot for a magnetic transducer appears as shown in Fig. 2.53. The blocked resistance obviously is not a constant, and the idealized circuit shown in Fig. 2.51b must be modified. The modification usually consists of arranging resistances and inductances in some combination series-parallel configuration, and assigning a phase shift to the coupling factor $\phi_m$.

To match impedances or calculate efficiency, the impedance rather than the admittance usually is desired, regardless of the transducer type. An impedance plot of a piezoelectric transducer is shown in Fig. 2.54.

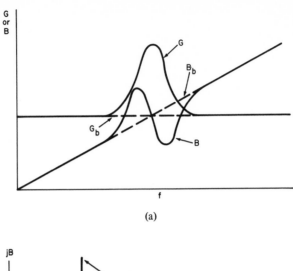

(a)

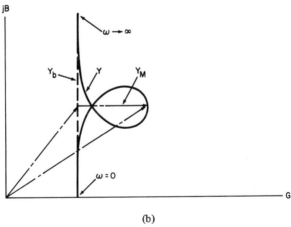

(b)

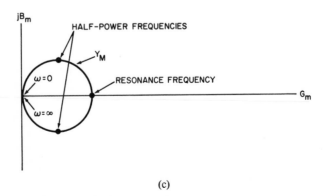

(c)

Fig. 2.52. Admittance of an electroacoustic transducer.

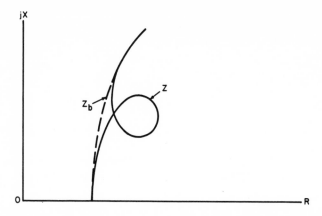

Fig. 2.53.   Impedance of a transducer with magnetic coupling.

The particular vectors shown in Fig. 2.52b are for the frequency of mechanical resonance—that is, the frequency at which $Z_m + Z_r$ is a minimum, $Y_M$ is a maximum, or the imaginary part of either $(Z_m + Z_r)$ or $Y_M$ goes to zero. Spurious resonances are indicated by secondary loops as shown in the dotted line in Fig. 2.54. Since $Z$ and $Y$ obviously are functions of $Z_r$, transducers must be radiating into their normal acoustic radiation load during an impedance measurement at frequencies near resonance. At frequencies far above or below resonance, however, $Z_M \ll Z_b$ and $Y_M \ll Y_b$, and the loading condition is not critical.

Note that the diameter of the motional loop is inversely proportional to $(Z_m + Z_r)$. Operating an underwater transducer in air is equivalent, essentially, to setting $Z_r$ equal to zero. This allows $\phi^2/Z_m$ to be measured alone or

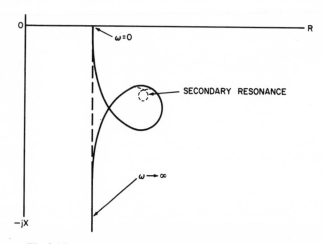

Fig. 2.54.   Impedance of a transducer with electric coupling.

independently of $Z_r$. This kind of measurement is used to compute the transducer efficiency; it is discussed further in Section 2.14.

The electrical impedance of electroacoustic transducers is analyzed in more
depth elsewhere in the literature.[53-55]

## 2.14  Efficiency

The steady-state power delivered to a transducer either is dissipated in the
electrical or mechanical resistance within the transducer, or it is radiated away.
Insofar as the electrical analog of a transducer is concerned, the radiated power
is considered as dissipated in the radiation resistance. The efficiency is the ratio
of the output radiated power to the input or total power delivered to the transducer. Two methods are used to measure efficiency. In the direct method, the
input and output powers are measured directly. In the impedance method, the
ratio of the input and output powers is inferred from impedance measurements.
The impedance method is easier, but, because of necessary assumptions, it also is
more susceptable to error and, therefore, of limited usefulness. The two methods
do not always agree. When they do not agree, and when the efficiency of a transducer in conventional free-field conditions is desired, the direct method is preferred.   When the conditions are other than free-field—as, for example, in
industrial ultrasonics—the impedance method may be preferred.

Unlike most electroacoustical values, efficiency has a theoretical limit—100%.
This fact can be quite helpful.  Anyone of long experience with highly efficient
transducers probably has obtained measured values of efficiency higher than
100%.  A measured value of, say, 105% is not to be ignored and can, in fact, lead
to a very accurate conclusion—provided one has a good estimate of his measurement error.  Suppose this estimate is ±10%. Then, a measured efficiency of 75%
means, in fact, that the efficiency probably is in the 65% to 85% range.  With
the same measurement error, the measured 105% implies that the real efficiency
probably is in the 95% to 115% range.  Efficiencies of more than 100% being
impossible, it is concluded that the real efficiency must be in the relatively narrow range from 95% to 100%.  Such logic is no substitute for a good measurement and must be used with restraint.  Nevertheless, it is true that measured
values (above 100%) are not automatically discarded as useless.

### 2.14.1  Direct method

In the direct method, the input power is measured, as it would be in any
purely electrical measurement, by using any one of the familiar relationships:

$$P_i = i^2 R_s = \frac{e^2}{R_p} = ei \cos\theta, \qquad (2.98)$$

where $P_i$ is the input power, $i$ is the input rms current, $e$ is the input rms voltage,
$\theta$ is the phase angle between $e$ and $i$, $R_s$ is the series resistance measured across

the input terminals, and $R_p$ is the parallel resistance measured across the input terminals. The resistances $R_s$ and $R_p$ will be functions of the electrical, mechanical, and radiation resistances, of course, and normally will not be frequency-independent constants.

The output power $P_o$ is obtained from a measurement of the sound pressure on the acoustic axis, and a measurement of the directivity factor $R_\theta$ or directivity index $D_i$. The characteristic impedance $\rho c$ of the medium is presumed known. Then

$$P_o = \overline{I}(4\pi r^2) = \left(\frac{I_0}{R_\theta}\right)(4\pi r^2), \tag{2.99}$$

where, as in Eq. (2.79), $\overline{I}$ is the intensity averaged over all directions and $I_0$ is the intensity on the axis, both at a distance $r$, and $R_\theta$ is the directivity factor. Then, if $p_r$ is the rms pressure on the axis at distance $r$, $I_0 = p_r^2/\rho c$, and

$$P_o = \frac{p_r^2(4\pi r^2)}{R_\theta \rho c}. \tag{2.100}$$

The efficiency $\eta$ is, then,

$$\eta = \frac{P_o}{P_i} = \frac{(4\pi r^2 p_r^2)}{(R_\theta \rho c i^2 R_s)}. \tag{2.101}$$

If $r$ is taken as 1 meter, the ratio $p_r/i$ is the transmitting current response $S$, and Eq. (2.101) simplifies to

$$\eta = \left(\frac{S^2}{R_\theta R_s}\right)\left(\frac{4\pi}{\rho c}\right). \tag{2.102}$$

Equation (2.102) applies as it is, if MKS units are used. If the hybrid system of practical electrical units and cgs acoustical units are used,

$$\eta = \left(\frac{S^2}{R_\theta R_s}\right)\left(\frac{4\pi}{\rho c}\right)10^{-3}. \tag{2.103}$$

Letting $K = (4\pi/\rho c)10^{-3}$ and putting Eq. (2.103) into its decibel form yields

$$\eta_{dB} = 20 \log S - D_i - 10 \log R_s + 10 \log K. \tag{2.104}$$

The constant $10 \log K$ depends on the medium. For sea water at 20°C, 35 parts per 1000 salinity, and atmospheric pressure, $K = -70.9$ dB. For measurements in fresh water tanks and as a function of temperature and pressure, the constant is slightly different:

|                        | 10 log $K$ | | |
| --- | --- | --- | --- |
|                        | 5°C | 15°C | 25°C |
| Atmospheric pressure   | −70.5 | −70.7 | −70.7 |
| 1000 psig              | −70.6 | −70.8 | −70.8 |

The output power of a transducer also can be measured by reverberation techniques.[56]   Such a technique is not applicable to a conventional efficiency measurement, however, because the radiation resistance of the transducer when radiating into a reverberation tank is not the same as when the transducer is radiating into a free field.

### 2.14.2  Impedance method

At the resonance frequency of an electric coupling transducer, the motional reactance is zero, and the analog circuit in Fig. 2.51a becomes the circuit in Fig. 2.55 where $R_m$ is the mechanical resistance and $R_r$ is the radiation resistance.  The efficiency obviously is the ratio of the power dissipated in $R_r$ to the total power dissipated in the whole circuit.  From Figs. 2.52c and 2.55, it can be seen that the diameter of the motional admittance circle with a normal water load is given by $D_w = \phi^2/(R_m + R_r)$.  When the transducer is operated in air, $R_r$ is zero for all practical purposes and the circle diameter in air is $D_a = \phi^2/R_m$.  It can be shown from conventional circuit analysis that the efficiency is given by

$$\eta = \frac{\dfrac{i_r^2 R_r}{\phi^2}}{i^2 R} = \frac{D_w(D_a - D_w)}{G D_a}, \tag{2.105}$$

where $G$ is the total conductance at resonance.

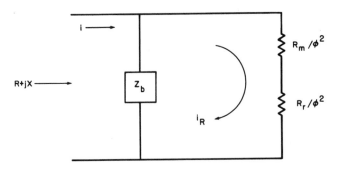

Fig. 2.55.  Electrical analog of an electroacoustic transducer when the motional reactance $j(X_m + X_r)/\phi^2$ is zero.

Similarly, for transducers with magnetic coupling, it can be shown that

$$\eta = \frac{D_w(D_a - D_w)}{RD_a}, \tag{2.106}$$

where $D_w$ and $D_a$ now are the diameters of motional impedance circles and $R$ is the total resistance at resonance.

The impedance method of computing efficiency should be used with caution. Electrical impedance can be measured more accurately than can acoustical pressure, and therefore one might think the impedance method is superior to the direct method. This is not true. Aside from measurement errors, the impedance method is sensitive to the initial assumptions that the transducer is described accurately by the analogs in Fig. 2.51, that the impedances are lumped parameters, that the impedances are independent of each other, and that there are no stray impedances. Many wierd looking impedance curves that only generally resemble Fig. 2.52 give ample evidence that these assumptions often are untenable. This is particularly true for magnetic transducers. It is true also for reasons unconnected with the transduction element itself. To illustrate, many piezoelectric transducers consist of crystals or ceramic elements immersed in oil and encased in a rubber boot. Removing the water load does not reduce the radiation impedance to zero. The oil and rubber remain, loading the crystal. If the remaining oil and rubber happen to be near a quarter-wave thickness, the radiation impedance actually could be higher in air than in water! More details about the theory of this technique are available in the literature.[45,54,55]

The impedance method should be reserved for circumstances where convenience outweighs the need for absolute accuracy.

## 2.15 Linearity and Dynamic Range

Linearity and dynamic range are related concepts in that both pertain to a dependence of the transducer calibration on the signal level.

Linearity has a very precise mathematical meaning. A transducer is linear if its output is proportional to its input—that is, if the quotient output/input is constant or independent of the absolute value of either the output or the input. The signal range over which a transducer is linear is found by measuring output vs. input over a wide range of signal levels. When the output is plotted as a function of input, using rectangular coordinates and linear scales, the transducer is linear where the plot is a straight line. For a hydrophone, the output is open-circuit voltage and the input is free-field pressure. For a projector, the output is free-field pressure and the input is current or voltage.

Dynamic range has a less precise definition than does linearity. It generally is a measure of the signal amplitude range in which a hydrophone can be used to detect and measure a sound pressure. The standard definition is "the difference between the overload pressure level and the equivalent noise pressure level."

The term "overload" has no precise meaning in either a qualitative or a quantitative sense. The overload may be caused by signal distortion, overheating, magnetic saturation, damage, etc. The method of overload determination must be specified. Any appropriate quantitative criteria, such as percentage of harmonic content of the signal, also should be specified.

The equivalent noise pressure is the rms sinusoidal pressure that will produce an rms voltage equal to the inherent noise voltage of the transducer when the noise is measured in a 1-Hz band centered in the sinusoidal frequency. Thus, the equivalent noise pressure is a theoretical threshold at which the signal-to-noise ratio is 1, or 0 dB. In practice, the threshold or minimum detectable signal may be either higher or lower than the equivalent noise pressure. Measurements seldom can be made in a 1-Hz band. Bandwidths wider than 1 Hz generally are used, thereby raising the rms inherent noise voltage output and masking a sinusoidal signal having a rms voltage output equal to the equivalent noise pressure voltage. On the other hand, modern signal processing techniques enable signals well below a noise level to be detected and measured. The measurement of equivalent noise pressure is discussed in Section 2.16.2.

The overload pressure level is measured by merely subjecting a hydrophone to gradually increasing free-field pressures until the overload condition is observed. Since the overload condition is somewhat arbitrary, it is possible for a transducer to be nonlinear and yet not be overloaded. Magnetostrictive transducers, for example, are inherently nonlinear, and usually show nonlinear response well below their maximum useful signal level or overload point. The reverse also is true. That is, a transducer may be overloaded and yet linear. The overload point of a moving-coil transducer usually is set by the heating of the voice coil wire. The (pressure output)/(current input) quotient, however, is essentially independent of the heating effect; therefore, a moving-coil transducer with a hot voice coil still can be linear. In some literature, linear range and dynamic range are synonymous. This is valid only if one chooses nonlinearity as the criterion for overload, and if the transducer is linear down to its inherent noise level. The latter condition seldom exists, since noise will interfere with signal levels well above the equivalent noise pressure level.

Dynamic range is not applied to projectors, because the minimum signal that a projector can produce is of negligible interest. It is the limitations at the high end of the signal amplitude range that are important.

Some sonar transducers are driven at signal levels above the linear range. The resulting nonlinear effects (distortion, etc.) are accepted as less important than other technical or economic considerations. Test or calibration measurements can be made on nonlinear transducers, but the measurements have very limited application. The formal definitions of transmitting current response, free-field voltage sensitivity, impedance, efficiency, etc., apply only to linear transducers, and the terms have no standard meaning in nonlinear cases. When similar measurements are made on nonlinear transducers, the absolute value of at least one of the parameters (pressure, voltage, or current) must be specified. Since harmonic distortion is a common factor in nonlinear systems, it is necessary also to specify whether the data apply to the fundamental frequency only or to the combined fundamental and harmonic frequencies. In general, the measurement conditions must be completely specified for a nonlinear transducer, and the data cannot be extrapolated to other conditions.

## 2.16 Noise Measurements

There are two standard general definitions of noise. The first is that noise is any undesired sound. Thus, if one sonar signal interferes with a second sonar signal, the first one is noise even though it may be a pure sinusoid. Sixty-hertz "hum" or other power frequency interference likewise is noise. The second definition is that noise is an erratic, intermittent, or statistically random oscillation.

Some noises may be erratic and intermittent but still confined to certain discrete frequencies. Such noise has a line spectrum, the term being borrowed from optical spectroscopy. Other noise has a continuous spectrum; that is, its frequency components are distributed continuously over a frequency region.

Insofar as measurements are concerned, we are interested in noise in the sense of the second definition, and our attention will be confined to noise in a continuous spectrum.

Such noise can be assumed to be the superposition of an infinite number of sinusoidal signals, each of a different frequency and of random amplitude about some mean amplitude. The relative mean amplitude of each frequency component varies with the type of noise. When the mean amplitude is independent of frequency, the noise is called white noise, from the analogy with white light.

The amplitude of ambient sea noise decreases 5 dB per octave as the frequency increases. In most practical cases, the amplitude is a smoothly changing function of frequency. The total sound energy in a finite band of frequencies is distributed among an infinite number of frequencies. The sound energy in any single frequency component, thus, is vanishingly small so that noise must be measured in a band of frequencies.

The sound energy in a band of frequencies depends on the bandwidth and how the amplitude of the frequency components varies with frequency. If the noise is essentially white, the energy is proportional to the bandwidth. The rms pressure in a band of acoustic noise has no unique relationship to the sound energy. In most practical cases, however, the rms pressure squared (or, mean of the pressure squared) is proportional to the energy, and therefore also proportional to the frequency bandwidth. An acoustic noise thus is measured by the rms pressure squared $p^2$ and the bandwidth $\Delta f$ in which $p^2$ is measured. The pressure spectrum level or PSL is defined by the equation

$$PSL = 20 \log\left(\frac{p}{p_0}\right) - 10 \log \Delta f, \qquad (2.107)$$

where $p_0$ is the reference pressure of 0.0002 $\mu$bar, and $\Delta f$ is the bandwidth in Hz. Thus, PSL at a frequency $f_0$ is the rms pressure level above 0.0002 $\mu$bar in a 1-Hz band centered on $f_0$. The measurement ordinarily cannot be made with a 1-Hz filter, and 20 log $\Delta f$ therefore is greater than zero. The noise must be essentially white in the band $\Delta f$, or an average PSL is measured. The selection of a practical bandwidth is a compromise. The bandwidth must be narrow enough to ascertain variations in the PSL as a function of frequency, but not so narrow that the random instantaneous noise amplitude becomes so large that $p^2$ cannot be measured accurately. Figure 2.56 shows how a noise signal appears on a recorder chart when a white noise is measured through different filters.

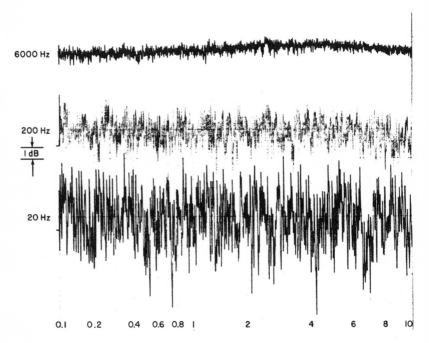

Fig. 2.56. Noise signal measured through a 6000-Hz, a 200-Hz, and a 20-Hz, sweeping, bandpass filter.

Insofar as electroacoustic measurements are concerned, noise levels are measured for two purposes. First, it may be some acoustic noise itself that is of interest, as, for example, ship noise. The measurement of noise itself requires a noise meter, and the calibration of a noise meter is discussed in Section 2.16.1. Second, the inherent noise in the meter or measuring system is of interest because it is the limitation on the minimum measurable signal, or low limit of the dynamic range. This limitation is expressed as the equivalent noise pressure. It is discussed in Section 2.16.2.

### 2.16.1 Noise meter calibration

A noise meter can be calibrated most simply by putting the hydrophone in a known noise sound field. However, the noise field can be known only if it is measured by a second calibrated standard meter or system. Ultimately, one must depend on one of the absolute hydrophone calibration techniques described in this chapter for continuous-wave sinusoidal sound pressure. Given such a calibrated hydrophone, consider the noise-measuring system shown in Fig. 2.57. The electroacoustic element of the hydrophone is represented by the Thevenin generator voltage $e_g$ and impedance $Z$. The voltage $e_g = Mp$, where $M$ is the known free-field voltage sensitivity and $p$ is the unknown sound pressure. The voltage $e_i$ is a known voltage that can be placed across the calibration resistor $R$. The meter itself includes the hydrophone preamplifier, filters, and all other electronic components. It may also include the signal generator for $e_i$. The reading of the voltmeter, recorder, oscilloscope, or whatever else is used to measure or observe the system output, is indicated by $e_o$. If $R$ is small in comparison with $Z$ and the meter input impedance, then the ratio $e_o/e_g = e_o/e_i = K$, where $K$ is a meter calibration constant. Then

$$\frac{e_o}{e_g} = \frac{e_o}{Mp} = K, \qquad (2.108)$$

or

$$\frac{e_o}{p} = MK. \qquad (2.109)$$

If we were dealing only with sinusoidal sound pressures, Eq. (2.108) would constitute the calibration formula, where $e_o/p$ is the system calibration in terms of the hydrophone calibration $M$ and meter calibration $K$.

When $p$ is the rms noise pressure in a band of frequencies, $M$ and $K$ must be known for the frequency band, and $e_o^2$ must be proportional to $p^2$ or to the total power in the frequency band. Ordinary voltmeters, even when calibrated in terms of rms voltages, are not power meters. Combining Eqs. (2.107) and (2.109) produces

$$PSL = 20 \log e_o - 20 \log MK - 20 \log p_0 - 10 \log \Delta f. \qquad (2.110)$$

The value of $MK$ at the bandpass center frequency is used. Any change of $M$ and $K$ with frequency then is accounted for in the effective bandwidth $\Delta f$. Figure 2.58 shows $(MK)^2$ plotted as a function of frequency. When both coordinate scales are linear, the area under the solid-line curve is proportional to the power through the hydrophone-meter filter system. A planimeter or other graphical technique is used to determine this area, and then an ideal filter characteristic

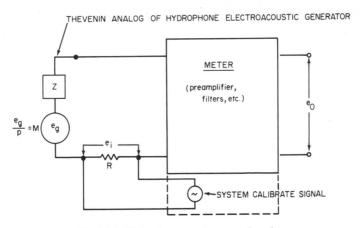

Fig. 2.57. Meter for measuring acoustic noise.

shown as a dashed line is drawn having the same area under the curve. The height of the ideal filter bandpass characteristic $(MK)^2$ is taken as the value of $(MK)^2$ at the center frequency $f_0$. The ideal or effective bandwidth then is $\Delta f$ as shown. The selection of the center frequency $f_0$ is somewhat arbitrary. The frequency of maximum $(MK)^2$ could have been chosen. Then, since the product $(MK)^2 \Delta f$ is fixed, 10 log $\Delta f$ would decrease by the same amount that 20 log $MK$ would increase, and Eq. (2.110) would be unaffected. Thus, $MK$, $p_0$, and $\Delta f$ in Eq. (2.110) all are known, and the PSL is determined by the meter output $e_o$.

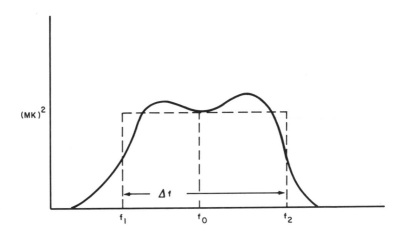

Fig. 2.58. Real (solid line) and equivalent ideal (dashed line) filter characteristic.

## 2.16.2  Equivalent noise pressure

The equivalent noise pressure is the normally incident sinusoidal rms pressure that produces the same hydrophone open-circuit voltage as does the inherent electrical noise of the hydrophone, when the electrical noise is measured as the rms voltage in a 1-Hz band.  Equating these two voltages and solving for the pressure $p$, we obtain

$$p = \frac{e_n}{M}, \tag{2.111}$$

where $M$ is the free-field voltage sensitivity and $e_n$ is the noise voltage.  Theoretically, $e_n$ is measured in much the same way as the hydrophone electro-acoustic generator voltage $e_g$ described in Section 2.16.1  From Eq. (2.108),

$$e_n = e_g = \frac{e_o}{K}, \tag{2.112}$$

Converting $e_n$ to a 1-Hz band gives

$$20 \log e_n = 20 \log e_o - 20 \log K - 10 \log \Delta f. \tag{2.113}$$

Usually, the inherent noise of an electroacoustic generator without its pre-amplifier is too low to measure.  That is, the electrical noise of the measuring system, or the ambient noise in the medium, is greater than the generator noise.  Then, the inherent noise is computed by assuming the noise is all of thermal origin as given by

$$\frac{e_n^2}{\Delta f} = 4kTR, \tag{2.114}$$

where $k$ is the Boltzmann gas constant $1.38 \times 10^{-23}$ joules per degree Kelvin, $T$ is the absolute temperature in degrees Kelvin, and $R$ is the equivalent series resistance of the transducer.  The resistance $R$ may be a function of the acoustic load, pressure, temperature, and so forth, and therefore must be measured under the proper environmental conditions.  For the temperature 20°C, Eq. (2.114) reduces to

$$\frac{e_n^2}{\Delta f} = \left(\frac{1.61}{10^{20}}\right)R. \tag{2.115}$$

Combining Eq. (2.111) and (2.115) produces

$$20 \log p = -197.9 + 10 \log R + 10 \log \Delta f - 20 \log M. \tag{2.116}$$

If the equivalent noise pressure of the hydrophone, including a preamplifier or other associated circuit, is needed, then the measuring technique described in Section 2.16.1 is used. The preamplifier then is included in the generator as pictured in Fig. 2.57 and the calibration signal $e_i$ is inserted between the preamplifier and the remaining part of the measuring system. There are some practical problems with this kind of measurement, if both the preamplifier output and meter input have one terminal at electrical ground. This situation is discussed in more detail in Section 3.6.

## REFERENCES

1.  T. A. Henriquez, "Diffraction constants of acoustic transducers," J. Acoust. Soc. Am. 36, 267 (1964).
2.  R. J. Bobber, "Diffraction constants of transducers," J. Acoust. Soc. Am. 37, 591 (1965).
3.  W. Schottky, "Das Gesetz des Tiefempfangs in der Akustik und Elektroakustik," Zeitschrift für Physik 36, 689 (1926).
4.  S. Ballantine, "Reciprocity in electromagnetic, mechanical, acoustical, and interconnected systems," Proc. Inst. Rad. Engr. 17, 929 (1929).
5.  W. R. MacLean, "Absolute measurement of sound without a primary standard," J. Acoust. Soc. Am. 12, 140 (1940).
6.  R. K. Cook, "Absolute pressure calibration of microphones," J. Acoust. Soc. Am. 12, 415 (1941).
7.  Summary Technical Report of NDRC, Div. 6, Vol. 10, "Sonar Calibration Methods" (1946).
8.  E. M. McMillan, "Violation of the reciprocity theorem in linear passive electromechanical systems," J. Acoust. Soc. Am. 18, 344 (1946).
9.  R. J. Bobber and C. L. Darner, "A linear passive nonreciprocal transducer," J. Acoust. Soc. Am. 26, 98 (1954).
10. R. J. Bobber, "A general reciprocity parameter," J. Acoust. Soc. Am. 39, 680 (1966).
11. L. L. Foldy and H. Primakoff, "General theory of passive linear electroacoustic transducers and the electroacoustic reciprocity theorem I," J. Acoust. Soc. Am. 17, 109 (1945); and Part II, 19, 50 (1947).
12. E. L. Carstensen, "Self-reciprocity calibration of electroacoustic transducers," J. Acoust. Soc. Am. 19, 961 (1947).
13. G. A. Sabin, "Transducer calibration by impedance measurements," J. Acoust. Soc. Am. 28, 705 (1956).
14. R. B. Patterson, "Using the ocean surface as a reflector for a self-reciprocity calibration of a transducer," J. Acoust. Soc. Am. 42, 653 (1967).
15. R. J. Bobber and G. A. Sabin, "Cylindrical wave reciprocity parameter," J. Acoust. Soc. Am. 32, 923(A) (1960); 33, 446 (1961).
16. B. D. Simmons and R. J. Urick, "Plane wave reciprocity parameter and its application to calibration of electroacoustic transducers at close distances," J. Acoust. Soc. Am. 21, 633 (1949).
17. L. G. Beatty, "Reciprocity calibration in a tube with active-impedance termination," J. Acoust. Soc. Am. 39, 40 (1966).
18. L. G. Beatty, R. J. Bobber, and D. L. Phillips, "Sonar calibration in a high-pressure tube," J. Acoust. Soc. Am. 39, 48 (1966).
19. C. C. Sims and T. A. Henriquez, "Reciprocity calibration of a standard hydrophone at 16,000 psi," J. Acoust. Soc. Am. 36, 1704 (1964).

20. G. A. McMahon, "Coupler-reciprocity system for hydrophone calibration at high pressure," J. Acoust. Soc. Am. 36, 2311 (1964).
21. A. N. Golenkov, "Calibration of infrasonic hydrophones by the reciprocity method in small water chambers," Measurement Techniques 8, 637 (1959).
22. H. G. Diestel, "Reciprocity calibration of microphones in a diffuse sound field," J. Acoust. Soc. Am. 33, 514 (1961).
23. W. J. Trott and E. N. Lide, "Two-projector null method for calibration of hydrophones at low audio and infrasonic frequencies," J. Acoust. Soc. Am. 27, 951 (1955).
24. E. C Wente, "A condenser transmitter as a uniformly sensitive instrument for the absolute measurement of sound intensity," Phys. Rev. 10, 39 (1917).
25. E. C. Wente, "The Thermophone," Phys. Rev. 19, 333 (1922).
26. G. W. C. Kaye, "Acoustical work of the National Physical Laboratory," J. Acoust. Soc. Am. 7, 167 (1936).
27. R. Glover and B. Baumzweiger, "A moving coil pistonphone for measurement of sound field pressure," J. Acoust. Soc. Am. 10, 200 (1939).
28. L. L. Beranek, *Acoustic Measurements* (John Wiley & Sons, Inc., New York, 1949), Section 4.4.
29. C. C. Sims and R. J. Bobber, "Pressure phone for hydrophone calibrations," J. Acoust. Soc. Am. 31, 1315 (1959).
30. C. C. Sims, "Hydrophone calibrator," U.S. Navy Underwater Sound Reference Laboratory Research Report No. 60, 12 April 1962 (AD 279-904); see also J. Acoust. Soc. Am. 36, 401 (1964), "Rapid calibrator for small hydrophones."
31. F. Schloss and M. Strasberg, "Hydrophone calibration in a vibrating column of liquid," J. Acoust. Soc. Am. 34, 958 (1962).
32. Summary Technical Report of NDRC, Div. 6, Vol. 11, "Sonar Calibration Measurements," page 42 (1946).
33. H. F. Olson, "Mechano-electronic transducers," J. Acoust. Soc. Am. 19, 307 (1947).
34. R. J. Bobber, "Electronic hydrophone for calibrations at very low frequencies," J. Acoust. Soc. Am. 26, 1080 (1954).
35. L. G. Beatty, "The dunking machine method of hydrophone calibration at infrasonic frequencies," U.S. Navy Underwater Sound Reference Laboratory Research Report No. 35 (1955) (AD 75-330).
36. A. N. Golenkov, "Absolute calibration of infrasonic pressure detectors in an air and water resonator with hydrostatic excitation," Measurement Techniques No. 5, pp. 444-450 (May 1965); also paper K41, 5th International Congress on Acoustics, Liege, Belgium, Sep. 1965.
37. T. F. Hueter and R. H. Bolt, *Sonics* (John Wiley & Sons, Inc., New York, 1955), p. 43.
38. G. Fieldler, "Siemens-Sonotest," U.S. Pat. 2,531,844, Nov. 28, 1950 (manufactured by Siemens-Reiniger Company, Erlangen, Germany).
39. A. R. Laufer and G. L. Thomas, "New method for the calibration of a plane hydrophone," J. Acoust. Soc. Am. 28, 951 (1956).
40. B. B. Bauer, "A laboratory calibrator for gradient hydrophones," J. Acoust. Soc. Am. 39, 585(L) (1966).
41. J. D. Kraus, *Antennas* (McGraw-Hill Book Company, Inc., New York, 1950), Chaps. 2, 3, and 4.
42. H. F. Olson, *Acoustical Engineering* (D. Van Nostrand Co., Inc., Princeton, N. J., 1957), Chap. II.
43. V. M. Albers, *Underwater Acoustics Handbook* (Pennsylvania State University Press, 1960), Chap. 11.
44. H. Stenzel, *Leitfaden zur Berechnung von Schallvorgängen* (Julius Springer, Berlin, 1939). In English translation by A. R. Stickley, "Handbook for the Calculation of Sound Propagation Phenomena," NRL Translation No. 130.

45.  Summary Technical Report of NDRC, Div. 6, Vol. 13, "Magnetostriction Transducers," Chap. 5 (1946).

46.  H. Stenzel, "Die akustische Strahlung der rechteckigen Kolbenmembran," Acustica 2, 263 (1952).

47.  C. T. Molloy, "Calculation of the directivity index for various types of radiators," J. Acoust. Soc. Am. 20, 387 (1948).

48.  F. Spandöck, "Grenzen der Güte elektroakustischer Wandler," Elektrotechnische Zeitschrift A76, 598 (1955).

49.  Sonar Transducer Computer (slide rule), Edo Corporation, College Point, L.I., New York; Sonar Performance Calculator (slide rule), Raytheon Company, Submarine Signal Division, Portsmouth, R.I.

50.  Summary Technical Report of NDRC, Div. 6, Vol. 10, "Sonar Calibration Methods," Chap. 4 (1946).

51.  P. M. Kendig and R. E. Mueser, "A simplified method for determining transducer directivity index," J. Acoust. Soc. Am. 19, 691 (1947).

52.  A. E. Reznekov and A. Ya. Snytka, "The problem of measuring the axial concentration coefficient in ultrasonic radiators," Measurement Techniques, No. 7, p. 654 (July 1965).

53.  F. V. Hunt, *Electroacoustics* (John Wiley & Sons, Inc., New York, 1954).

54.  F. A. Fischer, *Grundzüge der Elektroakustik* (Fachverlag Schiele & Schön, Berlin, 1950); English translation by S. Ehrlich and F. Pordes, *Fundamentals of Electroacoustics* (Interscience Publishers, Inc., New York, 1955).

55.  Summary Technical Report of NDRC, Div. 6, Vol. 13, "Magnetostriction Transducers," Chaps. 2 and 3 (1946).

56.  W. L. Brud, J. D. Donnelly, and L. E. Kinsler, "Investigations and application of reverberation measurements of acoustic power in water," J. Acoust. Soc. Am. 35, 1621 (1963).

# Chapter III

# FUNDAMENTALS OF FREE-FIELD MEASUREMENT PRACTICE

## 3.1 Introduction

Most underwater electroacoustic measurements fall in the general category of free-field far-field measurements. Nearly all the other methods described in Chapter II are specialized and not widely used, but facilities for free-field measurements are widespread. Virtually every naval laboratory engaged in undersea research and development has a facility of some kind, as do many naval contractors and some universities. Such facilities are relatively large because free-field far-field measurements cannot be made on a laboratory bench except, perhaps, at megahertz frequencies. Facilities usually are far from ideal in providing the conditions assumed by the theory; consequently, correct measurement practice becomes very important.

The theory of free-field far-field electroacoustic measurements makes few demands on measurement practice. All that is needed is (1) a free field, (2) a projector-hydrophone separation large enough to satisfy far-field criteria, (3) a means of measuring input current or voltage and output open-circuit voltage, and (4) values of a few parameters like distance, water density, and frequency. The parameters in (4) are readily available, but the other three needs are deceptive in their apparent simplicity. The free-field requirement in particular is a very large and complicated problem. A true free field or a uniform boundless medium is, or course, only an idealized concept. A major share of the practical problems in underwater electroacoustic measurements pertain to achieving a useful approximation to a free field.

The theoretical requirements, along with convenience and economy, lead to various measurement practices that are discussed in the sections that follow. Details of measurement practice vary greatly from place to place and, of course, they change with time. For the most part, the subjects discussed here are fundamental to measurement practice, although not all the subjects apply to all measurement situations.

## 3.2 Natural Sites and Facilities

Natural sites like lakes, ponds, large springs, rivers, flooded quarries, reservoirs, and ocean inlets all have been used for free-field measurements. Such sites as

109

artificial pools and indoor tanks are used also, but they usually require pulsed sound techniques and are discussed separately in Section 3.12. The basic requirements are (1) enough space so that interference from boundary reflections can be eliminated by pulsing techniques, anechoic boundaries, or spreading losses due to long distances, (2) a low ambient noise level, and (3) a water medium that is relatively free of anything that will cause refraction and scattering, like currents, temperature gradients, marine life, bubbles, and pollutants. Protection from rough weather also is desirable from the point of view of low ambient noise and platform stability, as well as for comfort and convenience.

Facility platforms are of various kinds—piers, bridges, barges, or other semi-mobile floating structures, and boats or ships. Piers and bridges provide the best stability and convenience. Where the body of water is large and deep, however, a floating structure must be used and stability and convenience are obtained through sheer size of the structure and the connections to the shore or bottom.

The critical dimension of natural bodies of water is the depth, because it usually is smaller than the horizontal dimensions and because the top or water-air surface and the bottom usually are the best reflecting boundaries. The side boundaries of natural bodies of water usually are relatively distant and have slopes that form a natural wedge-shaped sound trap with the water-air surface; that is, near-horizontal sound rays will be reflected many times between the sloping bottom and the top surface, losing a little sound energy into the bottom or into the air each time.

Sand, silt, or muck on the bottom will be partial absorbers of sound, provided that there is no decaying organic material in them. If the bottom does contain decaying organic material, however, bubbles of gas (usually methane) form continually, and it actually becomes a water-gas surface and a good reflector.[1,2] Where both the top and the bottom are good reflectors, the interference is more than merely twice that for the top alone. The two surfaces, which usually are approximately parallel, produce multiple reflections or a standing wave between the top and bottom. Such interference can be many times the magnitude of a single reflection interference.[3] Concave bottoms can produce focused reflections and thereby cause unusually high interference.

There is no simple criterion for the minimum acceptable depth for a facility site. The type of transducer, the kind of measurement and the accuracy required, the frequency range, and whether continuous wave or pulsed sound is used—all these affect the required depth. The experience of some facilities, however, provides some general guidance. Depths as small as 20 feet have been used, but largely for the ultrasonic frequency range. For measurements at high audio and ultrasonic frequencies, depths of 25-50 feet are typical; for frequencies below 1 kHz, however, the 25-50 foot depth is marginal. If the measurements are being made on wide-band transducers with approximately constant response or sensitivity, boundary interference usually can be recognized and corrections can be made. Transducers with resonances below 1 kHz should be calibrated in deeper water where transducer depths of the order of 50 feet or more are feasible.

Fish can be a problem if one must rig the transducers at a shallow depth where fish are present. The gas-filled bladders that many fish have act as bubbles that resonate in the audio-frequency range.

Producers of ambient noise include boat or ship traffic, nearby machinery (particularly pumps coupled to the water), trucks, railroads, rain, and wave motion. Surprisingly, large airplanes are a source of noise interference because their noise level is so high. Even with a 30-dB air-to-water transmission loss, the noise from an airplane can produce a high noise level in the water.

Temperature gradients are troublesome when they are present at or near the depth at which the transducers are placed. The sound waves are refracted and this of course can cause errors in measurements. Figure 3.1 shows some temperature profiles or thermoclines in Lake Gem Mary at Orlando, Florida, before measures were taken to eliminate the gradients. Some species of fish apparently prefer certain water temperatures, which leads to concentrations of fish at certain depths. Temperature gradients in small quiet bodies of water are greatest near the surface and in warm weather. In deep lakes, the gradient becomes negligible, for purposes of electroacoustic measurements, at depths of 50-100 feet. A spring usually will be almost isothermal and have no gradients. Small lakes or ponds can be made isothermal by forced vertical circulation of the water. A high-capacity low-pressure pump is used for this purpose at the Dodge Pond Facility of the Navy Underwater Sound Laboratory in New London, Connecticut. At Lake Gem Mary in Orlando, Florida, high-pressure air is released through a grid of perforated pipes supported near the bottom beneath the measurement working area. The bubbles rise to the surface, and produce vertical circulation in the process. This circulation, maintained for a few hours each night, keeps the whole 800-ft-diameter, 30-ft-deep lake approximately isothermal. Vertical circulation also inhibits the production of methane bubbles by anaerobic bacteria on the bottom.

Clean water is helpful although not necessary. Artificial pools and tanks can be kept clean by circulation and filtering. Thin plastic liners such as would be used for a deep artificial swimming pool can be used to accomplish the same purpose in natural bodies of water. The liner is suspended in the water and forms an enclosed pool within the larger lake or pond. The plastic is acoustically transparent so the free-field characteristics of the large natural body of water are retained, but the confined water can be filtered to keep it clean.

The facilities shown in Figs. 3.2 to 3.7 are representative of natural sites used by naval activities and contractors. The TRANSDEC facility shown in Fig. 3.7 is an artificial pool, but is unusually large, and more nearly characteristic of an outdoor natural site facility than of an indoor artificial pool or tank.

## 3.3 Transducer Preparation and Positioning

Transducers that are being readied for immersion in the water should be thoroughly washed with a wetting agent. It is vitally important that all air in cracks, slots, corners, and so forth be completely eliminated. It is important also that the temperature of the transducer be equalized with that of the water and

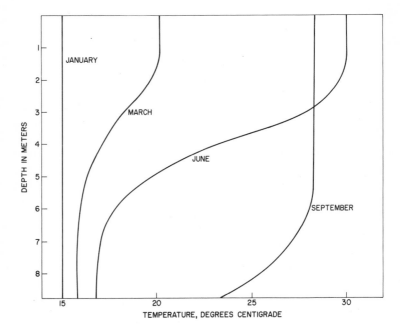

Fig. 3.1. Typical thermoclines in Lake Gem Mary, Orlando, Florida. Average depth of the lake near the calibration facility is 8-9 meters.

Fig. 3.2. Lake Facility of the Underwater Sound Reference Division of the Naval Research Laboratory at Lake Gem Mary near Orlando, Florida. The structure consists of three parallel and essentially identical piers supported by widely spaced tubular piling driven deep into the bottom of the lake. Water depth beneath the piers is 8-9 meters.

Fig. 3.3.   Leesburg Facility of the Underwater Sound Reference Division, Naval Research Laboratory, near Leesburg, Florida.  The structure consists of a floating platform and walkway supported by steel Navy pontoons filled with foamed plastic.  The water source is a slow-flowing spring 30 meters deep over a 30 × 60 meter area.

Fig. 3.4.   Facility of the Applied Research Laboratories of the University of Texas.  The lake actually is a reservoir behind a large dam a few hundred yards to the right and out of the picture.  The water level is subject to large and rapid changes, and the floating structure is loosely tied to the shore so as to allow for the change.

Fig. 3.5. Facility of the Navy Underwater Sound Laboratory at Dodge Pond near New London, Connecticut. The pond is about 12 meters deep. The structure is floating and supported by pontoons. The water level is stable. The structure including the walkway (and driveway) also is stable and firm and functions somewhat like a floating pier.

Fig. 3.6. Facility of the San Diego Division of the Naval Undersea Research and Development Center on Lake Pend Oreille in northern Idaho. The lake is about 200 meters deep beneath the floating barge, and measurements are made at depths of 30-60 meters. Long anchor lines connect the barge to the shore and bottom.

Fig. 3.7. TRANSDEC Facility of the Naval Undersea Research and Development Center, on Point Loma, San Diego, California. The very large artificial pool is spanned by a Bailey Bridge-type structure.

stabilized within itself. If a transducer that has been lying in the heat of the sun or for any other reason is unusually warm is put into cool water, air bubbles may collect on its surface. The warm transducer will heat the water layer next to the transducer. If the water already is saturated with air, the air will come out of solution and cling to the transducer because air is less soluble in warm water than in cold water. Uneven temperatures within a transducer also may cause stresses and strains. It is good practice to soak a transducer several hours before measurements are made.

The rigging structure that suspends or holds a transducer in the water should be acoustically as invisible as possible. In practice, this means a structure that is as light as is feasible, consistent with other requirements of mechanical strength and rigidity. Lattice-work is preferable to single large beams. Pipes and hollow rods should be free flooding. The structure should be as remote as possible from the transducer diaphragms or active faces and the acoustic path between the projector and hydrophone. Care must be taken so that parts of the transducer that normally vibrate, intentionally or otherwise, are not clamped or damped by the rigging. Figure 3.8 shows a typical rigging of small transducers.

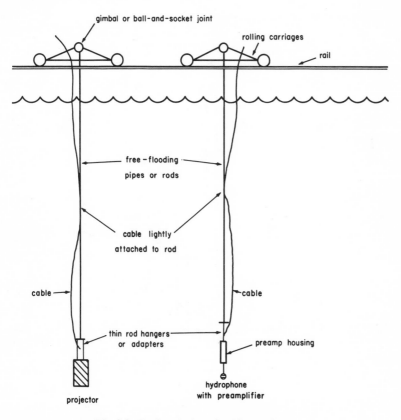

Fig. 3.8. Typical rigging of small transducers.

Both rigid and free-hanging rigging is used. In the rigid type, the transducer is rigidly connected to the supporting platform. In the free-hanging type, a gimbal or a ball-and-socket-type suspension is used so that the transducer hangs freely from the platform. The free-hanging type is preferable where the transducer is a symmetrical or balanced load, and where especially deep rigging is used. The rigid type is used where unbalanced loads are difficult to avoid. For example, if a transducer consists of a cylindrical housing with the diaphragm or acoustic center at one end, rotation for directivity pattern measurements must be about an axis at that end, as shown in Fig. 3.9. Counterbalancing is possible but difficult with a free-hanging suspension. Precise counterbalancing must be done in the water so that buoyancy effects are included. For unusually heavy unbalanced loads, even rigid rigging may need counterbalancing as shown in Fig. 3.10. Counterbalancing for a rigid structure need not be precise. The counterbalancing weight should be kept remote from the transducer.

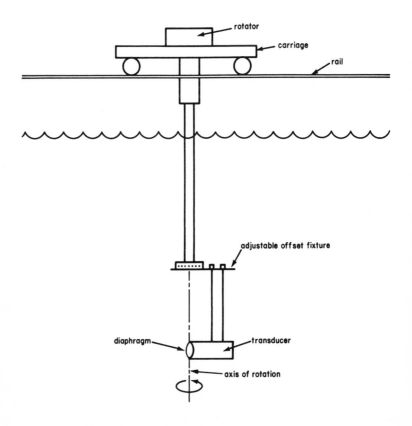

Fig. 3.9. Rigid rigging for rotating an unbalanced load.

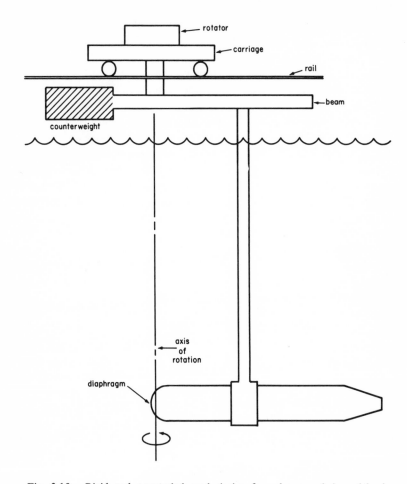

Fig. 3.10.   Rigid and counterbalanced rigging for a heavy unbalanced load.

In most facilities, the transducers are suspended from carriages that can be moved along rails on the platform. This arrangement makes it easy to adjust the distance between the projector and the  hydrophone.

There are four normal positioning requirements:  (1) The projector and hydrophone must be at the same depth. (2) The projector and hydrophone separation must be known. (3) The direction of the acoustic axis of each transducer must be known. (4) When rotation is involved, the axis of rotation must be known.

All positions are determined relative to the acoustic center of the transducer. The choice of the acoustic center can be arbitrary.  Any point on, or even remote from, the transducer can be chosen. However, if the real acoustic center, or point on a projector from which the transmitted sound appears to emanate, is not the same as the chosen acoustic center, then the hydrophone must be placed so far away that the separation of the two centers is negligible. That is, the projector-to-hydrophone distance would have to be about 100 times the distance between the real and the chosen acoustic centers or farther. Consequently, in practice, the acoustic center is chosen to be as near as possible to the real center. The real acoustic center is known accurately only for some symmetrical radiators like spheres and cylinders, where the acoustic center and the center or symmetry are the same. For piston radiators, the center of the piston face is used. When the transducer is of some unusual configuration, the location of the acoustic center may not be evident. Then, distance loss measurements can be made. For example, measure the pressure at two different distances $d_1$ and $d_2$. If the assumed position for the acoustic center is the correct position, the ratio of the measured pressures should conform to the inverse square spreading law; the pressure level differences should be 20 log $(d_2/d_1)$. If the measured difference is lower than the computed difference, the assumed acoustic center is too far forward. If the difference is too large, the assumed center is too far to the rear. This test is illustrated in Fig. 3.11. Obviously, if both $d_1$ and $d_2$ are large, the error due to $\Delta d$ in Fig. 3.11 will be small. In this test, it is assumed, of course, that there are no distance loss errors for other reasons such as are listed in Section 3.5.

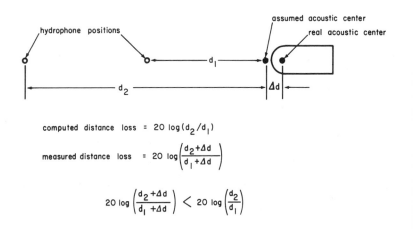

$$\text{computed distance loss} = 20 \log(d_2/d_1)$$

$$\text{measured distance loss} = 20 \log\left(\frac{d_2+\Delta d}{d_1+\Delta d}\right)$$

$$20 \log\left(\frac{d_2+\Delta d}{d_1+\Delta d}\right) < 20 \log\left(\frac{d_2}{d_1}\right)$$

Fig. 3.11. Distance-loss test for finding the real acoustic center.

Good precision in positioning is possible, and position errors are not critical. It is easy, for example, to position the projector and hydrophone with a separation error of less than 2%, and a 2% error would cause a pressure level error of less than 0.2 dB.

Inaccurate orientation of the acoustic axis is more serious than position errors. A one-degree misalignment of the axis can result in pressure level errors of several dB where the level is measured on the side of the main lobe of the beam pattern. Large transducers sometimes are oriented acoustically; that is, the orientation that produces maximum response is taken as the acoustic axis.

Errors in depth can lead to the unusual observation of a negative distance loss. The apparent pressure level will go up instead of down as the projector-to-hydrophone distance is increased, if one of the transducers has a narrow beam. The effect is illustrated by Fig. 3.12. At the short distance, the hydrophone is below or to the side of the main beam. When the separation is increased, the hydrophone angle error becomes smaller or the acoustic path moves closer to the maximum of the main beam. The signal increase due to being higher up on the main beam exceeds the distance loss, thereby causing a reversal of the normal distance loss.

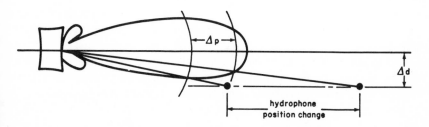

Fig. 3.12. Inverse distance loss $\Delta p$ due to depth error $\Delta d$.

For recording directivity patterns, transducers almost always are rotated about a vertical axis, with the transducer being reoriented in the hanger to obtain patterns in various planes. The mechanical rotator usually is above the water, except in some very deep water facilities.

## 3.4 Proximity Criteria

A projector and hydrophone are separated by the minimum acceptable distance in order to minimize interference from reflections. The criteria for the minimum distance or proximity are a function of the size and configuration of both transducers and of the type and desired accuracy of the measurement.

The proximity criterion for a projector alone comes from the requirement implied in the definition of the transmitting current or voltage response that the pressure be that in a spherically diverging wave. The reference distance is one meter from the projector. If the wave is not spherically divergent at one meter, however, the pressure must be measured at some larger distance and extrapolated back to one meter by making the assumption that the pressure is inversely proportional to the distance.

The proximity requirement for a hydrophone comes from the definition of the free-field voltage sensitivity in which the input free-field pressure is specified as that in a plane progressive wave. Plane waves can only be approximated in a free field, so the practical requirement is that the hydrophone intercept a segment of a spherical wave that is indistinguishable from a plane wave. That is, the segment must be very small or the radius of curvature of the wave must be very large.

The question of sufficient distance between projector and hydrophone can be answered experimentally. With a constant current into the projector, the output voltage of the hydrophone can be measured at two or more distances. If the voltage is inversely proportional to the distance, the proximity criterion is satisfied. However, if the desired proportionality is not found, the error may be due to causes other than proximity, and the question is not answered. For such reasons, as well as for measurement design and planning, proximity criteria and an understanding of proximity effects are useful.

Proximity criteria are available in the literature[4,5,6,7] for transducers of common shapes like pistons and lines. These criteria apply to single transmitting transducers in that they define the distance at which the Fresnel zone or near field ends and the Fraunhofer zone or spherically divergent far field begins. When applied to projector-hydrophone combinations, these criteria are valid only if the hydrophone is essentially a point sensor. If neither the projector nor the hydrophone is a point, a proximity criterion for the combinations must be established. This criterion is not merely the sum of the individual criteria for the two transducers.

Although proximity criteria for single transducers usually are visualized in terms of where the spherically divergent far field of a projector begins, the criteria apply also to the transducer as a hydrophone. From reciprocity theory, it is apparent that the proximity criterion for the combination of a large piston and a small point transducer, for example, must be the same, regardless of which is the projector and which is the hydrophone.

The combination of a large circular piston and a small point transducer is a common and particularly suitable example to illustrate the theory and rationale of proximity criteria.

If the large piston is the projector, the sound pressure on the piston axis, as would be measured by a point hydrophone, is shown in Fig. 3.13. The dashed curve showing the inward extrapolation of the far-field pressure meets the solid-line curve very gradually, indicating that there is no exact boundary between near field and far field. It is not surprising, therefore, that the proximity criteria of different authors do not always agree.

If the large piston were the hydrophone and the projector were a point source on the axis of the piston, the waves impinging on the piston would be spherical rather than plane. The magnitude of the pressure at the periphery of the piston would be less than at the middle, and the pressure would vary in phase as one moved from the middle to the periphery. The average free-field pressure at the position of the piston face clearly would be less than the pressure at the middle or axial point of the piston diaphragm. If one plotted this average free-field

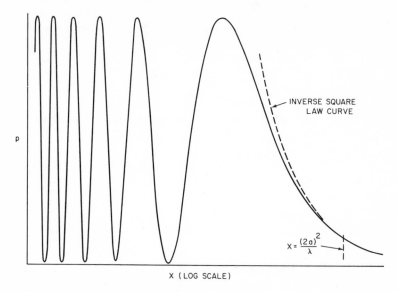

p

X ( LOG SCALE )

$X = \dfrac{(2a)^2}{\lambda}$

INVERSE SQUARE
LAW CURVE

Fig. 3.13.  Relative pressure $p$ at distance $x$ on the axis of a circular piston projector of radius $a$ for sound of wavelength $\lambda$.  Also, the average free-field pressure over the area of a circular piston hydrophone of radius $a$, from a point projector at distance $x$ on the hydrophone axis.

pressure as a function of the point projector's position on the axis, the shape of the curve would be identical to that in Fig. 3.13. The proximity criterion for the piston hydrophone case would be the same as for the piston projector case.

The proximity criterion for a circular piston in a rigid baffle is found by analyzing the expression for the axial pressure:

$$p = 2\rho c u \sin |\tfrac{1}{2}k[(x^2 + a^2)^{\tfrac{1}{2}} - x]|, \qquad (3.1)$$

where $\rho$ is the water density, $c$ is the speed of sound, $u$ is the piston velocity, $k = 2\pi/\lambda$ is the wave number, $\lambda$ is the wavelength, $x$ is the axial distance, and $a$ is the piston radius.

In the far field, Eq. (3.1) reduces to

$$p = \rho c u \left(\frac{\pi a^2}{\lambda r}\right). \qquad (3.2)$$

Mathematically, the proximity criterion relates to the question of what approximations are necessary to reduce Eq. (3.1) to Eq. (3.2). These approximations are found as follows:

The term $(x^2 + a^2)^{1/2}$ is developed by the binomial expansion into the infinite series

$$(x^2 + a^2)^{1/2} = x + \frac{a^2}{2x} - \frac{a^4}{8x^3} + \ldots, \tag{3.3}$$

and only the first two terms of the series are used. That is, the approximation

$$(x^2 + a^2)^{1/2} \simeq x + \frac{a^2}{2x} \tag{3.4}$$

is valid if

$$\frac{a^2}{2x} \gg \frac{a^4}{8x^3} \qquad \text{or} \qquad \frac{a}{x} \ll 2. \tag{3.5}$$

Substituting Eq. (3.4) into (3.1) produces

$$p = 2\rho c u \sin\left|\frac{ka^2}{4x}\right| = 2\rho c u \sin\left|\frac{\pi a^2}{2\lambda x}\right|. \tag{3.6}$$

As the second approximation, we use the common expression $\sin\theta \simeq \theta$ for small angles, or

$$\sin\left|\frac{\pi a^2}{2\lambda x}\right| \simeq \frac{\pi a^2}{2\lambda x}, \tag{3.7}$$

if

$$\frac{\pi a^2}{2\lambda x} \ll 1 \qquad \text{or} \qquad \frac{\pi a^2}{2\lambda} \ll x. \tag{3.8}$$

Substituting Eq. (3.7) into (3.6) yields

$$p = \rho c u \left(\frac{\pi a^2}{\lambda x}\right). \tag{3.9}$$

Equation (3.9) is the far-field expression where $p$ is inversely proportional to $x$.

The approximation errors of Eqs. (3.4) and (3.7) are shown in Fig. 3.14. This figure shows how the criteria depend on the arbitrary choice of acceptable accuracy. In general, the minimum value of $x$ at high frequencies is set by the acceptable error in Fig. 3.14b. This minimum distance $x$ becomes smaller as the frequency decreases until at low frequencies it reaches a constant value set by the acceptable error in Fig. 3.14a. This is illustrated in Fig. 3.15 for the case $a = 10$ cm where each straight line corresponds to one of the several criteria indicated. At and near the points where the lines intersect, the maximum error is the sum of the two errors.

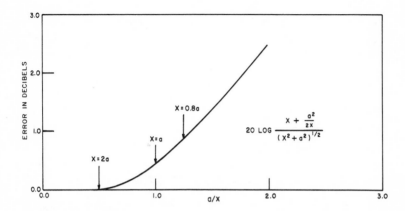

Fig. 3.14a. Error in using only the first two terms in the binomial expansion of $(x^2 + a^2)^{1/2}$.

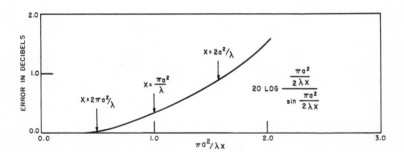

Fig. 3.14b. Error in the approximation that the sine of an angle equals the angle.

The standard criteria[6] for uniform circular pistons are

$$x \geqslant \frac{\pi a^2}{\lambda} \qquad (3.10)$$

and

$$x \geqslant a, \qquad (3.11)$$

but other criteria shown in Figs. 3.14 and 3.15 are used frequently.

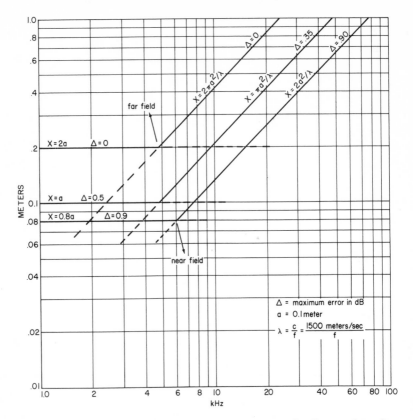

Fig. 3.15. Minimum distance $x$ between a circular piston of radius $a$ and a point transducer according to the proximity criterion shown on each line.

There are two proximity criteria because waves are characterized by two parameters—phase and amplitude. The criteria in Eqs. (3.5) and (3.11) and the error curve in Fig. 3.14a are independent of wavelength and relate to amplitude requirements. The criteria in Eqs. (3.8) and (3.10) and the error curve in Fig. 3.14b relate to the phase requirements.

Criteria for transducers other than uniform circular pistons are developed in a similar way. However, where the shape is not a simple circle, square, line, and so forth, calculations may become impossible. Fortunately, experience shows that loose approximations can be made about the shape of transducers.

For square pistons, the criterion is $x \geqslant w^2/\lambda$, where $w$ is the width of one side of the square. The criterion for a square and Eq. (3.10) for a circle can be combined into

$$x \geqslant \frac{\text{area}}{\lambda} \tag{3.12}$$

and used for any uniform piston shape (hexagon, octagon, and so forth) that approximates a circle or square.

Nonuniform pistons almost always are of the type having a shaded or tapered velocity amplitude that is maximum at the center and gradually reduces to zero at the periphery. The effective diameters or widths can be taken between the points having 0.5 normalized amplitudes—that is, between the half-shaded points. If the shading design is unknown, the safe step is to assume that there is no shading.

The criteria for lines or thin cylinders are

$$x \geqslant \frac{L^2}{\lambda} \qquad (3.13)$$

and

$$x \geqslant L, \qquad (3.14)$$

where $L$ is the line length. Both Eqs. (3.13) and (3.14) are very conservative, but they are useful in that they combine easily with piston criteria to provide two simple and general rules. From Eqs. (3.10), (3.11), (3.12), (3.13), and (3.14), one can derive the general rules for response measurements with pistons and lines:

$$x \geqslant \frac{(\text{maximum dimension})^2}{\lambda}, \qquad (3.15)$$

$$x \geqslant \text{maximum dimension}. \qquad (3.16)$$

Figure 3.16 is a chart in which Eqs. (3.15) and (3.16) are used for the general cases of transducers that have various maximum dimensions. These are conservative criteria that allow errors of 0.5 dB or less.

When distances that are too short to meet proximity criteria must be used, the corrections shown in Figs. 3.17 and 3.18 can be used.[5]

The general criteria given in Eqs. (3.15) and (3.16) apply only to such cases as the piston and thin cylinder or line where the diaphragm or active area of the transducer lies approximately in a plane normal to the acoustic axis. The criteria assure that both the amplitude and phase of a sound wave impinging on the plane from a distance $x$ are uniform and thereby simulate a plane wave. For transducers in which the diaphragm is not planar (a thick cylinder, for example) and for directivity pattern measurements where the diaphragm does not remain in one plane, additional limitations are necessary. Proximity criteria for such cases

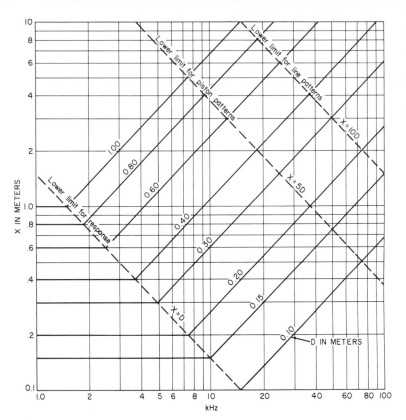

Fig. 3.16. Minimum distance $x$ between a transducer of maximum dimension $D$ and a point hydrophone, according to the criterion $x \geqslant D^2/\lambda$ and lower limits as shown. Speed of sound is taken as 1500 m/sec.

are not very amenable to calculation, but they can be analyzed by considering the diagram in Fig. 3.19. Assume that the circle shown either is a cross-section of a thick cylinder or represents the volume swept out by the rotation of a plane transducer. The spherical-wave segments impinging on the transducer position then must simulate plane waves over the entire volume occupied by the transducer. The spherical wave segments become more plane as the radius of curvature increases. Further, the phase of the pressure (but not the particle velocity) in a spherical wave is independent of the curvature. Consequently, if the phase proximity criterion of Eq. (3.15) is satisfied for the near edge of the transducer $(x_1 \geqslant D^2/\lambda)$, then the criterion of the far edge $(x_3 \geqslant D^2/\lambda)$ should be satisfied also.

With a similar argument, if Eq. (3.16) is satisfied by $x_1 \geqslant D$, then the criterion $x_3 \geqslant D$ is satisfied automatically. However, Eq. (3.16) assures amplitude uniformity only in a lateral direction. Here we also need amplitude uniformity in a

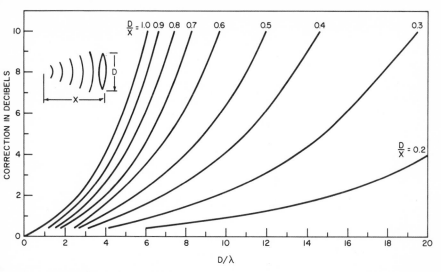

Fig. 3.17.  Spherical-wave correction for circular piston.  Correction to be added to measured response.  (From reference 5.)

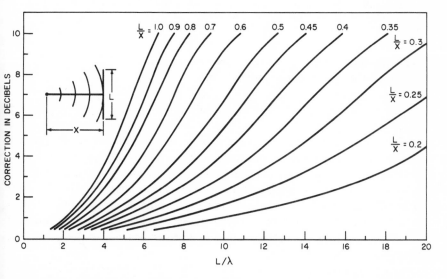

Fig. 3.18.  Spherical-wave correction for a uniform line.  Correction to be added to measured response.  (From reference 5.)

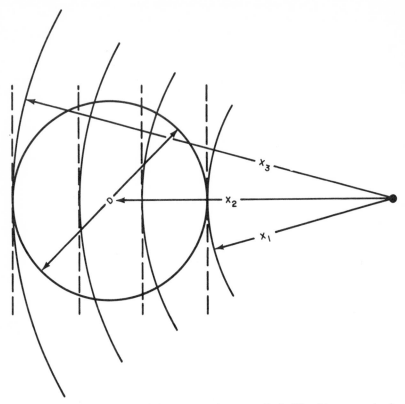

Fig. 3.19. Approximation of plane progressive waves (dashed lines) by segments of spherical waves over a volume of diameter $D$.

longitudinal direction. To assure a minimum variation of 1 dB between the near and far edge of the transducer, we must have

$$x \geqslant 10D. \tag{3.17}$$

The 1-dB variation does not necessarily correspond to a 1-dB error. The high pressure in the front and the low pressure in the rear usually will average out to the pressure in the middle, and the error will be considerably less than 1 dB.

Equation (3.17) is a more stringent requirement than $x \geqslant D^2/\lambda$, unless $D \geqslant 10\lambda$. Since very few transducers have dimensions of 10 wavelengths or more, Eq. (3.17) becomes the key criterion in designing calibration facilities. It is also the basis for the conclusion that pattern measurements require more space than response measurements do.

If one is measuring the end-fire response of a uniform line, Eq. (3.17) would be used without qualification. In many practical cases, however, a lesser distance $x$ can be used for one of three reasons.

First, in many pattern measurements, the interest is focused on the pattern near the acoustic axis—say in the 60° sector centered on the axis. If a piston transducer is rotated only through the angle from −30° to +30°, or if the accuracy and proximity criteria are applied only within this angle, then the distance to the near and far edge, or to $x_1$ and $x_3$ in Fig. 3.19, differ by not more than $D/2$. (See Fig. 3.59.) Then the criterion would be half that in Eq. (3.17).

A second practical case pertains specifically to the common circular piston transducer. Imagine in Fig. 3.19 that the circle represents a circular piston at 90° or 270° orientation. The piston area near the source at approximately the distance $x_1$ is smaller than the area at approximately the distance $x_2$. Similarly, the area at distance $x_3$ is less than at $x_2$. The piston functions as a tapered or shaded line—more sensitive at the center, with the sensitivity gradually diminishing toward the two ends. Consequently, errors in pressure magnitude at the ends, or at the near and far edges of the circular piston face will have less effect than if the transducer had uniform sensitivity (as would be true with a uniform line or square piston).

For these first two reasons, the criterion of Eq. (3.17) can be modified to

$$x \geqslant 5D. \tag{3.18}$$

The third reason pertains to transducers that are thick cylinders and others that have part of the diaphragm facing in the 180° direction. This part of the diaphragm is in an acoustic shadow. Regardless of what the free-field pressure is in the shadow zone, the applied pressure is low, and contributes little to the sensitivity. Consequently, the effective thickness of the transducer is less than the real thickness, and a less stringent criterion like Eq. (3.18) is permitted.

Equations (3.17) and (3.18) are used to define low limits in Fig. 3.16 that apply to nonplanar transducers or pattern measurements.

Having established that $x \geqslant 5D$, it makes little difference which of $x_1$, $x_2$, or $x_3$ in Fig. 3.19 is used as the transducer separation distance. However, it already has been specified that the acoustic center should be used. Thus $x_2$ would be the normal selection, and would tend to minimize errors to the greatest extent by averaging.

Proximity criteria for the case in which both transducers are of some finite size have been determined by Sabin for (1) two circular pistons of different diameters,[8] and (2) two parallel lines of the same length.[9] Figure 3.20 is a graph from Sabin showing proximity errors for the two-piston case. The curve $A \to \infty$ corresponds to the curve in Fig. 3.14b. Figure 3.21 is a plot of pressure versus distance for the two-line case. From Fig. 3.21, it can be seen that the criterion for errors of 1 dB is $L^2/\lambda$, and for negligible error, $2L^2/\lambda$.

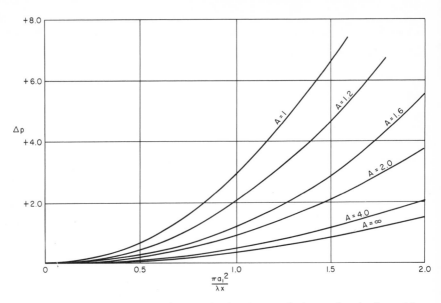

Fig. 3.20. The proximity error for two circular pistons; $\lambda$ is the wavelength of sound in the medium, $a_1$ is the radius of the circular piston source, $a_2$ is the radius of the circular piston receiver, $A = a_1/a_2$, $x$ is the separation distance between piston and receiver, $\Delta p$ is the proximity error in decibels to be added to the measured response. (From reference 8.)

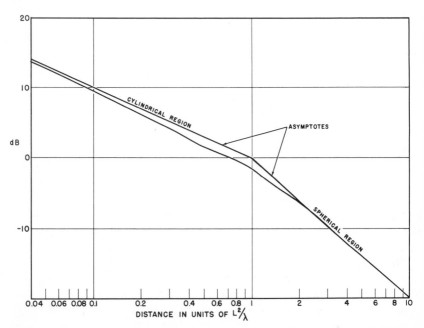

Fig. 3.21. The relative average pressure acting on a hydrophone as a function of the projector-to-hydrophone distance when the projector and hydrophone are two parallel lines of length $L$. (From reference 9.)

Yamada[10] has investigated the case of two rectangular transducers and gives a spherical wave approximation criterion:

$$x > \frac{k(1 + \gamma^2)[(\tfrac{1}{2}W)^2 + (\tfrac{1}{2}L)^2]}{6} ,$$  (3.19)

where $k$ is the wave number, $W$ is the projector width, $L$ is the projector length, and $\gamma$ is the ratio of hydrophone width to projector width. It is assumed that the two rectangles have the same shape. For the case of a square projector ($W = L$), and a point hydrophone ($\gamma = 0$), Eq. (3.19) reduces to

$$x > \frac{\pi}{6} \frac{W^2}{\lambda},$$  (3.20)

or about half of the criterion in Eq. (3.15). For the case of two identical squares ($\gamma = 1$), Eq. (3.19) reduces to

$$x > \frac{\pi}{3} \frac{W^2}{\lambda}.$$  (3.21)

Yamada's criteria are rather liberal as illustrated by one of his curves in Fig. 3.22. The ratio of the two curves for $x$ given by Eq. (3.19) is about 1.4, or the error is 3 dB, and corresponds approximately to a point in Fig. 3.20 for $A = 1$ and $\pi a^2/\lambda x = 1.0$. It would be necessary to use about twice the distance given by Eq. (3.19) to keep errors less than 1 dB, in which case Eqs. (3.20) and (3.15) essentially agree.

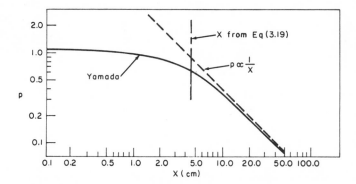

Fig. 3.22. Relative average free-field pressure at the position of a square hydrophone from an identical square projector at distance $x$ cm away. The wave number is 1 cm$^{-1}$. The side of the square is 5 cm. (From reference 10.)

## 3.5 Basic Measurements and Instrumentation

The basic parameters measured in a typical electroacoustic measurement are
(1) the projector input current $i$ or voltage $e$, (2) the hydrophone open-circuit
output voltage $e_{oc}$, (3) the distance separating the projector and hydrophone,
and (4) the frequency. These basic measurements can be made with instrumentation shown in Fig. 3.23 and an ordinary meter stick. In practice, however, the
instrumentation, aside from the meter stick, seldom is that simple. A power
amplifier in the transmitting system usually is necessary to increase the projector's acoustic output to a useable level. Similarly, a voltage amplifier may be
necessary in the receiving system. Electrical filters are used in the receiving system to obtain maximum signal-to-noise ratios. The projector current $i$ is
measured as the voltage $e_i$ across a series impedance so that all the electrical
measurements are of voltage. Then the same voltmeter is used for all the electrical measurements, and errors in voltage ratios are minimized. It can be seen
from Eqs. (2.1), (2.3), (2.6), and (2.19) that most calibration formulas contain
voltage ratios or voltage/current quotients. The signal generator usually is a wide-
range oscillator or a frequency synthesizer. Where an oscillator is used, a frequency standard or counter may be needed to monitor the generator signal, depending on the quality (and cost) of the oscillator. A typical calibration system
with these additional features, but still with discrete point-by-point frequency
changes, is shown in Fig. 3.24.

Still more elaborate systems for continuous sweeping through the frequency
range, analog recording, and using pulse techniques are shown in Sections 3.7
and 3.8.

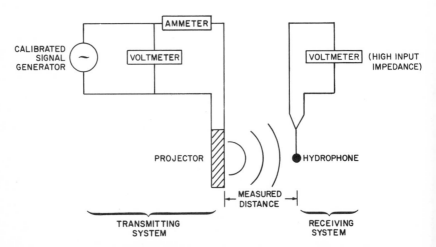

Fig. 3.23. Basic instrumentation for electroacoustic measurements.

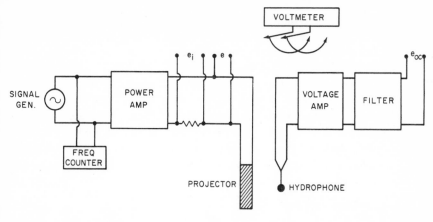

Fig. 3.24. Calibration instrumentation for point-by-point electroacoustic measurements.

The signal levels in calibration measurements usually are low. The range in typical basic measurements, based on hydrophone sensitivities of −90 to −110 dB re 1 V/μbar and projector responses to 40 to 80 dB re 1 μbar/A, is

| | |
|---|---|
| pressure level: | 40 to 70 dB re 1 μbar |
| hydrophone voltage level: | −70 to −40 dB re 1 V |
| projector current level: | −20 to 0 dB re 1 A |
| projector voltage level: | 0 to 60 dB re 1 V |

Voltage and current levels for impedance measurements with electrical bridges are even lower than these. If a transducer is linear, it makes no difference what the signal level is, so long as it is large enough to be well above the ambient acoustical and electrical noise levels and small enough to avoid overloading the equipment.

If the transducer is nonlinear, or if the transducer is exposed to signal levels above its linear range, then the defined meanings of sensitivity, response, impedance, and so forth, is lost. The special problems of high-signal measurements is discussed in Section 3.9.

The electrical measurements required by the calibration formulas (Eqs. (2.1), (2.3), (2.6), (2.19), etc.) should be made at not less than two separation distances. With the rolling carriage arrangement shown in Fig. 3.8, this distance change is easy to make and it provides a check or cross-check of several kinds. The two distances are chosen so that the distance loss of the signal is some convenient number of decibels. For example, if the distance is changed from 30 to 40 cm, the distance loss is 20 log (4/3) or 3.5 dB. Similarly, 20 log (5/4) = 2 dB, and 20 log (2/1) = 6 dB. If the distance loss measurement and theory agree, then all of the following measurement conditions are satisfied:

1. There is no proximity error.
2. The acoustic centers are properly chosen.
3. The system and the medium are stable.
4. The receiving system is linear.
5. The transducers are properly rigged.
6. There is no boundary interference or electrical crosstalk.

In the absence of the correct distance loss, one or more of these conditions probably are not satisfied. The distance loss test might fail at a single frequency because two errors of different kinds might cancel each other. The probability of error cancellation at several frequencies or over a frequency range is negligible.

### 3.6 Voltage Coupling Loss

When a hydrophone containing a preamplifier or other kind of associated network is calibrated, a choice must be made as to where the hydrophone output terminal points are. That is, where are the terminals across which the open-circuit voltage is to be measured? If the terminal points are selected at the end of the cable, then the preamplifier and the cable become an integral part of the hydrophone and affect the hydrophone sensitivity. If the terminal points are selected as close as possible to the generator (the electrodes of a high-impedance piezoelectric element, for example), then a measurement of the hydrophone voltage coupling loss becomes necessary.

Hydrophone voltage coupling loss is defined as the ratio of the open-circuit voltage of the hydrophone generator (usually a piezoelectric element) to the open-circuit voltage at the output of the preamplifier and cable or other type of associated network. Note that with this definition a true loss is a number greater than one or is a positive number of decibels.

The coupling loss and its measurement is straightforward in theory. In practice, however, the theoretically assumed conditions and the measurement are subject to several types of subtle errors that make the measurement difficult and, in some circumstances, impossible. Although we are concerned primarily with a hydrophone that contains a preamplifier, the theory and practice here applies equally well to any passive hydrophone and the first amplifier in the voltage-measuring system.

The coupling loss is the sum of two effects. One is the gain or loss of the preamplifier itself. The other is the voltage loss due to the fact that the preamplifier does not have an infinite input impedance and consequently the voltage across the preamplifier input is not a true open-circuit voltage. Figure 3.25 is a schematic diagram of a hydrophone with a preamplifier. The piezoelectric generator is represented according to Thevenin's Theorem by the generator open-circuit $e_{oc}$ in series with the generator impedance $Z_g$. The amplifier input impedance is $Z_a$. The amplifier input voltage $e_a$ will always be measurably less than $e_{oc}$, unless $Z_a \gg Z_g$. Since $Z_g$ often is many megohms, the assumption $Z_a \gg Z_g$ generally is not valid, and the voltage $e_{oc}$ is attenuated before it is applied to the preamplifier.

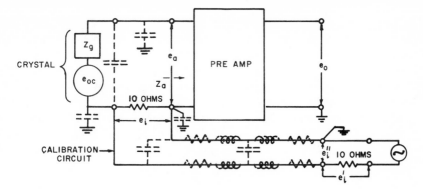

Fig. 3.25. Hydrophone circuit as represented by a Thevenin generator and a pre-amplifier. Stray impedances are shown in dashed lines.

The coupling loss is, by definition, the ratio $e_{oc}/e_0$. The loss is measured by inserting a calibration signal in series with both the piezoelectric generator and the preamplifier input in the manner shown in Fig. 3.25. The calibration resistor is kept small (typically, 10 ohms) so that it does not measurably attenuate the voltage $e_{oc}$ and so that the calibration input voltage $e_i$ is essentially an open-circuit voltage across the resistor. Then $e_i$ can simulate $e_{oc}$. That is, the input/output ratios $e_{oc}/e_0$ and $e_i/e_0$ are the same. The voltage $e_i$ is measured across a second external 10-ohm resistor as $e_i'$. This procedure is valid, if the shunt capacitance of the cable shown by the dashed symbols in Fig. 3.25 has an impedance much larger than 10 ohms. Alternately, the voltage $e_i''$ in Fig. 3.25 can be used if the series inductance and resistance of the cable can be neglected. If the cable is very long, say more than about 100 feet, neither $e_i'$ or $e_i''$ is the same as $e_i$, and the measurement becomes impractical. In such a case, end-of-cable calibrations are used.

Designers and users sometimes are tempted to use one conductor to serve as the low-potential or ground conductor for both the calibration circuit and the preamplifier output circuit. This is a mistake, since the two circuits then are coupled by the common small but finite impedance of the common conductor. Signals from the calibrator circuit are induced into the preamplifier output circuit, bypassing the preamplifier.

A common source of trouble in coupling measurements is the electrical grounding conditions. There are no simple rules to avoid such trouble except that the user should be alert to circuit complications due to stray impedance and multiple ground points. Crystal electrodes, cable shields, and the transducer housing all have measurable capacitance to ground or to the water medium. A single ground or zero potential point is difficult to achieve in practice. Fresh water is a much poorer conductor than salt water, and the electrical grounding conditions in the two media can be quite different. Figure 3.25 illustrates various stray impedances.

Near resonance frequencies when the motional impedance of the piezoelectric generator is a significant part of $Z_g$, the acoustic load on the generator during the coupling loss measurement must be the same as that during the sensitivity measurement.

Because of these various problems in the measurement of hydrophone voltage coupling loss and the advent of modern stable transistorized preamplifiers, the trend has been toward end-of-cable calibrations and elimination of the coupling loss measurement. Where the circuitry is still available, a coupling loss measurement can be used as a stability check on the circuit, but it is not otherwise used in a calibration measurement.

### 3.7 Automatic Systems

Underwater electroacoustic calibration, test, and evaluation measurements on one transducer usually are made at many frequencies or over wide frequency ranges. At some activities, measurements are made on large numbers of transducers. Consequently, various degrees and types of automation are used to reduce the time and tedium of many point-by-point frequency measurements. Automatic systems, however complicated they may be, still are only elaborations of the basic instrumentation shown in Figs. 3.23 and 3.24.

Many of the details of an automatic system are matters of individual preference, custom, economy, and easy availability of particular instruments or equipments. However, the general features of various systems are much the same, and the system in Fig. 3.26 illustrates these features. The components shown as solid-line blocks constitute the basic system used for continuous-wave (c-w) signals. The dashed-line blocks are major options. Automation of the basic system relates to three primary needs: (1) continuous frequency changes, (2) continuous recording of the hydrophone output signal, and (3) filtering a signal with a continually changing frequency.

Consider first the system shown in solid lines in Fig. 3.26. The signal is generated in a variable oscillator. The oscillator frequency range usually covers several decades, and often a motor-drive arrangement automatically sweeps through the entire frequency range. The frequency calibration of wide-range oscillators usually is not precise; consequently, a frequency counter or other type of frequency meter is used to monitor and measure the output of the oscillator.

The next stage is a voltage amplifier to control the signal level of the oscillator and provide the sufficient and proper voltage input level to succeeding stages.

The power amplifier provides the electrical, and ultimately acoustical, power needed to obtain a measurable signal level at the hydrophone.

Networks, often consisting of multitap transformers, are used to match the output impedance of the power amplifier to the projector to obtain maximum power transfer. Sometimes, however, projector current or voltage control is more important than maximum power. Then, deliberate mismatching can be used. The entire transmitting system that feeds the projector, for example, can

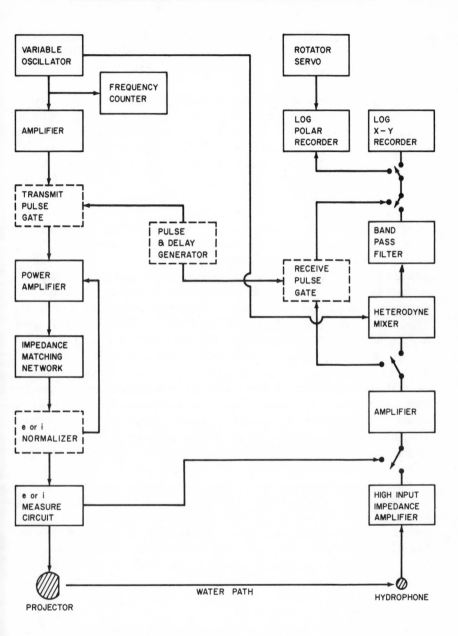

Fig. 3.26. Typical automatic calibration system. The basic continuous-wave signal system is shown in solid-line boxes. Options for pulsed sound and normalized or constant projector voltage or current are shown in dashed-line boxes.

be made to function approximately as a low-impedance constant-voltage genera-tor, or as a high-impedance constant-current generator. Other types of networks are used to obtain, for example, currents or voltages that change with frequency at some fixed rate.

Impedance matching or mismatching is used between all stages of the system to obtain optimum performance. When two stages are not properly matched, intermediate transformers or networks may be used to achieve or improve matching. Attenuators are used to minimize impedance variations as well as to attenuate signal levels. Impedance conditions are especially important at the input and output of an amplifier, if the amplifier gain calibration is to be used.

The projector input current or voltage must be measured for some types of calibrations, and should, in any case, be monitored to insure stability of the measurement conditions. Both the voltage $e$ and current $i$ measurement circuits are designed to have negligible effect on the amplifier-to-projector circuit. The $e$ measurement circuit is, typically, a high-impedance circuit connected in parallel with the projector; the $i$ measurement circuit is, typically, a low-impedance cir-cuit in series with the projector. In either case, the $e$ or $i$ measure signal is fed to the same receiving and recording system as the hydrophone output voltage, where it is subject to the same mixing, filtering, and recording. The calibration formulas in Section 3.15 all show that it is the ratio (or difference in decibels) of, for example, the hydrophone voltage measure to the projector current measure that is needed. Consequently, if both the $e$ or $i$ measure signal and the hydrophone signal are amplified, attenuated, mixed, filtered, recorded, and so forth, in the same way, the ratio is unaffected. The $e$ or $i$ measure circuit itself must be cali-brated, but the over-all system needs no calibration. It must, of course, be linear and stable, and for these reasons, electrical calibration-type measurements are used to test the system. But these are really monitor measurements rather than calibration measurements.

The $e$ measure is straightforward; a typical circuit is shown in Fig. 3.27a. The $i$ measure is more difficult. Being in series with the projector, it must carry the same current, which in some cases may be quite high. Electrical grounding conditions become complicated if the projector is electrically unbalanced. Figure 3.27b shows an old but typical arrangement using a small series resistor. Figure 3.27c shows a better circuit wherein one conductor of the projector cable is used as a single-turn primary winding of a transformer. The secondary winding is a toroid coil that surrounds the conductor. This circuit is similar to commercial "clamp-on" ammeters.

The $e$ and $i$ measure circuit calibration is essentially a determination of $e_e/e$ and $e_i/i$ in Fig. 3.27. If a standard resistance $R$ is substituted for the projector, the quantity $e_i/i$ becomes $e_iR/e$, and the current calibration becomes a measure-ment of two voltages by the same voltage-measuring system.

In hydrophone calibration measurements, the hydrophone output voltage must be measured across an effectively open circuit. Consequently, the first stage in the receiving system is a high-input-impedance amplifier such as a cathode-follower.

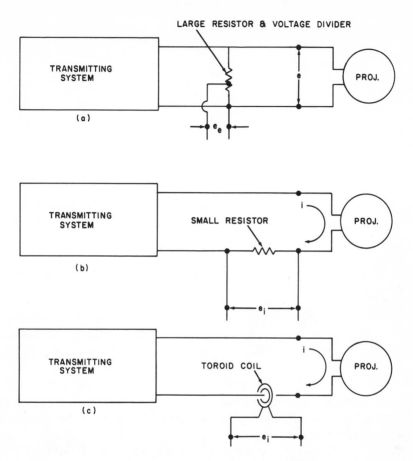

Fig. 3.27.  Typical circuits for measuring (a) the projector voltage and, (b) and (c), current.

The function of this first amplifier is really impedance matching rather than amplification; consequently, it is followed by a calibrated voltage amplifier.

The next two stages are a heterodyne mixer and a band-pass filter that together constitute a tracking filter. The heterodyne mixer changes the variable frequency to a fixed frequency $f_0$. The pass band of the filter then is fixed and centered on $f_0$.

The heterodyne principle consists essentially of mixing two frequencies so that sum and difference frequencies are produced, filtering out either the sum or difference frequency, and using the other. The combination of the variable oscillator in the transmitting system and heterodyne mixer in the receiving system actually is a combination of two oscillators and two mixers in either of two arrangements shown in Fig. 3.28. The beat-frequency oscillator in Fig. 3.28a has the advantage of a wider frequency range, but is more expensive and less readily available than the simple oscillator in Fig. 3.28b.

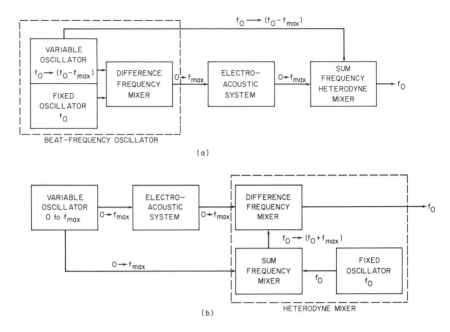

Fig. 3.28. Two variations of the heterodyning principle to change a variable signal frequency (0 to $f_{max}$) to a fixed frequency ($f_0$).

The band-pass filter rejects extraneous signal frequencies and improves the signal-to-noise ratio. It may be adjustable, having, for example, bandwidths of 20, 200, and 2000 Hz.

The recorders are logarithmic so that the signal amplitude is recorded in decibels. The data for frequency sensitivity or response is recorded on an x-y, strip, or linear recorder. Directivity pattern data are recorded in polar or linear form. The polar recorder turntable is connected to and synchronized with the mechanical rotator that rotates the transducer by a servo system.

It is convenient in many measurements to have the projector input current or voltage constant to an extent unattainable by passive impedance-matching techniques. In such cases, normalizing circuits are used as shown by the dashed-line box in Fig. 3.26. This is a circuit that feeds back a correction signal to one of the amplifier stages.

Many automatic systems operate with pulsed signals rather than the continuous-wave signals. The technique is discussed in detail in Section 3.8. The pulsing equipment consists of the three components shown in the dashed-line boxes in Fig. 3.26. The pulse generator feeds the pulses to both the transmit and receive gate circuits. The gate circuits essentially open and close the path or gate through which the oscillator signals must pass. The pulse generator also provides a means for delaying the signal fed to the receive gate to compensate for the time it takes a pulse to travel the water path at its relatively slow speed. The delay adjustment also permits passage or gating of selected portions of a pulse passing through the receive system. When not being used, the pulsing components of the system are bypassed.

The calibration data from a system as shown in Fig. 3.26 consists of two to four lines on a strip chart. Each line represents some voltage or current as a function of frequency. In addition to the measured data, constants or such quasi-constants as the reciprocity parameter, standard hydrophone calibration, test distance correction, and so forth must be added to obtain a hydrophone sensitivity or projector response (see Section 3.15). The data reduction may in fact be more time-consuming than the measurements. Various techniques have been used to expedite data reduction. If the projector current or voltage can be kept constant, the current or voltage can be treated as a constant instead of a measurement variable. Constants can be added to or subtracted from the signal voltages automatically by inserting special circuits into the receiving system. Curve-following techniques or voltage addition or difference circuits can be used to simplify the data reduction. When only one projector and one hydrophone are involved in a measurement, a completely automatic system is possible—one that produces calibration data instantaneously or in real time. All the necessary voltages and currents can be measured sequentially at a signal frequency and the data reduced quickly by digital computer techniques. This process is repeated at each frequency. Because of the high speed of digital computers, the frequency sweep rate need not be slower than for other methods. When a third transducer is necessary, real time computation is not very feasible because two or more acoustic signals are present and will interfere with each other. Also, the concept of direct substitution in comparison calibrations must be compromised. However, very rapid data reduction can be obtained by storing calibration data, not on a strip chart, but in the memory of a digital computer. This can provide a complete calibration in a few minutes. Such a quasi-real-time system is under development at the Underwater Sound Reference Division of the Naval Research Laboratory at this writing.

One obstacle to complete automation of calibration systems has been the fact that acoustic or electrical interference often is present and that the system, the transducers, or the medium are not stable. Variations or anomalies can be recognized in the data in a strip chart, and corrected. This is not true when the data are stored in a computer memory. Consequently, errors due to interference or instability must either be eliminated or be identified through some supplementary procedure such as redundancy of calibrations.

## 3.8  Pulsed Sound

Pulsed sound is a common technique[11] used since World War II for eliminating the effects of interference originating from boundaries, standing waves, and electrical crosstalk. The projector is driven with a pulse or short burst of an otherwise continuous and single-frequency signal. The length of each pulse then is only a small number of cycles. The hydrophone and receiving system are controlled so that an acoustic signal will be sensed and measured only during the short period of time when the direct projector-to-hydrophone signal pulse impinges on the hydrophone. Pulses arriving prior to this time (like crosstalk or purely electromagnetic signals) and pulses arriving after this time (like reflections from boundaries) are rejected by the receiving system. This process is called "gating."

Imagine, for example, the arrangement in Fig. 3.29. If the hydrophone output were connected to an oscilloscope, one would see the signal-versus-time picture shown in Fig. 3.30. The sharp clear pulses, with rectangular envelope, shown in Fig. 3.30 seldom are obtained in practice. The pulse shape usually is distorted by the filter characteristics of the electronic equipment and the transducers, and by the nonspecular reflection characteristics of the various reflecting boundaries.

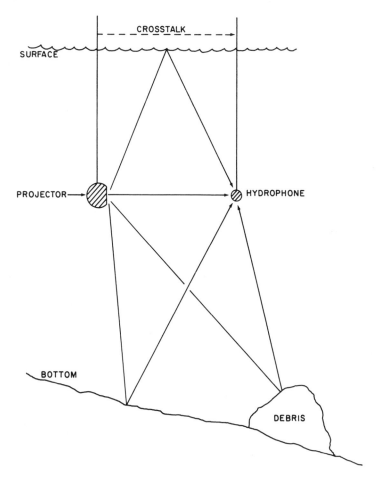

Fig. 3.29.  Typical measurement arrangement where electromagnetic crosstalk and various acoustic reflections can interfere with the direct signal.

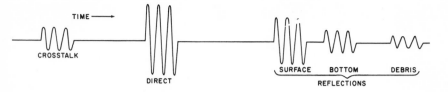

Fig. 3.30.   Oscillogram showing sequence of pulses at hydrophone position in Fig. 3.29.

The pulse length or duration must be long enough for a steady-state condition to be reached. That is, it takes a finite period of time for the pulse to reach its steady-state amplitude or the amplitude with which the system would oscillate if it were driven continuously. A typical pulse is shown in Fig. 3.31. The practical criterion for this transient period is that it consist of $Q$ cycles, where $Q$ has the usual meaning of the ratio of the reactive to the resistive impedance in the whole system being pulsed. Any oscillating electromechanical system has a certain amount of energy stored in it in the form of electrical charge, magnetic fields, mechanical inertia, and elastic deformation; the reactive impedance is a measure of this stored energy. Starting from rest, it takes approximately $Q$ cycles for the generator to feed the reactive or stored energy into the system, so that thereafter all the input energy flows through or is dissipated within the system. Theoretically, the signal rise is exponential and a system only approaches absolute steady-state asymptotically; however, it is within 95.5% of steady-state amplitude after $Q$ cycles and within 99% after $1.5Q$ cycles. (See Fig. 3.57.) The former is taken as a convenient and sufficiently accurate criterion of equivalent steady state.

A further requirement of the pulse length is that all parts of a large hydrophone reach steady state before the pulse terminates. Or, for the case of a large projector, the signal at the hydrophone position from all parts of the projector must reach steady state. In a typical case of a piston projector, a point hydrophone, and a response measurement, this requirement does not add to the pulse length, if the separation distance meets the proximity criterion of Eq. (3.12). For a directivity pattern measurement or a response measurement at 90° or 270°, however, the diameter of the piston must be added to the physical length corresponding to $Q$ cycles (see Fig. 3.59).

After a pulse signal is shut off, the system will continue to oscillate or ring at its natural or resonance frequency. This ringing will decay exponentially at the same rate as the initial signal increased. The duration of the initial transient will be the same as that of the decay transient, if steady state is reached between transients, and if the $Q$ of the system is not changed by the gating process.

The pulses are repeated at regular intervals. The pulse repetition rate must be low enough so that all reflections or reverberation dissipate between pulses. On the other hand, the pulse repetition rate must be high enough so that the meter or recorder operates without jitter. The time constant of the recording system

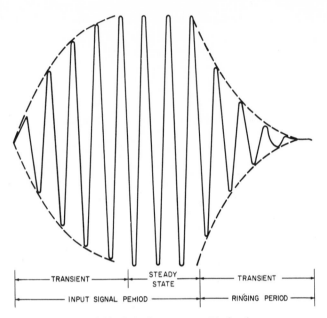

Fig. 3.31. Pulse in a system with $Q = 4$.

usually is small enough to hold steady at pulse repetition rates higher than 10 pps. These conflicting requirements on the pulse repetition rate give rise to the combination of pulsed sound and anechoic tank linings. Without some kind of acoustic absorber at the boundaries to accelerate the dissipation of acoustic energy, very low pulse repetition rates would have to be used in small tanks.

Pulses are formed by inserting a modulator or transmit gate circuit into the transmitting system as shown in Fig. 3.26. Similarly, the pulse receiver gate circuit is inserted into the receiving system as shown in the same figure. The receive gate is narrower, or of shorter time duration than the transmit gate, so that only the steady-state part of the receive pulse is detected and measured.

The pulsing technique has no high-frequency limit. Generally, the higher the frequency, the easier the technique becomes. At low frequencies, however, there is a definite limit. The minimum number of cycles in one pulse depends on the sophistication of the equipment and technique used. For purposes of illustration, however, suppose that one cycle is a typical minimum. The pulse length at 1 kHz would be 1 msec or 1.5 m long in water. Then, if the difference between the direct projector-to-hydrophone path and a boundary-reflection path were less than 1.5 m, the two pulses would overlap and interfere with each other at the hydrophone position. It is evident that for a given minimum pulse length and a given geometry of transducer separation and boundary distances, there is a low-frequency limit to the pulsing technique. In typical situations, this limit varies from 500 to 5000 Hz.

Almost all of the problems with a pulsing technique arise from the fact that, when examined in the frequency domain, pulsed signals contain a spectrum of frequencies rather than the single fundamental or carrier frequency, and that the transducers and some electronic components of the measuring system do not have uniform frequency characteristics or high fidelity. The spectral content of pulses is covered in detail in other references[12-14] and only the fundamentals of the spectrum analysis will be discussed here. The pulse spectrum depends on (1) the fundamental carrier, or test frequency, (2) the pulse shape, (3) the pulse length, (4) the pulse repetition rate, and (5) the initial and final phase of the pulse.

The pulse transmit gate circuit shown in Fig. 3.26 modulates the amplitude of the fundamental frequency with some kind of modulation signal. When the modulation signal is a rectangular wave, the process results in a pulsed signal that appears graphically as in Fig. 3.32. Mathematically, the modulation results in three separate signal frequencies, if the modulation signal is a sinusoid. If $f_0$ is the fundamental frequency and $f_1$ is the modulation frequency, the modulated signal consists of (1) the fundamental $f_0$, (2) an upper sideband $f_0 + f_1$, and (3) a lower sideband $f_0 - f_1$. If the modulation signal itself consists of a spectrum $f_1 + f_2 + f_3 + \ldots$, then the modulated signal will consist of a whole spectrum of upper sidebands $f_0 + f_1, f_0 + f_2, f_0 + f_3$, etc., and a whole spectrum of lower sidebands $f_0 - f_1, f_0 - f_2, f_0 - f_3$, etc.

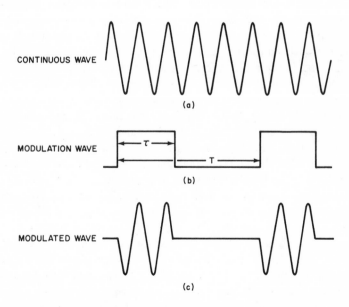

CONTINUOUS WAVE

(a)

MODULATION WAVE

(b)

MODULATED WAVE

(c)

Fig. 3.32. Rectangular pulses obtained by amplitude modulating a continuous wave with a rectangular wave; $\tau$ is the pulse length or duration and $T$ is the pulse repetition period.

Pulses having sawtooth, triangular, round, cosine-squared, and other shapes sometimes are used in various applications. In ordinary underwater electro-acoustic measurements, a modulation signal consisting of periodic square or rectangular waves as shown in Fig. 3.32b is used. Fourier's Theorem says that any periodic function is equivalent to the sum of simple harmonic functions whose frequencies are integral multiples of the repetition rate of the given function. That is, if $T$ is the period of the function and $t$ is time,

$$f(t) = A_0 + A_1 \cos \omega t + A_2 \cos 2\omega t + A_3 \cos 3\omega t + \cdots$$

$$B_1 \sin \omega t + B_2 \sin 2\omega t + B_3 \sin 3\omega t + \cdots \quad (3.22)$$

where $\omega = 2\pi/T$ and the $A_n$ and $B_n$ are constants including, in many cases, zero. Physically, this means that a rectangular wave has a spectrum of harmonically related sinusoidal waves. This spectrum constitutes the sideband frequencies in a rectangular pulse signal.

The modulated signal shown in Fig. 3.32c is typical of the electrical signal at the output of the transmit gate circuit of Fig. 3.26 before it is distorted by the $Q$ or narrow-bandwidth characteristics of the transducer. The spectrum of such a signal will be that in Fig. 3.33. The envelope of amplitude of the spectral lines is set by the pulse length $\tau$ (in addition to the pulse shape). A long pulse or large $\tau$ results in a narrow spectrum centered on $f_0$. An infinite $\tau$ would be equivalent to continuous waves, and, in the limit, the envelope curve would collapse to a single line at $f_0$. Similarly, the condition $\tau = T$ would be a continuous wave because all the sideband spectral lines would fall at the zero-crossing points or all the $A_n$ and $B_n$ in Eq. (3.22) except $A_1$ and $B_1$ would be zero; only $f_0$ would remain. Short pulses or small $\tau$ result in a spreading out of the spectrum. Low repetition rates or large values of $T$ produce many closely spaced spectral lines. The spectrum between $f_0 - 1/\tau$ and $f_0 + 1/\tau$ is called the essential bandwidth (EBW). A rectangular pulse passed through a bandpass filter will be distorted to only a small extent, if the filter bandwidth is $2/\tau$. Pulse lengths of 0.1, 1, and 10 msec result in EBW's of 20,000, 2000, and 200 Hz, respectively. Narrowband filters and short pulse lengths clearly are incompatible.

The spectrum shown in Fig. 3.33 is symmetrical about the carrier frequency $f_0$. This is only an approximation. The low-sideband part of the spectrum extends beyond zero frequency. That is $f_0 - f_n$ eventually becomes a negative number as $n$ and $f_n$ become large. One can visualize the negative frequency part of the spectrum as being folded back on to and added to the positive frequencies, thereby causing asymmetry. This asymmetry is accentuated when the pulse contains an integral number of cycles. Then, if the pulse starts and ends at instantaneous zero, the amplitudes of the low-sideband frequencies are higher than the amplitudes of the corresponding high-sideband frequencies. If the pulse starts and ends at an instantaneous peak value, the reverse is true.

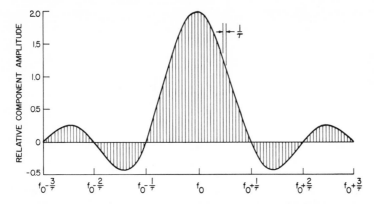

Fig. 3.33. Spectrum of a pulsed signal. The carrier frequency is $f_0$. The modulation envelope or pulse shape is rectangular. The pulse length is $\tau$ seconds. The pulse repetition period is $T$, or pulse repetition rate is $1/T$ pulses per second.

Pulses are coherent if they all begin at the same phase angle—all at a time of instantaneous zero and increasing voltage amplitude, for example. Such pulses provide minimum trouble with transient signals and maximum stability of the signal phase. It is possible to use only a fraction of a cycle per pulse with pulses that are coherent and that begin at zero-crossing points.

Electroacoustic transducers and acoustic materials as absorbers often are resonant, and almost always have characteristics that are a function of frequency. Consequently, when they are part of an electroacoustic system they will affect the spectrum of a pulsed signal. At a transducer resonance, the $Q$ of the transducer will introduce transients of the type shown in Fig. 3.31. At off-resonance frequencies, other effects distort the pulse spectrum and shape. For example, the transmitting current response of a projector below the projector resonance frequency is increasing at the rate 6 dB per octave or more (see Fig. 5.2). This slope will distort the pulse. That is, the acoustic pressure pulse out of the projector will differ from the current pulse into the projector as shown in Fig. 3.34. The amplitude of high-sideband frequencies will be increased; and the amplitude of the low sideband frequencies will be decreased. Most important, the frequency of maximum amplitude will be shifted upward. Since most systems measure the pulse peak, the measurement will be in error. The peak amplitude of the pulse will be a measure of the transmitting current response at the upper sideband frequency with the maximum amplitude rather than at the fundamental frequency.

A similar type of error is present when the insertion loss or echo reduction of some acoustic materials is measured near a resonance frequency. Figure 3.35a shows a reflection coefficient characteristic of a resonant anechoic coating. The characteristic is similar to that of a notch filter. The reflected pulse is distorted as shown in Fig. 3.35b. Again the peak reflected signal is a measure of the sideband rather than the fundamental frequency characteristics.

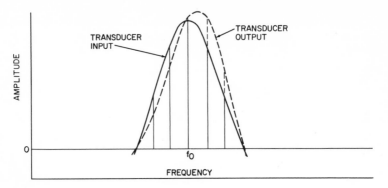

Fig. 3.34. Spectrum distortion within the essential bandwidth due to a transducer response that increases with frequency.

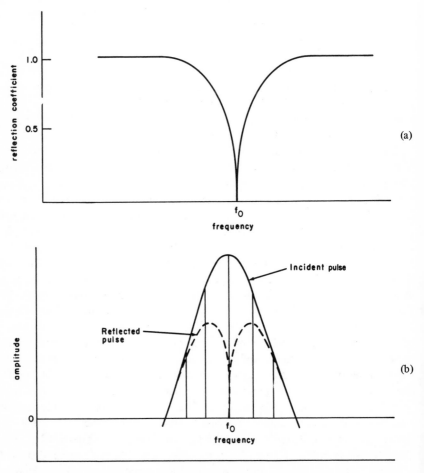

Fig. 3.35. Distortion of a pulse spectrum in the EBW of an acoustic rectangular pulse reflected from a resonant absorber with a reflection coefficient characteristic shown in (a).

Errors caused by the spectrum peak frequency being shifted away from the fundamental can be minimized by using very narrow receive pulse gates and centering the receive gate in the middle or steady-state part of the transmitted pulse as shown in the two pulses at the input and output of the receive gate in Fig. 3.36. The sum of the sideband frequencies constitutes a signal that include the transient part of the pulse—that is, the part at the beginning and end where the pulse is forming or decaying. Figure 3.37 shows how the sum of the steady-state or fundamental frequency $f_0$ and the sideband frequencies results in periodic pulses. Gating in on the middle of a pulse thus discriminates against sideband frequencies and will correct a peak-frequency shift.

Typical pulses at 5 points in the measuring system are shown in Fig. 3.36.

It would seem from Figs. 3.33 and 3.37 that errors due to the high amplitudes of sideband frequencies could be eliminated by filtering. That is, after interfering pulses have been rejected by the receive gate, the pulse could be passed through a filter centered on $f_0$ and with a bandwidth narrow enough to reject or at least attenuate the sideband frequencies. Theoretically, from Fig. 3.37,

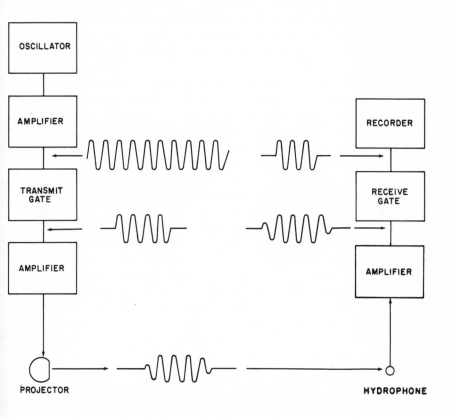

Fig. 3.36. Typical signal forms at five different points in the measuring system.

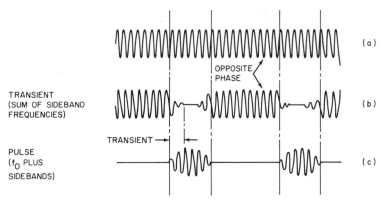

TRANSIENT
(SUM OF SIDEBAND
FREQUENCIES)

PULSE
($f_0$ PLUS
SIDEBANDS)

Fig. 3.37.  Illustration of how a steady-state or continuous-wave signal (a) of frequency $f_0$ adds to a signal (b) constituting the sum of all the sideband frequencies to form (c), a pulse train (a) + (b) = (c).

(c) − (b) = (a), or one could convert from pulsed sound back to a c-w signal! Unfortunately, this is only theory.  Narrow bandpass filters have high $Q$'s and otherwise act the same as highly resonant transducers.  Some types of filters indeed are resonant transducers.  When the $Q$ is large, the transient period illustrated in Fig. 3.31 is much longer than either $\tau$ or $T$.  In such cases, the filter will not pass a steady-state signal at the frequency $f_0$ and of the same amplitude as in the input pulse.  Figure 3.38 illustrates what happens in the filter.  The signal amplitude rises to only a small fraction of steady state during a time $\tau$ and then the pulse cuts off.  The amplitude slowly decays.  After $T$ seconds, the second pulse increases the amplitude, but again only by a small amount before the pulse again cuts off.  The amplitude again decays at a slightly faster rate than after the first pulse.  This process is repeated until the signal increase during $\tau$ equals the signal decay during $T - \tau$.  A quasi-steady-state condition is reached where the amplitude is only a small fraction of the true steady state.

The ratio $\tau/T$ expressed as a percentage is called the duty cycle, and is a measure of the percentage of time that the transducer is vibrating.  When transducers are driven at high power levels, the duty cycle becomes important because the power limitations of a transducer are set by the average power over a period of time large in comparison with a pulse length.  For example, a transducer that is limited to 1 kW with a c-w signal may, unless otherwise limited, transmit at a 10-kW pulse level with a 10% duty cycle.

## 3.9  High Signal Measurements

Some projectors are used regularly at signal levels beyond their linear range. This results in distorted output waves that contain harmonic frequencies and are mathematically described in Eq. (3.22).  The harmonic distortion is accepted as

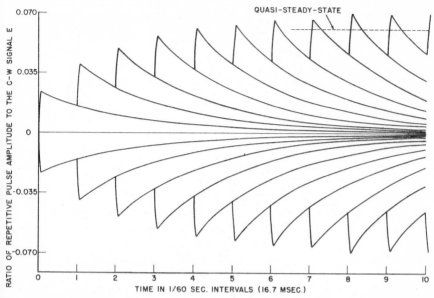

Fig. 3.38. Amplitude buildup of repetitive pulses to a quasi-steady-state in a circuit of $Q$ = 343. Pulse duration $\tau$ = 1 msec. Pulse repetition period $T$ = 1/60 sec.

being secondary in importance to high signal output. Such transducers must be evaluated at the particular signal levels that will be used in practice. Linearity of the transducer is assumed in conventional and standard definitions of response, sensitivity, impedance, and so forth. For measurements beyond the linear range, these conventional terms are not strictly correct, although they are used. If they are used, they should always be qualified by specifying the voltage or current level at which the measurement is made. The measurement will pertain only to the fundamental frequency, but some measure of the wave distortion or harmonic content should be specified also.

High-level continuous-wave signals can be attenuated, the harmonic frequencies can be filtered out, and thereafter the signals can be measured with various conventional methods and instruments. However, high-power nonlinear transducers almost always are pulsed at a low duty cycle. As explained in Section 3.8, pulsing and narrow bandpass filtering are incompatible. One then has the problem of measuring the amplitude of distorted waveforms without bandpass filters. Further, when the impedance or input power is desired, the phase angle between the current and voltage at the fundamental frequency must be measured. For impedance or power measurements, all of the usual measuring devices such as bridges, phase meters, vector locus indicators, power meters, Z-angle meters, and so forth, suffer from a deficiency in one or more of the following characteristics:  power-handling capability, frequency range, impedance range, harmonic rejection, and ability to operate under pulsed conditions.

One technique that has been used successfully is illustrated by the simplified diagram in Fig. 3.39.[15]   The transducer voltage or current pulse is sampled by a step-down current transformer consisting of a toroid coil surrounding a single conductor.  Simultaneously, the signal in a continuous-wave reference circuit is sampled.  The two signals are added and displayed on a cathode-ray oscilloscope. The reference signal contains only the fundamental frequency.  The amplitude and phase of the reference signal is adjusted until a null condition in the steady-state part of the pulse is observed on the oscilloscope.  As shown in Fig. 3.37 the sideband frequencies add up to zero, or are effectively absent in the steady-state part of the pulse.  Then the reference signal is equal in amplitude and opposite in phase to the fundamental frequency component of the transducer signal pulse.  The null condition as it would be observed on the oscilloscope is illustrated in Fig. 3.40.  There will be a signal residue in the null because of the harmonic distortion frequencies in the signal.  If the harmonic distortion is small, the residue is small and does not introduce measurable error in the nulling technique. If the residue is large, a low-pass filter is used to attenuate the harmonic frequencies.

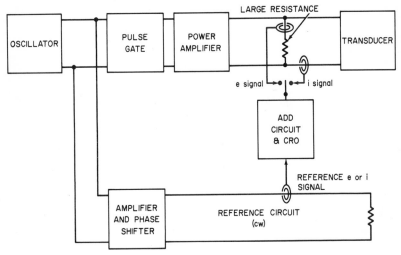

Fig. 3.39.  Nulling circuit for measurement of voltage, current, and phase when a transducer is driven with high-power pulsed sound.

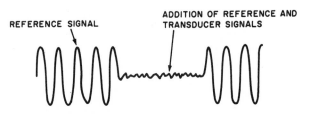

Fig. 3.40.  Typical CRO display when the pulse and reference signals have been balanced to a null.

The three transformers should be identical to minimize errors. In practice, the current and reference signal transformers can be one and the same.

The reference circuit is a low-signal continuous-wave circuit. The reference voltage and current are readily obtained by conventional calibration methods. Phase difference between the reference current and voltage is controlled and measured by the phase shifter.

### 3.10 Interference Identification

Signal interference is of four general types. First, there is acoustical and electrical noise from nearby equipment, traffic, weather conditions, and so forth. Such interference is readily recognizable by its irregular nature.

Second, there is interference from other regular signal sources such as the 60-Hz power line frequency and its harmonics. Local radio stations may interfere if one is working in the 500 to 1500 kHz frequency range. Different acoustical experiments in the same or nearby bodies of water may interfere with each other. Such interference is identified by the purity and perhaps stability of the interfering signal frequency.

Third, there is interference from reflections, crosstalk, and standing waves, which collectively will be referred to as wave interference. The reflection and standing-wave interference is similar to such optical phenomena as diffraction, interference fringes, and the Lloyd's mirror effect. Crosstalk is an electrical or electromagnetic signal that unintentionally is transmitted directly from the transmitting equipment to the receiving equipment, bypassing the acoustic path. A wave interference signal travels a path different from that of the direct signal being measured, and for this and other reasons will differ in amplitude and phase, but it always has the same frequency as the direct signal. The interference is identified by a regular periodic amplitude change as a function of frequency, as illustrated in Fig. 3.41. The frequency interval $\Delta f$ can be used to provide a clue as to the type and source of wave interference.

If two waves from the same source travel paths that differ by the distance $\Delta x$, their phase difference at the end of the paths will be $k\Delta x$ or $2\pi f\Delta x/c$, where $k$, $f$, and $c$ have the usual definitions of wave number, frequency, and speed. If $\Delta x$ is some number of whole wavelengths, the waves interfere constructively or add. If $\Delta x$ is some odd number of half-wavelengths, the waves will interfere destructively or subtract. As the frequency and wavelength changes, the waves alternately add and subtract, resulting in the oscillating amplitude in Fig. 3.41. The frequency interval $\Delta f$ corresponds to a change of $2\pi$ radians in $2\pi f\Delta x/c$, or

$$\frac{2\pi\Delta f\Delta x}{c} = 2\pi, \tag{3.23}$$

or

$$\Delta x = \frac{c}{\Delta f}. \tag{3.24}$$

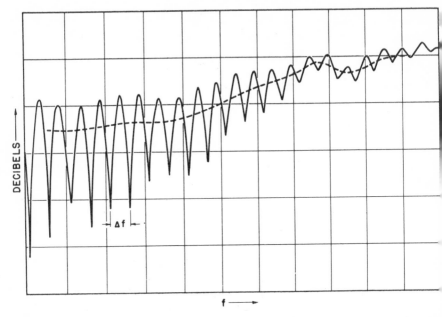

Fig. 3.41. Measured hydrophone output voltage versus frequency, illustrating a typical oscillating interference pattern resulting from a surface reflection. Solid line is measured sum of direct and reflected signals. Dashed line is computed direct signal.

After $\Delta x$ is found from the measurement of $\Delta f$ and Eq. (3.24), it can be related to various measurement dimensions like the depth and transducer separation. The source of the interference is identified thereby, and steps can be taken to eliminate it. With crosstalk, the nonacoustic interference path is essentially zero and $\Delta x$ is merely the projector-to-hydrophone distance $d$. With standing waves between the projector and hydrophone, $\Delta x = 2d$. For boundary reflection interference, $\Delta x$ depends on the geometry of the boundary and transducer arrangement. For a surface reflection as shown in Fig. 3.42,

$$\Delta x = 2[h^2 + (\tfrac{1}{2}d)^2]^{\tfrac{1}{2}} - d. \qquad (3.25)$$

The curves in Fig. 3.43 are plots of Eq. (3.25), of $x = d$, and of $x = 2d$; they are useful graphical aids for identifying the three common types of wave interference.

If the ordinate scale in Fig. 3.41 were linear rather than logarithmic or in decibels, the oscillating amplitude pattern would be approximately sinusoidal. The direct signal then is the average of the maximum and minimum amplitudes. The dashed line in Fig. 3.41 then is found by taking the arithmetic average. The technique and graphical aids and charts for doing this are given in Section 6.3.2 and Figs. 6.3, 6.4, and 6.5, where interference techniques are described for measuring echo reduction.

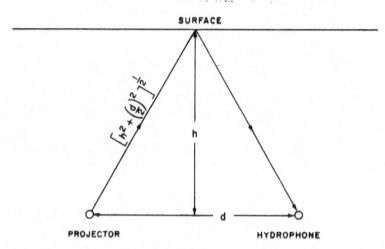

Fig. 3.42.   Diagram for calculating path difference $\Delta x$ for the case of a surface reflection.

The interference in Fig. 3.41 is seen to decrease with frequency.  This is typical of surface reflections where the transducers become more directional as the frequency increases.  Standing waves between two plane transducers require that the transducers be large enough in wavelengths to be good reflectors, and that they be aligned with their diaphragms parallel within a dimensional error small in comparison with a wavelength.  Consequently, standing waves occur usually only at intermediate frequencies in the high audio and low ultrasonic frequency range.  A crosstalk signal generally is independent of the acoustic signal amplitude; therefore, if crosstalk is present, it will be more evident when the acoustic signal is low.  For example, if a resonant transducer is being measured, crosstalk may be evident above and below resonance but not at resonance when the acoustic signal is high and the ratio of cross-talk amplitude to acoustic amplitude is low.  These characteristics of interference aid in making educated guesses as to what kind of interference is present.

In shallow lakes where both the surface and bottom are reflecting boundaries, interference becomes particularly troublesome and usually is the limiting factor in setting the useful low-frequency limit of the facility.  Figure 3.44 illustrates the kind of data obtained.  The interfering signal is acutally the sum of many multiple reflections between the surface and bottom.[3]  There is still a discernable $\Delta f$ frequency interval, but it is a large fraction of the frequency.  In Fig. 3.44, $\Delta f$ is 200 Hz.  The amplitude of the interference is not a smooth sinusoid but a sequence of sawtooth and sharply peaked waveforms.  Obviously, it is difficult to apply the technique of Fig. 6.3 to ascertain the direct signal in Fig. 3.44.

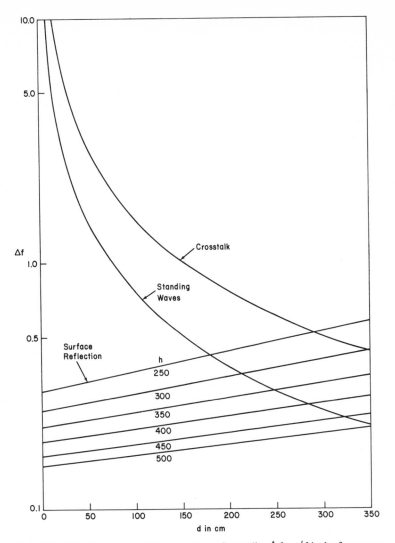

Fig. 3.43.  Interference identification chart.  Crosstalk:  $\Delta f = c/d$ is the frequency interval in Hz, $c$ is the speed of sound in water ($1.5 \times 10^5$ cm/sec), and $d$ is the separation of the transducers in cm.  Standing waves: $\Delta f = c/2d$.  Surface reflections:  $\Delta f = c/[2(h^2 + \frac{1}{4}d^2)^{\frac{1}{2}} - d]$ and $h$ is the depth in cm.

The fourth type of interference is unique to underwater acoustics—resonant gas bubbles. Gas bubbles as used here means not only a spherical bubble drifting freely in the water or clinging to a surface, but also tiny amounts of gas trapped in holes, crevices, slots, screw heads, and so forth.  A bubble driven at its resonance frequency oscillates vigorously, reradiating sound and having a measurable effect over an area some 20,000 times as large as the bubble cross section.[16]  The

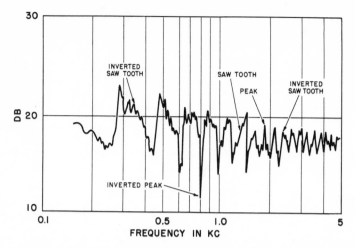

Fig. 3.44. Measured hydrophone output voltage where projector and hydrophone both are at a depth midway between the water-air surface and bubble-covered bottom. The transducers are separated by a distance equal to 1/8 of the water depth. The projector transmitting response and hydrophone receiving sensitivity both are essentially constant with frequency.

resonance frequency of a spherical air bubble is proportional to the square root of the absolute pressure and inversely proportional to the static radius.[16] As a convenient reference, a bubble near the surface, or at one atmosphere of pressure, and one centimeter in diameter will resonate at 667 Hz.[16] From this reference, the resonance frequency of smaller bubbles at higher pressures can be calculated using the proportions just stated. Bubbles usually are small in comparison with a wavelength and therefore the shape is not critical. The resonance frequency of other shapes can be assumed to be approximately the same as for a spherical bubble of the same volume.

Small gas bubbles can be quite tenacious and stable. Thus it becomes important to examine thoroughly and test an anomaly in recorded data as illustrated in Fig. 3.45 to ascertain whether it is a valid characteristic of the transducer or a perturbation due to a bubble in the medium. Since the resonance frequency of a bubble depends on the static pressure, a change in depth will shift the frequency. Such a test might still be inconclusive, however, inasmuch as a transducer may have bubbles on the inside—particularly in a fluid that acoustically couples crystals to the water. A general understanding of how bubbles interfere with acoustic measurements is helpful.

Consider a bubble whose radius is small in comparison with a wavelength of sound in water. The bubble is in a sound field where the free-field sound pressure is $p_f$. The acoustic impedance of the bubble itself consists of the compliance $C$ of the enclosed gas and a resistance $R$ arising from losses that occur when

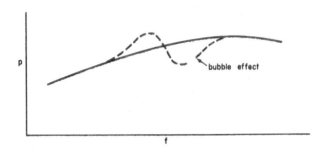

Fig. 3.45. Typical effect of a gas bubble in water near a hydrophone.

a gas is compressed and expanded. The mass of the moving gas is negligible. The analog of the acoustic generator acting on this bubble is obtained by using Thevenin's Theorem. The blocked (or open-circuit) pressure is obtained by letting the bubble impedance become infinite and ascertaining the pressure acting on the blocked bubble. If the bubble is small, this pressure is the free-field pressure. Next, we turn the generator off and view the generator impedance at the generator terminals. That is, we look at the generator from the load, or in acoustical terms, we look into the medium from the bubble—and we see the radiation impedance $R + j\omega m$. For a small spherical radiator, $\omega m \gg R$. Thus, our analog is as shown in Fig. 3.46. The velocity $u$ is the velocity of the spherical boundary, and the inward direction is positive. Figure 3.46 is a conventional series resonant circuit. For constant $p_f$, the relative amplitude and phase of $u$ is proportional to the bubble admittance shown in the circle diagram of Fig. 3.47. Assume that a hydrophone and bubble are closely spaced so that the spacing distance $r \ll \lambda$. Also, assume that the hydrophone and bubble are side by side, so that the free-field pressure acting on each is the same in both amplitude and phase. This would be the condition of a bubble clinging to the periphery of a diaphragm. Then the total pressure $p_H$ at the hydrophone position and everywhere near the bubble is the sum of $p_f$ and the pressure $p_r$ radiating from the pulsating bubble, as depicted in Fig. 3.48. The bubble is acting like a small spherical radiator and $p_r$ is given by the well-known equations such as $p_r = j\omega\rho U/r$ where $U$ is the volume velocity. That is, the radiation load on the bubble is a mass reactance and $p_r$ leads the outward velocity by 90°. Since we chose positive velocity as inward, $p_r$ will lead the negative velocity by 90°, or will lead the positive velocity by 270°. Consequently, a locus of $p_r$ relative to $p_f$ is obtained by rotating the circle in Fig. 3.47 through 270°. At the resonance frequency, the velocity $u$ depends on $R$, and the ratio $p_r/p_f$ depends on the $Q$ of the resonant system and the distance $r$. The sum $p_h = p_f + p_r$ is then as shown in Fig. 3.49.  Note from Fig. 3.49 that the resonance frequency is not the frequency of maximum or minimum pressure, nor that at which $p_H = p_f$.

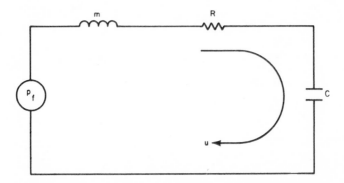

Fig. 3.46.  Analog circuit of a gas bubble in water driven by a free-field pressure $p_f$; $m$ is the radiation water mass load on the bubble, $R$ is the resistance in the gas of the bubble and in the radiation impedance, $C$ is the compliance of the gas in the bubble, $u$ is the linear velocity of the water-gas surface of the bubble with inward direction taken as positive.

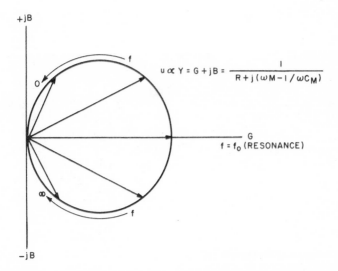

Fig. 3.47.  The admittance of a mass $m$, resistance $R$, and compliance $C$ in series.

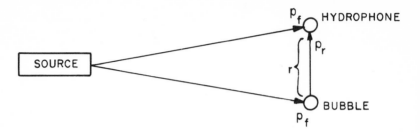

Fig. 3.48.  Arrangement wherein the free-field pressure $p_f$ impinges on both a hydrophone and a gas bubble at distance $r$ away.  The sound pressure $p_r$ reradiated or scattered from the bubble also impinges on the hydrophone.

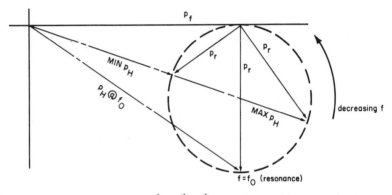

Fig. 3.49.  Phasor diagram showing $\vec{p}_H = \vec{p}_f + \vec{p}_r$ as a function of frequency for the arrangement in Fig. 3.48.

It is evident from Fig. 3.49 that the ratio $p_H/p_f$ will vary with frequency as illustrated in Fig. 3.45.  If $r$ becomes large, the size of the circle will diminish and the phase of $p_r$ will be affected.  The phase angle of $p_r$ is $-kr$ radians.  A larger $r$ will result in a larger negative angle or a clockwise rotation of the $p_r$ phasors in Fig. 3.49.  The phase of $p_r$ will be affected similarly if the bubble is behind the hydrophone.  If the bubble is in front of the hydrophone, the $p_r$ phasors will rotate in counterclockwise direction.  The effects of the bubble position on $p_H$ is illustrated in Fig. 3.50.  If the phase shift due to bubble position is near $\pi/2$ a mirror image of Fig. 3.50 is obtained.  Consequently, a wide variety of anomalous configurations is possible, but Fig. 3.50 still is typical of the most common bubble interference.

## 3.11  Interference Elimination

There are various remedies for different kinds of interference.  The remedies are not all compatible; thus, if more than one kind of interference is present,

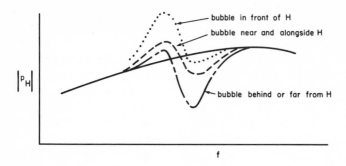

Fig. 3.50.  Magnitude of the pressure at the hydrophone for various locations of bubble.

compromises must be made.  Not all interference problems have remedies.  For example, it is virtually impossible to make free-field far-field measurements in a small tank at infrasonic frequencies because of the boundary conditions.  Then, an alternate calibration method like a coupler must be used.

Interference from noise and spurious signals is eliminated or minimized (see Fig. 2.51) by the use of narrowband filters.  This procedure is applicable only to continuous-wave signals, of course.

Interference from reflections and crosstalk is best eliminated by using the pulsing techniques described in Section 3.8.

Standing waves are eliminated by rotating one or both transducers a few degrees, which eliminates the parallel-planes condition without measurably affecting the sensitivity.  Increasing the transducer separation will also reduce the interference due to standing waves, but it may increase interference due to reflections.

Bubbles are eliminated by thoroughly washing the transducers with a wetting agent, temperature-stabilization of transducers, proper design of transducers, proper design of transducer hangers and other underwater rigging equipment, control of marine life, and removal of gas-producing organic material on the bottom of the body of water.

When pulsing techniques cannot be used to eliminate reflections, other steps can be taken, although they are, for the most part, only partial solutions.  The transducer separation distance should be kept to a minimum and the distance to the boundary should be made a maximum so that the amplitude ratio of the direct signal to reflected signal is a maximum.  Directional transducers should be used if possible to discriminate against signal transmission along reflection paths.  Absorbers can be used at the reflecting boundaries.  Baffles can be used to intercept reflections and deflect them in harmless directions.  The baffle technique, however, is not as simple and useful as it might appear.  Good rigid reflectors would be very heavy and ponderous.  Good pressure-release reflectors are not durable and are sensitive to static pressure. Furthermore, baffle edges scatter and diffract the sound waves, providing secondary sources of interference.

The initial positioning of the two transducers relative to a reflecting boundary can be helpful. If one transducer is insensitive in one direction (to the rear, for example), the transducer should be oriented so that the reflecting boundary is in the insensitive direction. That is, the main lobe of the transducer should be pointed away from the boundary. However, the optimum arrangement is not necessarily the same for a response measurements as for a directivity pattern measurement in which the unknown transducer is rotated. This fact is illustrated in Fig. 3.51, where a directional projector is being evaluated with an omni-directional standard hydrophone. The arrangement in Fig. 3.51a is optimal for response because the zero response at $180°$ or to the rear of the projector eliminates reflections from the boundary, whereas in Fig. 3.51b, both a direct and a reflected signal impinge on the hydrophone. If the arrangement in 3.51a is used for a pattern measurement, we see from Figs. 3.51c and 3.51d that the pattern level at zero degrees is unaffected by reflections, but at $180°$ all the signal consists of the reflection, and a false minor lobe will appear at $180°$. If the positions of the two transducers are reversed, the zero-degree measurement in Fig. 3.51e is subject to interference, but the $180°$ measurement in Fig. 3.51f is not. The optimal arrangement then reduces to a choice of the errors in (d) or in (e). Note that the interfering reflected signal in the two cases is the same, but the direct signal is zero in (d) and a maximum in (e). The interference then will have a much larger effect in (d) than in (e), thereby making (e) the preferred arrangement. To illustrate with an example, suppose the reflection path is 10 times as long as the direct path. Then the false minor lobe at $180°$ in (d) will be 20 dB down from the major lobe, or the front-to-back ratio will be 20 dB instead of infinite. In (e), the major lobe at zero degrees will be subject to an error of $20 \log (1 \pm 0.1)$, or about $\pm 1$ dB, which is a relatively small error. Since pattern errors are meaningful only in terms of the level differences at various angles, even this small error disappears in this example because whatever the error in (e), it will be the same at all angles and consequently the pattern configuration will be unaffected.

Selective positioning is useful in discriminating against vertical boundary reflections, but is not very helpful in minimizing surface or bottom reflection interference. Occasionally one can point a pattern null in the direction of a reflection path as illustrated in Fig. 3.52, and thereby eliminate the interference. However, since null angles shift with frequency, this technique is limited to a single frequency or a narrow band of frequencies.

Insofar as a passive interference like reflection is concerned, it makes no difference whether a transducer is transmitting or receiving. The reciprocity principle applies to reflections as well as to direct signals. If an active interfering source is present somewhere, however, the system no longer is passive, and reciprocity does not hold. Suppose for example we have the situation shown in Fig. 3.53 with one omnidirectional transducer and one narrow-beam transducer

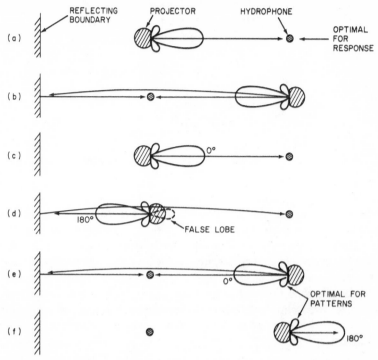

Fig. 3.51. Optional arrangements for a directional projector and an omnidirectional hydrophone relative to a reflecting boundary. (a) is preferred to (b) for response; (e) and (f) are preferred to (c) and (d) for patterns.

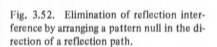

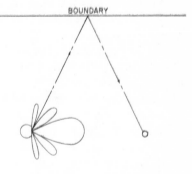

Fig. 3.52. Elimination of reflection interference by arranging a pattern null in the direction of a reflection path.

that has zero sensitivity at $180°$ or to the rear. Then, if the rear of the directional transducer is pointed at the interference source and the directional transducer is used as the hydrophone, the interference will have no effect. That is, the hydrophone will sense only the sound from the projector. If the signal direction is reversed and the narrow-beam transducer is used as a projector, the omnidirectional hydrophone will sense the sound from both the projector and the interference source.

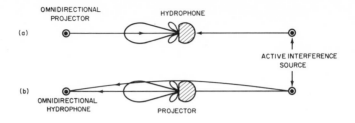

Fig. 3.53. Effect of reversing the direction of the signal transmission. The interference signal is not sensed by the hydrophone in (a) but is sensed in (b).

The direct signal as given by the dashed line in Fig. 3.41 is the average of the maximum and minimum signals. A technique wherein the average signal over a band of frequencies is measured, then, effectively would eliminate the effect of reflections. Two such techniques are feasible. In one, a band of noise centered on the frequency of interest is used; in the other, a warbled or frequency-modulated signal is used. Neither technique is applied very often in underwater electroacoustic measurements because the frequency resolution of the sensitivity that is obtained by this averaging procedure generally is unacceptable.

## 3.12 Tank Facilities and Sizes

Tank facilities for underwater electroacoustic measurements have the advantages of convenient location and controllable environments. As used in this Section, the term tank facility refers only to those tanks in which free-field measurements can be made. Therein lies the main disadvantages of tank facilities: poor free-field conditions. Unless the tank is unusually large like the TRANSDEC Facility in Fig. 3.7, for example, the usefulness of a tank facility depends on the extent to which reflections or the interference from reflections can be eliminated. When the reflections are eliminated or attenuated by absorbers at the tank boundaries, the term anechoic, meaning "free from echoes," is used. Figure 3.54 is a picture of a typical indoor tank.

Most such facilities are open tanks that are similar to, but smaller than, facilities on natural water sites. An exception is the closed anechoic tank in which the deep ocean environment can be simulated with high hydrostatic pressure and low temperature. If necessary, the salinity can be controlled also, but this seldom is necessary for electroacoustic measurements. A cross-sectional diagram of such a tank is shown in Fig. 3.55. Closed high-pressure tanks introduce the additional complications of (a) controlling the position and orientation of the transducers from outside the tank through pressure seals, (b) access ports that limit transducer size, and (c) a relatively small size because high pressure and large size are not compatible.

Fig. 3.54. Indoor tank facility of the Naval Research Laboratory in Washington, D.C. The tank is made of cypress wood, is 30 feet in diameter and 22 feet deep, with most of the depth recessed into a hole beneath the building.

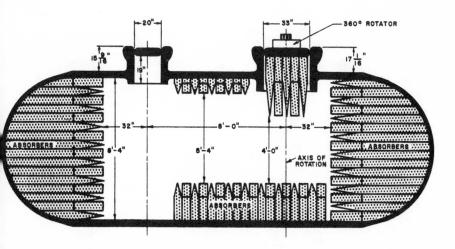

Fig. 3.55. Cross-sectional diagram of a 1000-psi anechoic tank at the Underwater Sound Reference Division of the Naval Research Laboratory at Orlando, Florida.

Because most tanks are small, pulsed-sound techniques are used to eliminate the interference that originates at tank wall boundaries. In addition, absorbers or anechoic coatings also are used on the tank walls, bottom, and sometimes the surface. Various types of rubber materials have been used in open tanks. For high-pressure tanks like that shown in Fig. 3.55, a cement and sawdust mixture called Insulkrete has been used.[17] Wood by itself is a fair absorber and, since cylindrical wooden tanks have other industrial uses, such tanks are economically attractive.[18] Tanks of cedar, redwood, or cypress have been the most popular.

The major question in designing and using a tank facility is its frequency range. The necessary tank size is roughly proportional to the wavelength of the acoustic signal. Consequently, attention is focused on the large wavelength or the low-frequency limit. There is no simple answer to a question like "How large must a tank be to be useable at 1 kHz?" The size depends on the pulse length and repetition rate, and the projector-to-hydrophone distance. These values, in turn, depend on the kind of measurements to be made, the acceptable accuracy, the transducer's size and $Q$, the frequency, the type of voltage sensing and measuring system, and the echo reduction of the boundaries.

If pulsing is used, the tank shape is not important. It is the proximity of the boundary that is nearest to the direct projector-to-hydrophone acoustic path that is controlling.

To arrive at some general criteria for tank dimensions, a number of simplifying but realistic assumptions can be made. The first of these, illustrated in Fig. 3.56, is that the nearest reflecting boundary is either parallel to the direct acoustic path (sidewall, bottom, or surface), or perpendicular to the direct path (end walls).

The second assumption is that any absorption at the boundaries is primarily for the rapid dissipation of the reverberation between pulses. Most anechoic linings are only partially effective, particularly at low frequencies. Single reflections are attenuated but not eliminated. The pulsing described in Section 3.8 is based on the concept that the difference between the direct projector-to-hydrophone path and the first reflection path is greater than a pulse length. That is, the hydrophone must be receiving the steady-state part of the direct pulse before the leading edge of the reflected pulse reaches the hydrophone. The minimum path difference then is $\tau$ seconds or $c\tau$ meters, where $c$ is the speed of sound in meters per second. The minimum tank length $L$ and minimum width (or depth) $W$ then can be computed from Fig. 3.56 as

$$L = d + c\tau, \tag{3.26}$$

$$W = [(d + c\tau)^2 - d^2]^{1/2} = (2dc\tau + c^2\tau^2)^{1/2}. \tag{3.27}$$

These basic equations can be put in terms of transducer parameters by making further assumptions.

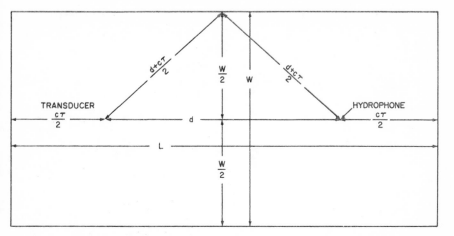

Fig. 3.56.  Direct and reflected signal paths in test tank; $d$ is the required measurement distance, $\tau$ is the pulse duration in seconds, $c$ is the speed of sound, $c\tau$ is the minimum difference between direct and reflected path lengths, $L = d + c\tau$ is the length of the tank, and $W = [(d + c\tau)^2 - d^2]^{1/2}$ is the width or depth of the tank.

It takes $Q$ cycles for a pulse to reach effective steady state, where $Q$ applies to the whole transmitting system, not just to the projector.  The minimum pulse length is assumed to require $Q$ cycles or $Q\lambda$ meters for cases in which the transducer has a negligible diaphragm dimension in the direction of sound propagation.  When this is not true, an additional pulse length is needed to cover the entire transducer with the effective steady-state signal.

The pulse-length criterion of $Q$ cycles bears directly on the question of acceptable measurement accuracy.  Figure 3.57 shows the asymptotic approach to steady state.  Where $n/Q = 1$, the amplitude is still 0.4 dB or 4½% too low.  Better accuracy can be obtained with longer pulse lengths, but only at the expense of larger tank dimensions, as is evident from Eqs. (3.26) and (3.27).

The pulse-length criterion of only $Q$ cycles also implies that the voltage-measuring system can operate with the sawtooth-shaped pulse shown in Fig. 3.57.

Another assumption is that one of the two transducers is small in comparison with a wavelength—say one is a point hydrophone.  The other transducer is assumed to be large but with a maximum dimension of five wavelengths.  Theoretical patterns of 5-wavelength transducers are shown in Fig. 3.58.  The 10-dB-down beam widths are less than 20° and as narrow as most transducer beam widths get.  Because of proximity criteria like Eq. (3.15), the linear dimensions of a tank are approximately proportional to the square of the transducer dimension, so it is well to set a reasonable limit.  When measurements are to be made on larger or very narrow-beam transducers, special criteria can be developed.

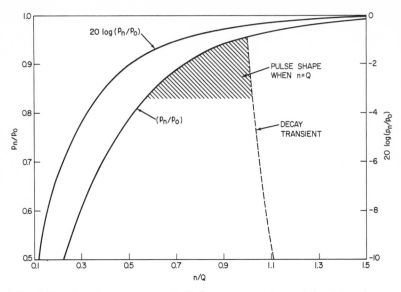

Fig. 3.57. Sound pressure magnitude from a resonant transducer driven by a step-function electrical pulse. Curves computed from $p_n/p_0 = 1 - e^{-\pi n/Q}$ where $p_0$ is the steady-state pressure ($n \to \infty$), $p_n$ is the pressure after $n$ cycles, $n$ is the number of cycles, and $Q$ is the $Q$ of the transducer.

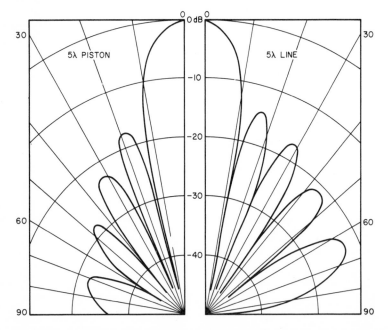

Fig. 3.58. Theoretical directivity patterns for a piston five wavelengths in diameter and a line five wavelengths long.

The last assumption is that the maximum distance $d$ is set by the proximity criterion in Eq. (3.17). Combining this equation with the maximum transducer dimension $D = 5\lambda$ produces for the $d$ in Fig. 3.56

$$d = 5D = 25\lambda. \tag{3.28}$$

The use of Eq. (3.17) also implies that the steady-state part of the longest pulse must be $D/2$ meters or 2½ wavelengths long. Figure 3.59 illustrates the pulse-length requirement for the conditions assumed in Eq. (3.17) or for measuring the pattern of a transducer in the 60° sector centered on the axis. For this case of maximum pulse length and $D = 5\lambda$,

$$c\tau = Q\lambda + 2\tfrac{1}{2}\lambda = (Q + 2\tfrac{1}{2})\lambda. \tag{3.29}$$

Then, combining Eqs. (3.28) and (3.29) with Eqs. (3.26) and (3.27) yields

$$L = (27.5 + Q)\lambda, \tag{3.30}$$

$$W = [50(Q + 2\tfrac{1}{2}) + (Q + 2\tfrac{1}{2})^2]^{\tfrac{1}{2}}\lambda. \tag{3.31}$$

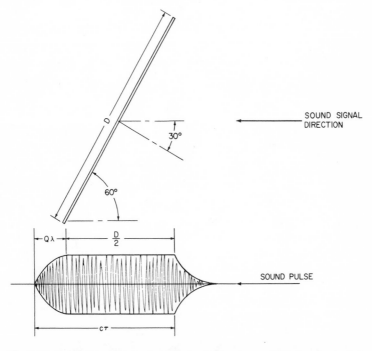

Fig. 3.59. Illustration of how a transducer of diameter or width $D$ and oriented at 30° off axis requires a pulse with a steady-state length of $D/2$.

Equations (3.30) and (3.31) are plotted in Fig. 3.60 with wavelength converted to frequency.

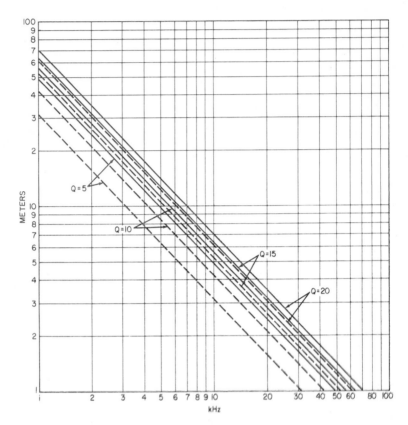

Fig. 3.60. Length (solid line) and width or depth (dashed line) of a tank for measuring a pattern of a transducer with a maximum dimension of five wavelengths.

### 3.13 Acoustically Transparent Pressure Vessels

Closed tanks that are large enough for free-field measurements and also strong enough to contain hydrostatic pressures of several thousand pounds per square inch are very expensive. An alternative for some purposes is provided by small acoustically transparent pressure vessels. If an unknown transducer is placed in such a vessel and then the entire vessel is immersed in a larger body of water, conventional free-field measurements will be limited only by the dimensions of the large body of water. The hydrostatic pressure and temperature are applied only to the unknown; other transducers are outside the vessel as shown in Fig. 3.61.

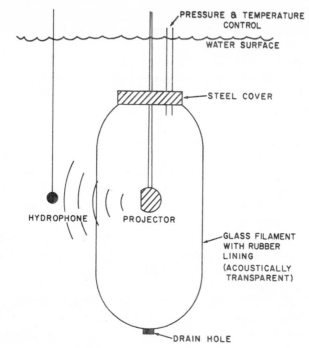

Fig. 3.61. Arrangement for using acoustically transparent pressure vessel to test and evaluate transducers.

Glass-filament-wound vessels have been used with this techniuqe.[19,20] They have a much shorter life in terms of pressure cycles than a comparable steel vessel does, but the relatively low cost compensates for the short life.

The vessels are made by winding glass filament on a mandrel. The filament is coated with a resin that provides the adhesive bond between filaments. A rubber liner serves as a water barrier. The winding technique requires an opening on each end. One opening is made large and used as an access port. The other is small and used as a drain hole. Transducers inside the vessel usually are attached rigidly to the steel cover if the vessel is small, and the transducer and vessel are moved or rotated together.

Because the filament-resin material is heterogeneous and anisotropic, its acoustical characteristics are not amenable to theoretical analysis. All of the current information is empirical.

Glass vessels are completely transparent only at low frequencies in the audio range. The insertion loss of the vessel walls increases gradually with frequency until it may be as much as 8 dB in the ultrasonic range. There may also be discernable resonances of the whole water-filled vessel at an audio frequency. Where the walls have significant insertion loss, they will also reflect sound. Internal reflections will occur in the vessel, and pulsing techniques are needed to eliminate interference.

The principal interference-causing reflection originates from the vessel wall behind the transducer. The low-frequency limit for the pulsing technique is set by this reflection path or the vessel radius. Increasing the radius does not necessarily improve matters, because, for a given pressure capability of the vessel, the wall thickness increases with the radius. There is a pressure-size relation that optimizes the crossover between the frequency range in which the vessel is essentially transparent and continuous-wave signals can be used and the frequency range in which pulsed sound is feasible.

A calibrated standard transducer is needed to determine the insertion loss of the wall as a function of frequency and pressure, or to serve as a standard in a comparison calibration as described in Section 2.2.1. If no change is observed as a function of pressure in an insertion loss measurement, however, it is safe to assume that both the insertion loss of the vessel and the transducer response do not change. The probability of equal and opposite changes over a wide frequency range is negligible. Such "no change" measurements have been observed[19,20] using the type F27 and F30 transducers described in Sections 5.9.1 and 5.9.2. If changes are observed, and if a standard calibrated elsewhere is not available, the internal transducer and the vessel are evaluated as a single unit.

If the transparent vessel is large enough to accommodate simultaneously two transducers separated by a distance that meets the proximity criteria of Section 3.4, it can function as a tank facility as described in Section 3.12.

### 3.14  Coordinate System for Transducer Orientation

A standard system[6] of left-handed polar coordinates like that shown in Fig. 3.62 is used to relate calibration measurements to a transducer. The system is fixed with respect to the transducer. The origin of the coordinates always is placed at the acoustic center of the transducer. Other relationships follow the conventions below, unless otherwise specified. It is assumed that a transducer normally transmits sound in, or receives sound from, a horizontal direction.

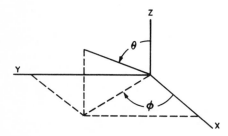

Fig. 3.62. Standard coordinate system for transducer orientation.

(a)  The positive $Z$ axis ($\theta = 0°$) is in the upward direction when the transducer is in its normal position.

(b)  The positive $X$ axis ($\phi = 0°$, $\theta = 90°$) is the direction of normal propagation or the acoustic axis.

(c)  Response or sensitivity is measured in the direction of the $X$ axis.

(d)  Point or spherical transducers are oriented in the coordinate system by an arbitrary choice, but reference points (scribe marks, serial numbers, screw heads, cable glands, etc.) that coincide with the $X$ and $Z$ axis must be specified. Figure 3.63 shows an example.

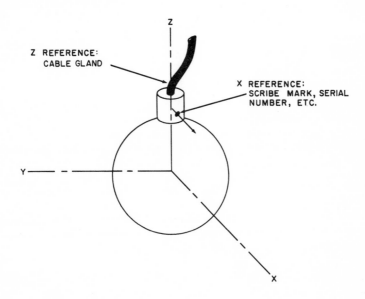

Fig. 3.63. Coordinate system for a point or spherical transducer.

(e)  Cylindrical or line transducers are oriented with the axis of the cylinder or line coinciding with the $Z$ axis. A reference mark in the $XZ$ plane in the direction of the positive $X$ axis is specified. Figure 3.64 shows an example.

(f)  Plane or piston transducers are oriented with the plane or piston face in the $YZ$ plane with the $X$ axis normal to the face at its acoustic center. A reference mark in the $XZ$ plane in the direction of the positive $Z$ axis is specified. Figure 3.65 shows an example.

When unconventional orientations or configurations are used, calibration data should be accompanied by special sketches showing the same information as Figs. 3.63, 3.64, and 3.65.

Polar directivity patterns identify the plane of the pattern by the direction of (1) the $0°$ radius vector (normally the acoustic axis, if it lies in the plane), and (2) the $90°$ radius vector. If the radius vector coincides with the $X$, $Y$, or $Z$ axis,

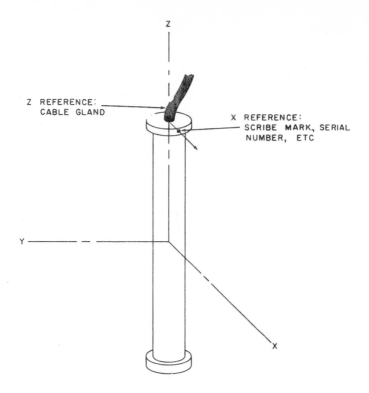

Fig. 3.64.  Coordinate system for a line or cylindrical transducer.

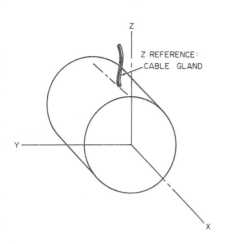

Fig. 3.65.  Coordinate system for a plane or piston transducer.

these symbols are used rather than the angles $\theta$ and $\phi$. For example, an $XY$ pattern means that $0°$ is in the direction of the $X$ axis and $90°$ in the direction of the $Y$ axis. Examples of $XY$, $XZ$, and $YZ$ patterns are shown in Figs. 3.66, 3.67, and 3.68, respectively. If the $0°$ or $90°$ vectors do not coincide with an axis, the directions are identified by $\theta$ and $\phi$. For the example in Fig. 3.69, the pattern is identified by $(\phi = 45, \theta = 0)$ or $(\phi = 45°, Z)$.

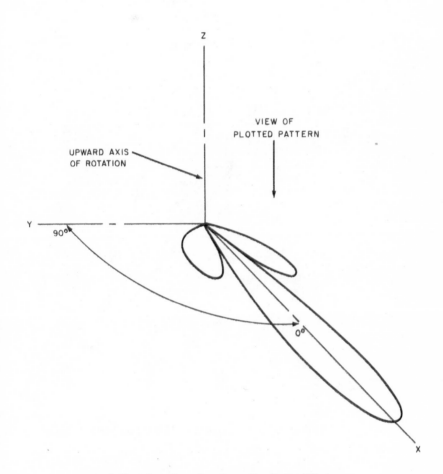

Fig. 3.66. Orientation of a polar pattern in the $XY$ plane.

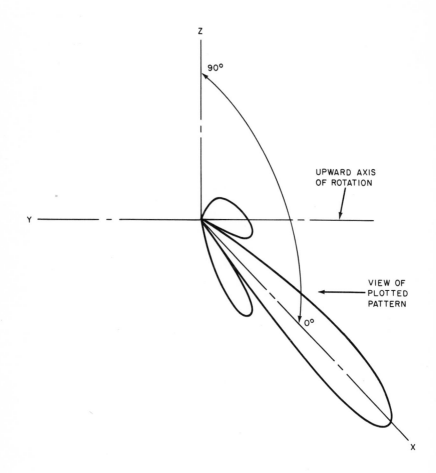

Fig. 3.67. Orientation of a polar pattern in the *XZ* plane.

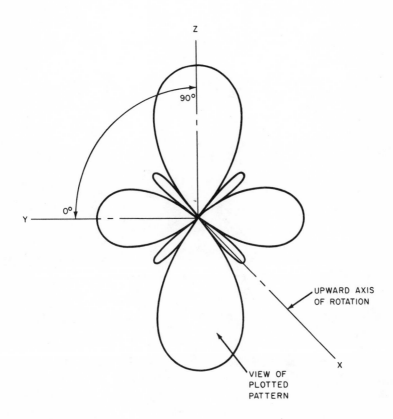

Fig. 3.68.  Orientation of a polar pattern in the *YZ* plane.

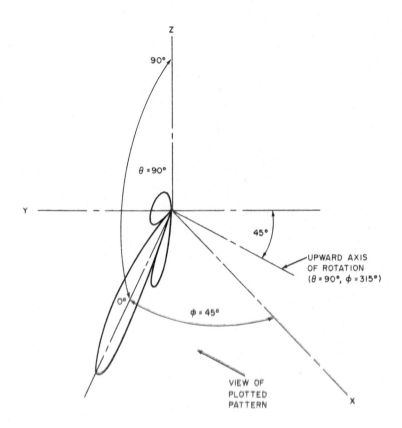

Fig. 3.69. Orientation of a polar pattern in the plane identified by (1) $0°$ radius vector is at $\phi = 45°$ and $\theta = 0°$, and (2) $90°$ radius vector is at $\theta = 0°$.

It is easy to confuse rotational directions, and axes of rotation are not used as a reference. If the patterns were measured by revolving the standard or reference transducer in a wide circle around the unknown transducer, the standard and the data plot would move together in the same, usually clockwise or compass-wise, direction. But patterns actually are measured by rotating the unknown in a direction opposite to the data plot. That is, to plot data for $0°$ to $90°$ or in a clockwise direction, the transducer must rotate from $0°$ to $-90°$ or in a counter-clockwise direction.

In some unusual cases, patterns are measured in configurations other than a plane. If, for example, the two transducers are at different depths and one is rotated about a vertical axis, the line joining the two transducers will sweep out a conical surface. In unconventional pattern measurements like this, the pattern identification scheme should be described in detail, preferably with a drawing.

### 3.15  Data Reduction and Analysis

When transducers are calibrated in free-field facilities and with automatic systems, the calibration equations of Chapter II need expansion and modification into practical formulas that account for units, constants, amplifier gains, attenuators, conversion to the decibel system, voltage and current measure calibration, voltage coupling losses, and so forth. The formulas are further modified to fit techniques for reducing the tedium of computing many data points.

Before, during, and after data reduction, certain examinations and analyses of the data can be made to determine consistency among the measurements and compliance with theory as given in Sections 2.11, 2.13, and 5.2.

The receiving sensitivity $M$ and transmitting response $S$ of a transducer almost always are given in the decibel system, and when they are the correct terminology is sensitivity or response *level*. Patterns almost always are plotted with decibel scales. Other parameters, like directivity index and efficiency, usually are given in decibels. Consequently, when speaking of the sensitivity $M$, for example, one actually means $20 \log (M/M_0)$, where $M_0$ is a reference value.

Measurements of a voltage $e$ with a system like that shown in Fig. 3.26 always involves the gain of the voltage amplifier. The amplifier is calibrated and the gain is read directly from dial settings. The gain $G$ is a measure of the ratio of output voltage to input voltage, or

$$G = 20 \log \frac{\text{output voltage}}{\text{input voltage}} . \tag{3.32}$$

Attenuation is treated as a negative gain.

Where a hydrophone voltage coupling loss is measured in decibels, it will be symbolized by $CL$:

$$CL = 20 \log\left(\frac{e_i}{e_0}\right) = 20 \log e_i - 20 \log e_0, \tag{3.33}$$

when $e_i$ and $e_0$ are taken from Fig. 3.25. Note again that $CL$ is a positive number for a true loss.

Where the projector voltage or current is used in a formula, the voltage or current must be related to the output voltage of the "$e$ and $i$ measure" circuit of Fig. 3.26. This is the same as the output voltage $e_e$ or $e_i$ in Fig. 3.27. These relationships are found by actually measuring $e_e$ or $e_i$ as functions of $e$ and $i$, respectively, and then defining

$$K_e = 20 \log e_e - 20 \log e, \qquad (3.34)$$

$$K_i = 20 \log e_i - 20 \log i. \qquad (3.35)$$

The value of $K_e$ would be expected to be equal to 20 times the logarithm of the voltage divider ratio in Fig. 3.27a; $K_i$ would be equal to 20 times the logarithm of the resistance in Fig. 3.27b, and be a function of the toroid transformer turns ratio in Fig. 3.27c.

Equations (3.33) and (3.34) represent dimensionless ratios; consequently, the units of voltage are unimportant. It is only necessary that the same unit be used consistently in each equation. The units in Eq. (3.35) are those of the MKS system and $K_i$ is the logarithm of volts per ampere.

### 3.15.1  Calibration formulas

In deriving calibration formulas, it will be assumed that all measured voltages are subject to finite amplifier gains, and all hydrophone voltages are subject to coupling losses. This is done for the sake of completeness; such gains and losses do not always exist.

A free-field voltage sensitivity level obtained by comparison with a standard hydrophone is given by Eq. (2.1), which, expanded and modified, is

$$20 \log M_x = 20 \log M_s + (20 \log e_x - G_x + CL_x)$$

$$- (20 \log e_s - G_s + CL_s), \qquad (3.36)$$

where the $x$ subscript denotes a quantity associated with the unknown and the $s$ subscript, with the standard. The units of $M_x$ will be the same as those for the standard calibration $M_s$—that is, volts per unit pressure (one of the unit pressures shown in Fig. 1.1). The voltages are referred to one volt.

A transmitting current response $S_x$ obtained by measuring the transmitted pressure with a standard hydrophone is given by Eq. (2.6), which, expanded and modified, is

$$20 \log S_x = (20 \log e_s - G_s + CL_s) + 20 \log d - 20 \log M_s$$

$$- (20 \log e_i - K_i - G_i). \qquad (3.37)$$

The units of $S_x$ will be unit pressure per ampere when the unit pressure is the same as that used in $M_s$. The voltages $e_s$ and $e_i$ are referred to one volt, and the distance $d$ to one meter.

A transmitting voltage response $S_x{'}$ is taken from Eq. (2.7); the formula is

$$20 \log S_x{'} = (20 \log e_s - G_s + CL_s) + 20 \log d - 20 \log M_s$$

$$- (20 \log e_e - K_e - G_e). \qquad (3.38)$$

A free-field voltage sensitivity obtained by a reciprocity calibration is given by Eq. (2.17), which, expanded and modified, is

$$20 \log M_H = \tfrac{1}{2}[(20 \log e_{PH} - G_{PH} + CL_H) + (20 \log e_{TH} - G_{TH} + CL_H)$$

$$- (20 \log e_{PT} - G_{PT} + CL_T) - (20 \log e_i - K_i - G_i)_T$$

$$+ 20 \log J + 20 \log d]. \qquad (3.39)$$

The units of $M$ depend on the units of $J$, which is given in Figs. 3.70 and 3.71 for all four reference pressure levels of Fig. 1.1.

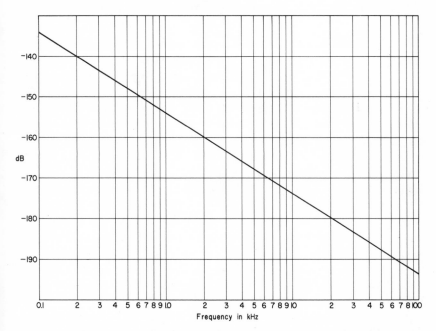

Fig. 3.70.   Reciprocity parameter $20 \log J$ as a function of frequency in cgs units; $J = M/S = (2d/\rho f) \times 10^{-7}$ where $M$ is in volts per microbar, $S$ is in microbars per ampere at $d$ cm, $d = 100$ cm, and $\rho = 1.00$ g/cm$^3$. Note:  Subtract 148 dB when reference pressure is changed from 1 $\mu$bar to 0.0002 $\mu$bar.

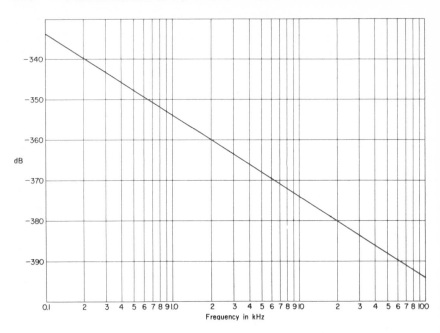

Fig. 3.71. Reciprocity parameter 20 log $J$ as a function of frequency in MKS units; $J = M/S = (2d/\rho f) \times 10^{-12}$ where $M$ is in volts per micronewton/meter$^2$, $S$ is in micronewton/meter$^2$/ampere at $d$ meters, $d$ = 1m, and $\rho$ = 1000 kg/m$^3$. Note: (1) Add 240 dB when reference pressure is changed from 1 $\mu$N/m$^2$ to 1 N/m$^2$. (2) Add 52 dB when reference pressure is changed from 1 $\mu$N/m$^2$ to 20 $\mu$N/m$^2$.

Equation (3.39) is cumbersome if all 14 terms are used. In practice, this usually is not necessary. The distance $d$ can be combined with $J$ from Table 3.1 and Fig. 3.71 by adding 20 log $d$, with $d$ in meters, to $J$. The electrical impedances of the projector P and the reciprocal transducer T usually are low in comparison with the input impedance of the first receiving amplifier in Fig. 3.26. Thus, when they are used as hydrophones, P and T will have zero coupling loss, or $CL_P = CL_T = 0$. The hydrophone itself may have no coupling loss if it has no preamplifier or if end-of-cable calibrations are used. Then $CL_H = 0$. With a receiving system that has good linearity over a large dynamic range, the amplifier gains can be the same for all four measurements in a reciprocity calibration, and thereby cancel out. Still further simplification is obtained if the current or $e_i$ is held constant by a normalizing circuit as shown in Fig. 3.26, and a circuit with a 6-dB-per-octave insertion loss is used to combine $J$ with $e_{TH}$. All these simplifications reduce Eq. (3.39) to

$$20 \log M_H = \tfrac{1}{2}[(20 \log e_{PH} - 20 \log e_{PT}) + 20 \log e_{TH}' + K_0], \quad (3.40)$$

where $e_{TH}'$ includes the 6-dB-per-octave loss equivalent to $J$ and $K_0$ includes all system constants including current, distance, and a reference level for $e_{TH}'$.

Table 3.1. The reciprocity parameter as used in Eq. (3.39) for five different reference pressures used in the definitions of free-field voltage sensitivity and transmitting current response. The units of $d$ and $\rho$ are meters and kilograms per cubic meter where the reference pressure is in newtons per square meter, and centimeters and grams per cubic centimeter where the reference pressure is in microbars per square centimeter.

| Reference Pressure | Reciprocity Parameter ($J$) |
|---|---|
| 1 N/m² | $2d/\rho f$ |
| 1 $\mu$N/m² | $(2d/\rho f) \times 10^{-12}$ |
| 20 $\mu$N/m² | $(2d/\rho f) \times 10^{-10}$ |
| 1 $\mu$bar | $(2d/\rho f) \times 10^{-7}$ |
| 0.0002 $\mu$bar | $(2d/\rho f) \times 4 \times 10^{-15}$ |

Roshon[21] uses Eq. (3.40) and largely graphical techniques to compute $M_H$ over a wide frequency range. The difference between the first two terms in parentheses is graphically added to the $e_{TH}'$ term, resulting in a curve proportional to $M_H$. Then, a computation at just one frequency is all that is necessary to account for $K_0$ and reduce the curve to the absolute level.

If a fourth measurement in which T is the projector and P is the hydrophone (see Fig. 2.5d) is added to the conventional reciprocity trio, Eq. (2.18) can be expanded and modified into a formula similar to Eq. (3.39), but with the $P$ and $T$ subscripts interchanged. Such an interchange affects only the "$PT$" and "$i$" parenthetical expressions. Equating these expressions constitutes a check on the reciprocity of P and T. That is, if P and T are reciprocal, then

$$(20 \log e_{PT} - G_{PT} + CL_T) + (20 \log e_i - K_i - G_i)_T =$$

$$(20 \log e_{TP} - G_{TP} + CL_P) + (20 \log e_i - K_i - G_i)_P \qquad (3.41)$$

The value of $K_i$ is independent of the projector, T and P usually are similar transducers so that the gains cancel out, and $CL_T$ and $CL_P$ usually are zero. Then Eq. (3.41) reduces to

$$20 \log e_{PT} + (20 \log e_i)_T = 20 \log e_{TP} + (20 \log e_i)_P. \qquad (3.42)$$

The numerical values of the two sides of Eqs. (3.41) or (3.42) may differ by a few tenths of a decibel because of random error. An average of the two expressions then can be used in Eq. (3.39) instead of only the left-hand expression.

### 3.15.2  Conversion of reciprocity parameter and level

The reciprocity parameter $J$ in Eqs. (2.17) and (3.39) is defined in Section 2.3 and Eq. (2.13) as the ratio $M/S$. In the literature[22],[23] this $J$ is shown to be an acoustical transfer admittance $U/p$, where $U$ is the volume velocity of a simple source and $p$ is the free-field pressure in a spherically diverging wave at the distance $d$. From this, then, $J$ is

$$J = \frac{M}{S} = \frac{2d}{\rho f},$$  (3.43)

where $d$ is the reference distance of the transmitted pressure in the definition of $S$—that is, one meter; $\rho$ is the density of water; and $f$ is the frequency. If all the parameters in Eq. (2.17) and (3.39) were consistent or in a single system of units, and if the reference voltages, currents, and pressures used in the definitions of $M$ and $S$ were the units of the system, then Eq. (3.43) would be a complete formula for $J$. Where the units are mixed (MKSA volts and amperes, cgs microbars and centimeters, and reference pressures other than one newton per square meter, for example), a conversion constant must be added to Eq. (3.43). These constants are shown in Table 3.1 for five different reference pressures. In each case, it is assumed that the same unit system (that is, MKS or cgs) is used for $2d/\rho f$ as for the reference pressure. It should be noted that even though $20~\mu\text{N/m}^2$ and $0.0002~\mu\text{bar}$ are the same pressure, $20 \log J$ is different for the two cases because different units are used for $2d/\rho f$. This difference accounts for the factor $10^{-5}$ in the conversion contants. That is,

$$\frac{2d(\text{m})}{\rho\left(\frac{\text{kg}}{\text{m}^3}\right)f(\text{Hz})} = 10^{-5}\frac{2d(\text{cm})}{\rho\left(\frac{\text{g}}{\text{cm}^3}\right)f(\text{Hz})}.$$  (3.44)

The remaining part of the conversion factor accounts for the reference pressure level differences shown in Fig. 1.1. The parameter $20 \log J$ is plotted as a function of frequency in Figs. 3.70 and 3.71.

Since the free-field voltage sensitivity of a given hydrophone is proportional to the reference pressure, the sensitivity levels will differ by the same amount as the pressure levels shown in Fig. 1.1. One then can compute $M$ with one reference pressure level and use Fig. 1.1 to change it to another. Similarly, the reference level of the transmitting current response can be changed by using Fig. 1.1 and inverting the difference. Table 3.2 shows the relative levels of $M$, $S$, and $J$. The level differences can be used to convert from one system to another. For example, $M$ referred to 1 volt per micronewton per square meter will be 100 dB lower than when referred to one volt per microbar. The $20 \log J$ column of Table 3.2 also can be obtained from the conversion factors in Table 3.1 and Eq. (3.44).

Table 3.2.  Conversion factors or relative levels of sensitivity, response, and the reciprocity parameter as a function of the reference pressure.

| Reference Pressure | Conversion from 1 N/m² | | |
|---|---|---|---|
| | $20 \log M$ | $20 \log S$ | $20 \log J$ |
| 1 $\mu$N/m² | −120 | +120 | −240 |
| 1 $\mu$bar | −20 | +20 | −40 |
| 20 $\mu$N/m² ⎱<br>0.0002 $\mu$bar ⎰ | −94 | +94 | −188 |

### 3.15.3  Data consistency

Calibration, test, and evaluation data on underwater electroacoustic transducers, like any experimental data, can and should be examined and analyzed for internal consistency and consistency with theory.  There are many ways of doing this, especially if all voltages and currents are measured and all responses and sensitivities are plotted as continuous functions of frequency.  Such plots are assumed in the paragraphs that follow.  Each paragraph describes the examination and analysis associated with each type or combinations of types of data.

### A. *Transducer Input or Output Voltages and Currents*

The basic raw data of a measurement are several lines on a strip chart representing hydrophone voltage and projector current or voltage as a function of frequency.  These plots are examined first for evidence of the various types of interference discussed in Section 3.10.  If, in accordance with good practice, the measurements are made at two distances between the projector and hydrophone, the difference in levels is checked for proper "distance loss."  In a reciprocity calibration the "reciprocity check" discussed in Section 2.3, Figs. 2.5b and 2.5d, and Eq. (3.41) is made.  The projector voltage and current (or voltage proportional to current) of a sharply resonant transducer usually will peak or dip at the resonance frequency unless the voltage is normalized.  These peaks and dips should be consistent with the theory of Figs. 2.51, 2.53, and 2.54 in that (a) the current peaks and the voltage dips at the resonance of a piezoelectric transducer, and (b) the current dips and voltage peaks at the resonance of an electromagnetic transducer.

### B. *Response and Sensitivity*

The surest test for the validity of a computed response or sensitivity is to obtain data by different and independent methods and compare results. The free field reciprocity and two-projector null methods, for example, would be completely independent.    Few places have facilities for such checks on measurements. More common are semi-independent techniques like comparing continuous-wave and pulsed-sound results, or examining results in overlapping frequency ranges. When a wide-band hydrophone is calibrated, the frequency range of the measurement usually is limited by the projector. A moving-coil projector would be used in the audio range to, say, 20 kHz; typically, a piezoelectric projector would be used in the range 5 to 50 kHz. The two measurements would overlap in the range 5 to 20 kHz, and would be semi-independent in this range. That is, some of the measurement conditions would be the same and others would be different in the measurements in the two ranges. Repetitive measurements also can be made to identify random errors. Agreement with theory as given in Section 5.2 and Figs. 5.2a, 5.2b, and 5.3 should be examined. In a resonant transducer, the free-field voltage sensitivity will peak at a lower frequency than the transmitting current response. This is evident from the relationship $20 \log M - 20 \log S = 20 \log J$ and the fact that $J$ decreases at a 6-dB-per-octave rate. This frequency difference is small and not shown in Fig. 5.2, but it may be discernible in some cases.

### C. *Response and Sensitivity versus Patterns*

If the response or sensitivity is measured in two or more directions, and if directivity patterns are measured in a plane including the two or more directions, the differences must be consistent. For example, if a hydrophone sensitivity is measured for both the acoustic axis ($X$ direction) and at 90° (or $Y$ axis direction), and at a given frequency the latter is 6 dB lower than the former, this same 6 dB difference should appear in the pattern at the same frequency.

### D. *Response versus Impedance*

The transmitting current response $S$ and transmitting voltage response $S'$ are related according to Ohm's Law:

$$20 \log S - 20 \log S' = 20 \log Z, \qquad (3.45)$$

where $Z$ is the transducer impedance.

Equation (3.45) is a consistency check if the projector current, voltage, and impedance are all measured.    Sometimes Eq. (3.45) is used to find one of the three parameters when only the other two are measured.    It is evident that in a resonant transducer, $S$ and $S'$ will not necessarily peak at the same frequency because, as is shown in Fig. 2.52, the maximum $Z$ is not at the resonance frequency.

### E. *Patterns*

Patterns can be examined for agreement with the theory of Section 2.11 and Figs. 2.41, 2.42, and 2.43. The width of the main beam and the difference in level between the main beam and the first minor lobe are the two parameters that usually are examined. This requires some knowledge or at least educated guesses about the actual size and configuration of the transducer. Beam patterns become narrower as the frequency increases. Any violation of this rule usually indicates that a pattern is being measured at a harmonic frequency. Where patterns are measured in several planes, there should be consistency between certain levels. The front-to-back differences in $XY$ and $XZ$ patterns should be the same. The difference in level in the $Y$ and $Z$ axes directions should be consistent in all patterns. If patterns are taken in the three principal planes, then a $Y$ and $Z$ axis check would show that

$$(XZ @ 90°) - (XY @ 90°) = (YZ @ 0°) - (YZ @ 90°). \qquad (3.46)$$

### F. Impedance

If the transducer impedance is measured by more than one technique, the results should be consistent, of course. There are three techniques. The "e and i measure" calibration data give only a general idea as to the impedance. Vector impedance locus plotters (VILP) automatically display impedance in the form shown in Figs. 2.52b, 2.53, and 2.54. Such plots are convenient and useful, but not very accurate. For high accuracy, impedance bridges are used, and the data are plotted as in Fig. 2.52a. The plotted data should be examined to ascertain that maximums, minimums, and slopes are all consistent with the theory as given in Section 2.13.

### G. Coupling Loss

The voltage coupling loss is independent of the acoustic load on a transducer except near the resonance of a sharply resonant transducer. Consequently, with wide-range hydrophones, bench measurements in air should produce the same results as regular measurements in water. Since electrical grounding conditions often affect coupling loss measurements, a comparison in air and water environments is useful to detect this source of error. If they do not agree, it usually means that the calibration resistor is being shunted by a ground loop in one of the two conditions. The coupling loss usually is approximately constant down to a low cut-off frequency which is not to be confused with the sensitivity cut-off frequency described in Section 5.2 and Fig. 5.3. Figure 3.72 is a simplified version of Fig. 3.25 showing the piezoelectirc generator and the parallel resistances and capacitances that load the generator. Except at the very low frequencies, the resistances $R_g$ and $r_a$ are much larger than the reactances $1/\omega C_g$ and $1/\omega C_a$, and the coupling calibration voltage $e_i$ is divided across the two reactances. This division is constant with frequency. At some low frequency, typically 1 to 100 Hz, $1/\omega C_a$ becomes equal to $R_a$. This is the cut-off frequency. At frequencies below the cut-off, $e_i$ is divided across $R_a$ and $1/\omega C_g$, and the ratio $e_i/e_a$ increases at the rate 6 dB per octave as the frequency is decreased. At a still lower frequency, $e_i$ will divide across $R_g$ and $R_a$, and the ratio $e_i/e_a$ again will become constant, but this usually happens at too low a frequency to observe. An unusually high cut-off frequency indicates that $R_a$ is smaller than usual—as, for example, when moisture gets into the hydrophone.

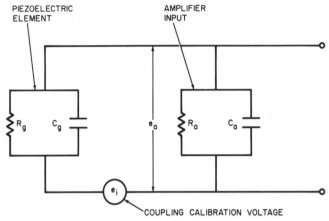

Fig. 3.72. Simplified coupling measurement circuit. Stray capacitances and leakage resistances are lumped with $C_g$ and $R_g$ or with $C_a$ and $R_a$ according to whether they are in the crystal or the amplifier side of the coupling calibration voltage.

### H. *Efficiency and Other Parameters*

Various electroacoustic parameters, like efficiency, are functions of the measured parameters response, sensitivity, directivity, and impedance. They are obtained by computation. It follows that any peaks, dips, or anomalies in the frequency curves of the measured parameters must appear in the computed parameters—unless, of course, they coincidentally cancel out. Computed parameters should be examined for consistency in the contours of the curves.

### 3.15.4 Data accuracy

The calibration of an underwater electroacoustic transducer is a measurement of a dynamic system in an unstable environment. The transducer itself vibrates in many complex ways. Ideally, the electroacoustic element itself, coupling fluids, and acoustic windows vibrate freely. At the same time, all other parts of a transducer ideally do not vibrate at all. The transducer is expected to be sensitive to dynamic pressures of the order of one microbar or $1.5 \times 10^{-5}$ psi, and insensitive to static pressures of $10^3$ psi or more. The water medium never is the boundless, homogeneous, and stable medium it is assumed to be. It is understandable, then, that underwater electroacoustic measurements are not as accurate and precise as some other types of calibration measurements.

Most activities will claim an accuracy of ±1 dB for a measurement on an unknown transducer performed once, and with only a nominal effort at data examination and analysis. Where several independent, semi-independent, and redundant measurements can be made, accuracy of ±0.5 dB can be expected, and perhaps in some exceptional cases it may be as good as 0.2 dB.

As used here, accuracy does not have the precise mathematical meaning that is possible when many measurements are made and average deviations from the mean can be determined. It is the kind of criterion one would put in a specification and is a measure of the data spread under various measurement conditions after the data in each case have been examined, analyzed, and perhaps corrected for observed error.

In an international round robin hydrophone calibration program,[24] accuracies of ±0.5 dB to ±1.5 dB were claimed by various participants. When the data from all the participants were analyzed, average deviations of 0.3 to 0.6 dB were found.

# REFERENCES

1. J. L. Jones, C. B. Leslie, and L. E. Barton, "Acoustic Characteristics of a Lake Bottom," J. Acoust. Soc. Am. 30, 142 (1958).

2. R. J. Bobber, "Acoustic Characteristics of a Florida Lake Bottom," J. Acoust. Soc. Am. 31, 250 (1959).

3. R. J. Bobber, "Interference Versus Frequency in Measurements in a Shallow Lake," J. Acoust. Soc. Am. 33, 1211 (1961).

4. H. Stenzel, *Leitfaden zur Berechnung von Schallvorgängen* (Julius Springer, Berlin, 1939). English translation by A. R. Stickley, "Handbook for the Calculation of Sound Propagation Phenomena," Naval Research Laboratory Translation No. 130.

5. *Sonar Calibration Methods,* Summary Technical Report of NDRC Division 6, Vol. 10.

6. "American Standard Procedures for Calibration of Electroacoustic Transducers, Particularly Those for Use in Water," Z24.24-1957 (USA Standards Institute, New York).

7. R. W. Bukmore and R. C. Hansen, "Antenna Power Densities in the Fresnel Region," Proc. IRE 47, 2119 (1959).

8. G. A. Sabin, "Calibration of Piston Transducers at Marginal Test Distances," J. Acoust. Soc. Am. 36, 168 (1964).

9. R. J. Bobber and G. A. Sabin, "Cylindrical Wave Reciprocity Parameter," J. Acoust. Soc. Am. 33, 446 (1961).

10. K. Yamada, "Acoustic Response of a Rectangular Receiver to a Rectangular Source," Papers of Ship Research Institute (Tokyo) No. 20, June 1967.

11. O. M. Owsley, "Testing Devices for Sound Projectors," U.S. Patent No. 2,451,509 (filed 5 July 1944).

12. S. Goldman, *Frequency Analysis, Modulation and Noise* (McGraw-Hill Book Co., Inc., New York, 1948).

13. C. Cherry, *Pulses and Transients in Communication Circuits* (Dover Publications Inc., New York, 1950).

14. O. H. Davie, *The Elements of Pulse Techniques* (Reinhold Publishing Corporation, New York, 1964).

15. R. E. Ford and C. W. Stoops, "The Measurement of Impedance at High Power," Naval Research Laboratory Report No. 6631, 27 Oct 1967.

16. *The Physics of Sound in the Sea,* Summary Technical Report of NDRC Division 6, Vol. 8, Chap. 28, "Acoustic Theory of Bubbles."

17. C. L. Darner, "An Anechoic Tank for Underwater Sound Measurements Under High Hydrostatic Pressures," J. Acoust. Soc. Am. 26, 221 (1954).

18. J. D. Wallace and E. W. McMorrow, "Sonar Transducer Pulse Calibration System," J. Acoust. Soc. Am. 33, 75 (1961).

19. C. E. Green and J. R. Roshon, "Sonar Calibration in a Controlled Pressure-Temperature Environment," J. Acoust. Soc. Am. 42, 1188(A) (1967).

20.   C. E. Green, "Pressure/Temperature Vessels for Calibrating Sonar Transducers," Naval Undersea Warfare Center Report TP45, May 1968.
21.   J. Roshon, "Electroacoustic Transducer Calibration Combined with Semiautomatic Data Reduction," J. Acoust. Soc. Am. 32, 1519(A) (1960). Also, Naval Electronics Laboratory Technical Memorandum TM-469 of 18 Apr 1961.
22.   W. Wathen-Dunn, "On the Reciprocity Free-Field Calibration of Microphones," J. Acoust. Soc. Am. 21, 542 (1949).
23.   R. J. Bobber, "General Reciprocity Parameter," J. Acoust. Soc. Am. 39, 680 (1966).
24.   W. J. Trott, "International Standardization in Underwater Sound Measurements," Acustica 20, 169 (1968).

# Chapter IV

# NEAR-FIELD METHODS

## 4.1 Introduction

The low limit of the frequency range in which useful calibration, test, or evaluation measurements can be made in a small body of water generally is a function of the minimum measurement distance set by the proximity criteria of Section 3.4. These criteria indicate that when a transducer diameter or length amounts to several wavelengths or more, the minimum measurement distance is many wavelengths. At frequencies of a few kilohertz, this distance becomes very large and interference from boundaries illustrated in Fig. 3.29 becomes severe. It also was pointed out in Section 3.4 that whether continuous-wave or pulsed sound signals are used, the minimum distance should be used to discriminate against boundary interference.

It became obvious in the late 1950's that the small lake, pond, and tank facilities of the Navy were running out of space (in wavelengths) as frequencies of a few kilohertz and large transducers were coming into use. If conventional far-field measurements were to continue, very large bodies of water and very large and expensive facilities would be needed. The only alternative would be to devise measurement techniques that would change or eliminate the free-field far-field transducer proximity requirements. If, for example, one could make measurements in the near field or Fresnel zone of a transducer and extrapolate the results to conventional far-field patterns and response, a great saving in space and money could be realized.

Some basic mathematical theory for extrapolating near-field data to far-field patterns and response was available,[1-4] but had not been used in practice. In 1958, the Navy Underwater Sound Reference Laboratory (USRL) recommended to the Office of Naval Research that a study be sponsored at some university with the aim of extending and applying these mathematical concepts to the real Navy problems of making calibration, test, or evaluation measurements on large sonar transducers. In 1959, Horton, Innis, and Baker at the Defense Research Laboratory (DRL) of the University of Texas undertook this task under the joint sponsorship of the Office of Naval Research and the Navy Bureau of Ships. At the same time, W. J. Trott at the USRL continued to investigate the same problem along lines that eventually led to an array that produces a near field consisting

193

in part of uniform plane progressive waves. The two approaches to this problem have become known as (1) the DRL method, and (2) the Trott array. Both have been successful, and each is discussed in the sections that follow.

## 4.2 Theory of DRL Method

The DRL method is based on formulas from Kirchhoff and Helmholtz[5-7] and the concept illustrated in Fig. 4.1. If a sound source is completely enclosed by a surface $S$, the pressure $p(P)$ at any point $P$ in the space exterior to $S$ and due to the sound source within $S$ can be determined by the surface integral

$$p(P) = (1/4\pi) \iint_{S}\left[p(Q) \frac{\partial}{\partial n}\left(\frac{e^{jkr}}{r}\right) - \left(\frac{e^{jkr}}{r}\right) \frac{\partial p(Q)}{\partial n}\right] dS, \qquad (4.1)$$

where $p(Q)$ is the complex pressure at a point $Q$ on the surface $S$, $n$ is the outward normal to $S$ at $Q$, $\partial/\partial n$ denotes differentiation in the normal direction, $r$ is the distance from $Q$ to $P$, and $k$ is the wave number. Equation (4.1), known as the Helmholtz formula, is valid only for the case of sinusoidal waves.

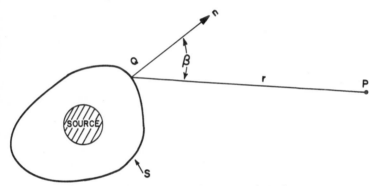

Fig. 4.1. Surface integration for the Helmholtz formula.

The direct use of the Helmholtz formula requires that the magnitude and phase of both the pressure and pressure gradient be measured over the surface $S$. The pressure gradient is difficult to measure with good spatial resolution, however, because pressure-gradient hydrophones generally have dimensions of 2 to 5 in. (see Section 5.12) and, in effect, measure the pressure gradient averaged over a volume of 8-125 in.[3]. Without a very small or probe pressure-gradient hydrophone, the pressure gradient at a point in a sound field cannot be accurately measured. To avoid this measurement, it is assumed in the DRL method that the wave propagation at the point $Q$ is approximately plane, and

$$\frac{\partial p(Q)}{\partial n} \simeq jkp(Q). \qquad (4.2)$$

This approximation is valid for surfaces of moderate curvature over which the pressure changes are not sharp. For the case of a cylindrical wave, for example, Horton shows that it is valid when the diameter of the cylinder is 5 wavelengths or more.[6] Experimental results on large cylindrical and other transducers also support the approximation. For general application of the DRL method, however, the approximation in Eq. (4.2) should be examined whenever the transducer and the surface $S$ do not constitute a large cylinder or sphere.

A second assumption is that $r$ is very large. This is automatically valid, of course, if Eq. (4.1) is being used to compute far-field patterns or response. Then

$$\frac{\partial}{\partial n}\left(\frac{e^{jkr}}{r}\right) \simeq \frac{jk}{r}\,e^{jkr}\,\frac{\partial r}{\partial n} = -j\frac{ke^{jkr}}{r}\cos\beta, \tag{4.3}$$

where $\beta$ is the angle between the normal and the line from $Q$ to $P$. Substituting Eqs. (4.2) and (4.3) into Eq. (4.1) and taking the magnitude of $r$ as approximately a constant yields

$$p(P) = \frac{-jk}{4\pi r}\iint_{S}\ (1 + \cos\beta)e^{jkr}p(Q)dS. \tag{4.4}$$

In any particular measurement, the magnitudes of $r$ and $k$ are constants, the magnitude and phase of $p(Q)$ are measured at closely spaced discrete points over the surface $S$, $\beta$ is computed for every point $Q$ from the geometry, and Eq. (4.4) is used to determine $p(P)$. The magnitude of the quotient of $p(P)$ on the transducer acoustic axis over the current driving the source is the transmitting current response. For a pattern, $p(P)$ is computed for a series of points on the arc of a circle centered on the source. The computations obviously are formidable, and an electronic computer is necessary to make the method feasible; however, once a computer is programmed for a particular surface $S$, the computation is easily made.

### 4.3 Practice of DRL Method

The practical use of the DRL method is illustrated by some of the work of Baker,[7] who experimented with the large cylindrical transducer shown in Fig. 4.2, which consisted of 48 vertical staves equally spaced about the axis. Measurements were made while groups of 12 adjacent staves were driven. The surface of integration was a cylinder 1.25 wavelengths larger in radius than the transducer and slightly longer than the transducer. A calibrated probe hydrophone was held in a fixed position $1.25\lambda$ from the transducer as the transducer was rotated in steps of $3.6°$. The pressure and phase were measured at 100 points in a circle around the transducer. The probe then was moved upward to a new level and the sequence repeated. The surface of integration was not closed in this example. No measurements were made above and below the transducer. It was assumed that the pressure above and below the transducer was small enough to be neglected. Figure 4.3 shows sample plots of data obtained at one level of the probe. The separation between measuring points should be less than 0.8λ–a common criterion for approximating a continuous plane with an array of points. The experiments showed that greater separation in the plane of a pattern being measured introduced scallops into the pattern; however, greater separation in the orthogonal or vertical plane seemed more tolerable. Figure 4.4 shows a pattern computed by the DRL method and measured by conventional far-field techniques. The agreement between angles of ±60° is quite good, even when only one set of 100 points at one probe level is used. Better results are obtained if a line hydrophone is used instead of the probe. If the line hydrophone is as long as the transducer, is designed so that it integrates the acoustic signal along the length of the line, and is positioned with the axis of the line parallel to the axis of the cylinder, then the whole cylinder is scanned in one rotation. The results of such a measurement are shown in Fig. 4.5. A line hydrophone consisting of a series of closely spaced discrete elements will integrate the signal when the elements are electrically connected in series and the output open-circuit voltage is measured, or when the elements are connected in parallel and the output short-circuit current is measured.

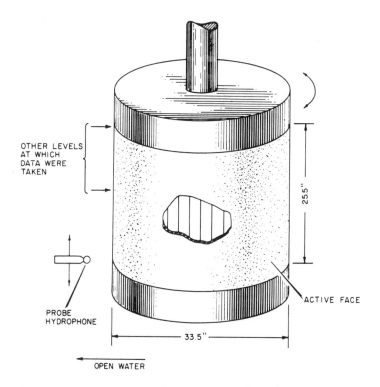

Fig. 4.2. Sketch of the large cylindrical transducer showing near-field probe and the position at which three-level data were taken. (From reference 7.)

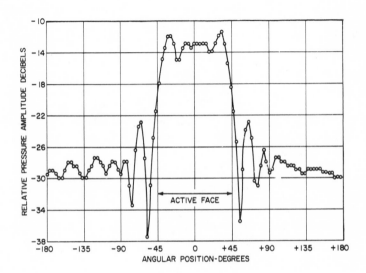

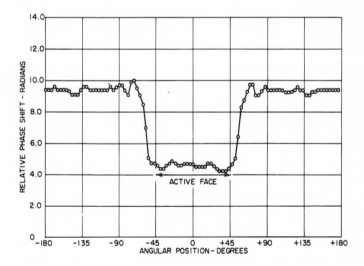

Fig. 4.3. Sample plots of 12-stave near-field data showing the position of the active face of the cylindrical transducer. (From reference 7.)

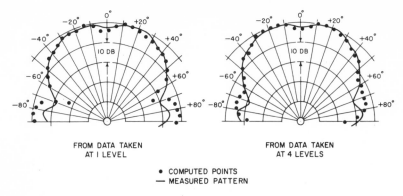

FROM DATA TAKEN              FROM DATA TAKEN
AT I LEVEL                   AT 4 LEVELS

• COMPUTED POINTS
— MEASURED PATTERN

Fig. 4.4.  Comparison of measured and computed horizontal far-field patterns of the cylindrical transducer—12 active staves.  (From reference 7.)

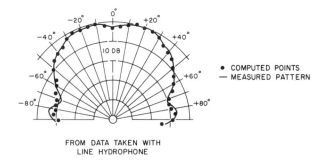

• COMPUTED POINTS
— MEASURED PATTERN

FROM DATA TAKEN WITH
LINE HYDROPHONE

Fig. 4.5.  Comparison of measured and computed horizontal far-field patterns of the cylindrical transducer—12 active staves. (From reference 7.)

Vertical patterns computed from near-field data with the arrangement in Fig. 4.2 require data at closely spaced probe levels.  Figure 4.6 shows patterns computed from data at 27 levels and 11 levels.  Level separation in both cases was less than 0.8λ.

Transmitting response and absolute source levels computed by the DRL method agreed within ±1 dB with conventional far-field calibration measurements.

Baker also made measurements on plane, dipole, line, and line-and-cone transducers.  Where there was disagreement with far-field measurements, it was of the order of 1 to 2 dB on the main lobe and high side lobes of the pattern.  Levels on low side lobes, 20 dB or more below the axis level, generally were too inaccurate to use.  However, the same is true for many conventional far-field pattern measurements.  Accuracy can be improved by closer spacing of the measurement points and more complete scanning of the integration surface.

The DRL scanning technique provides an added benefit of identifying subnormal elements in a multielement transducer.  Figure 4.7 shows the effect of

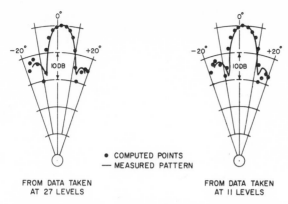

● COMPUTED POINTS
— MEASURED PATTERN

FROM DATA TAKEN
AT 27 LEVELS

FROM DATA TAKEN
AT II LEVELS

Fig. 4.6. Comparison of measured and computed vertical far-field patterns of the cylindrical transducer—six active staves. (From reference 7.)

one inactive stave in the transducer shown in Fig. 4.2. A near-field pressure anomaly usually will occur at the position of the subnormal element causing the anomaly. This is not always true, however, and care must be used in interpreting such effects. For example, two subnormal but identical staves separated by one normal stave could produce a near-field anomaly centered on the position of the normal stave.

When the DRL method is used with pulsed-sound techniques, the dimensional requirements of the volume of water probably approach the practical minimum. Only the invention of an ideal anechoic coating that would eliminate boundary interference could reduce the volume still further. Figure 4.8 shows the dimensions used by Baker. The tank diameter is less than 3 times the transducer diameter.

## 4.4 Trott Array Concept

In his first study of a feasible near-field technique, Trott[8,9] observed that the near- and far-field sound pressures produced by a large piston radiator were related in the same way as the spherical-wave and plane-wave reciprocity parameters (see Sections 2.3.1 and 2.3.5). If the same transducer is effectively a point on a spherical wave, as is assumed in a conventional spherical-wave reciprocity calibration, or a plane on a plane wave, as is assumed in a plane-wave reciprocity calibration, the free-field voltage sensitivity $M$ will be the same in each case. The transmitting response $S$, however, depends on the mode and extent of the wave propagation. Thus,

$$M = S_p J_p = S_s J_s \tag{4.5}$$

where $J$ is the reciprocity parameter and the subscripts $p$ and $s$ pertain to plane- and spherical-wave conditions, respectively. The near field of a large circular

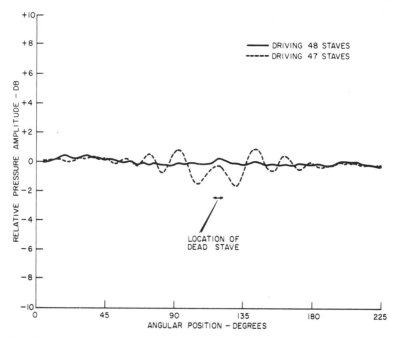

Fig. 4.7.   Near-field pressure-amplitude data for 48 and 47 active staves of the cylindrical transducer. (From reference 7.)

piston radiator consists essentially of a collimated beam of sound energy as shown in Fig. 4.9. The average pressure $p_{nf}$ in any cross-sectional near-field area of the beam is constant, and thus the near field approximates a collimated beam of uniform plane progressive waves.[10,11]  By Eq. (4.5), the far-field pressure $p_{ff}$ from the same large circular piston transducer being driven by the same current as for $p_{nf}$ then is related to $p_{nf}$:

$$\frac{p_{ff}}{p_{nf}} = \frac{S_s}{S_p} = \frac{J_p}{J_s} = \frac{S}{r_1\lambda},  \tag{4.6}$$

where $r_1$ is the reference distance in the definition of $S_s$, $\lambda$ is the wavelength, and $S$ is the cross-sectional area.

With a similar argument and use of the cylindrical-wave reciprocity parameter (see Section 2.3.4), the far-field to near-field pressure ratio for a line or thin cylinder transducer can be shown to be $Lr_2/r_1\lambda^{1/2}$, where $r_2$ is the reference distance for the cylindrical-wave transmitting response and $L$ is the line transducer length.

As in the DRL method, the average near-field pressure was obtained with a scanning and integrating technique using a point or line hydrophone.

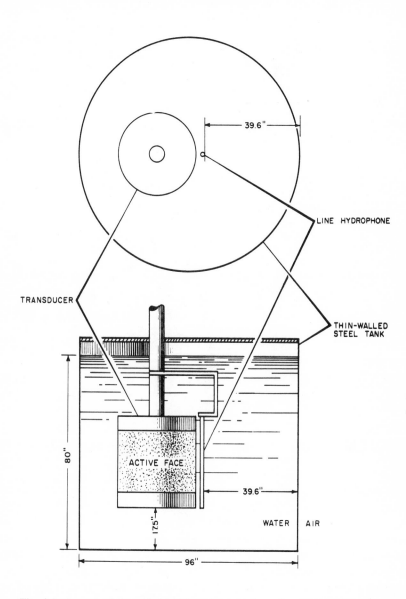

Fig. 4.8.  Layout of the cylindrical transducer in the tank.  (From reference 7.)

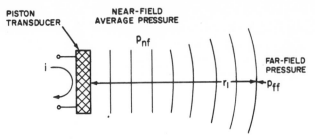

Fig. 4.9.  Near and far field of piston transducer; $S_p = p_{nf}/i$, $S_s = p_{ff}/i$.

The reciprocity parameter approach actually was equivalent to a special case of the DRL or Kirchhoff-Helmholtz method.  If we let $\beta = 1$ in Eq. (4.4), the magnitude of the integral becomes

$$\iint_S 2p(Q)dS \;=\; 2p_{nf}S, \tag{4.7}$$

or

$$|p(P)| \equiv |p_{ff}| = \left(\frac{k}{4\pi r_1}\right)(2p_{nf}S), \tag{4.8}$$

and

$$\frac{p_{ff}}{p_{nf}} = \frac{S}{r_1\lambda}. \tag{4.9}$$

Equation (4.9) is the same in Eq. (4.6).

Instead of expanding from a special to the more general case of the Kirchhoff-Helmholtz formula or the DRL method with its computational problems, Trott took a different approach.  He reversed the projector-hydrophone relationship and visualized the scanning transducer as a point source that would, with integration over a period of time, construct a plane wave according to the classical Huygens wavelet concept.  If the plane scanning area were large enough, the integrated sound pressure acting on the unknown transducer would be indistinguishable from the sound pressure in a plane progressive wave.  The question then is:  How large is large enough?  In attacking this question, Trott dispensed with the scanning and computational integration entirely by conceiving a large multielement array of small sources.  As a projector, each element or small source would produce Huygens wavelets.  The elements would be both small enough and widely space enough so that the array would be acoustically transparent. Then there would be no standing waves between the array and the unknown transducer, nor would the near presence of the array affect the radiation impedance of the unknown. The element spacing would still have to be $0.8\lambda$ or less for the array to simulate a uniform plane source. The array would not be rigorously consistent with the Huygens wavelet concept, because it would transmit in two opposite directions. Huygens' principle imposes a directivity function $(1 + \cos \beta)$ on each wavelet source—the same function as used in Eq. (4.4). Such directivity can be designed into a transducer, but practical difficulties outweigh the advantages of a unidirectional array.

An unknown transducer could be placed very close to such an array as shown in Fig. 4.10. The array would simulate an incident plane progressive wave. Conventional measurements then would be made with continuous-wave or pulsed-sound signals with virtually no separation of the array projector and unknown hydrophones. As in the DRL method, the whole electroacoustic system would be linear, passive, and reciprocal, so the direction of signal propagation could be reversed without invalidating the theory or the measurement data. That is, the unknown could transmit and the array receive the acoustic signal.

Returning to the question of how large the array must be so as to simulate the effect of an infinite array on an unknown transducer, we find that various authors show how this can be answered if the hydrophone is small or effectively a point.

Rayleigh's description[12] of Huygens' principle states that a plane wave of infinite extent can be replaced by the area of the first half-wave Fresnel zone $(\pi\lambda x_0)$ with the amplitude attenuated by the factor $1/\pi$, insofar as the effect at a point a distance $x_0$ in front of the plane is concerned.

Stenzel[13] shows that the pressure on the axis of a circular piston source is given by

$$p = \rho c u e^{-jkx} - \rho c u e^{-jk(r_0^2 + x^2)^{1/2}}, \qquad (4.10)$$

where $\rho c$ is the characteristic impedance of the medium, $u$ is the vibration velocity of the source, $r_0$ is the piston radius, and $x$ is the axial distance. The first term on the right-hand side of Eq. (4.10) represents the pressure in an infinite plane wave with velocity amplitude $u$. The second term represents a signal that appears to emanate from the edge of the piston and interferes with the plane-wave component, causing the near-field axial interference. If the edge diffraction or second part could be cancelled out by superimposing an out-of-phase ring source at the piston edge, the axial pressure in the near field would be uniform. A point hydrophone on the axis then would be subject only to the effective plane-wave component.

Uniform sound pressure in the near field on the axis is available directly with two other radiator configurations. von Haselberg and Krautkrämer[14] have shown that a plane circular radiator with the vibration amplitude distributed radially or "shaded" according to a Gaussian function $e^{-r^2}$ produces a constant pressure on

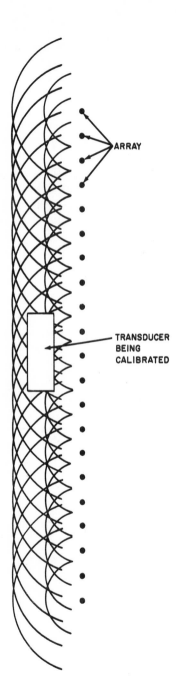

Fig. 4.10. Simulation of a plane progressive wave by an array of point sources.

the axis in the near field. It also has no minor lobes in the far-field pattern. von Haselberg and Krautkrämer point out that the requirements for freedom of the directivity pattern from minor lobes and freedom from undulation in the near field seem to be identical. All evidence supports this relationship between the near-field and far-field patterns, and Trott used this as a guide in developing his array. In particular, this guide identified a line of points with binomial coefficient shading as another type of radiator with a smooth near field. It has been known in radio antenna theory[15] that a line of $n$ point radiators, with half-wavelength spacing, and the source strength of the points set proportional to the coefficients of the binomial expansion $(a + b)^{n-1}$, has a pattern in the plane of the line with no side lobes. It follows, then, that the axial pressure in the near field of such a radiator will be free of undulations. A line source would have two-dimensional spreading even in the near field, of course. The axial pressure would be inversely proportional to the square root of the axial distance rather than constant. To obtain a constant field, the binomial line concept must be extrapolated to a plane source. Unlike the Gaussian radiator that is continuous and infinite, the binomial line is discrete and finite, and a good basis for the real array design discussed in the next section.

All of the theory here has been limited to the near-field pressure at a point or on the axis. The extension of the near-field uniform pressure to a volume large enough to accommodate a sonar transducer was the essence of the Trott array design.

## 4.5 Trott Array Design

The Trott Array design[16,17] is based on a replication of $m$ number of line arrays each consisting of equally spaced points with source strengths (or volume velocities) proportional to the coefficients of the expansion of a binomial of the $n$-th power. To take a simple example, if $n = 2$, the coefficients of the expansion of $(a + b)^2$ are 1,2,1. A line consisting of three point sources, with relative source strengths 1,2,1 and separated by half wavelengths will produce a smooth or non-undulating axial sound pressure and its directivity pattern will not have any side lobes. The pattern from any such binomial shaded line is given by $\cos^n \phi$, where $\phi = (\pi d/\lambda) \sin \theta$, $d$ is the element separation, and $\theta$ is the pattern angle. When $d = \lambda/2$, then $\phi = (\pi/2) \sin \theta$. It can be seen that as $\theta$ varies from 0 to 90°, $\cos \phi$ decreases smoothly from 1 to zero, or the pattern has no side lobes. The function $\cos^n \phi$ also will decrease smoothly from 1 to 0, and the pattern also will be free of side lobes. The function will decrease more rapidly and the beamwidth will become narrower as $n$ increases.

To obtain pressure uniformity in a transverse direction, or off the axis, $m$ number of these basic binomial lines are figuratively placed side by side with the separation $d$. Then, using the acoustic superposition concept, the source strengths at each position are summed as shown in Fig. 4.11, where $m = 6$ is used. The directivity pattern of $m$ uniform points is given by Eq. (2.5) as

$(\sin m\phi)/(m \sin \phi)$. The pattern of the replicated line, according to the Bridge product theorem given in Section 2.11.1, is the product

$$p(\theta) = \frac{\sin m\phi}{m \sin \phi} \cos^n \phi. \tag{4.11}$$

The term $(\sin m\phi)/(m \sin \phi)$ is zero whenever $m\phi = 2\pi, 4\pi, 6\pi, \dots$ . The side lobes as shown in Fig. 2.42 are rather high; consequently, the pattern given by Eq. (4.11) will have side lobes also, but they will be reduced in amplitude by the $\cos^n \phi$ term. This effect is shown for the case $n = 2$, $m = 6$, and $d = \lambda/2$, in Fig. 4.12.

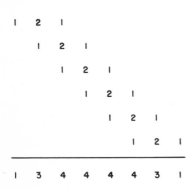

Fig. 4.11. Replication of 6 lines with binomial coefficient shading for the power 2 and summation of the coefficients.

Complete elimination of side lobes is not necessarily the optimal condition for obtaining maximum uniformity in the near field. Figure 4.13 illustrates how small undulations in the axial pressure can provide a larger region of uniform pressure in practice, if small but realistic limits are placed on the uniformity. Trott retained one small side lobe in the pattern, or small undulations in the near-field pressure to extend the limits of his uniform-pressure volume. The extension effect applies to the transverse as well as the axial direction. Optimizing the values of $m$ and $n$, so that the maximum plane-wave region is obtained with the minimum sacrifice in pressure uniformity, is the principal design problem with the Trott array.

The sequence of numbers describing the relative source strengths, as for example 1, 3, 4, 4, 4, 4, 3, 1 in Fig. 4.11, is referred to as Trott's shading function. It usually is normalized to one so that the shading function from Fig. 4.11 would be given as 0.25, 0.75, 1.00, 1.00, 1.00, 1.00, 0.75, 0.25.

The design of a plane array is obtained from the replicated line concept by using the product of a horizontal and a vertical line. With the Trott shading function used as shown in Fig. 4.14, the source strength of each element in a plane array is proportional to the product $[f(x)] [f(y)]$, where $f(x)$ is the shading function value in the horizontal direction and $f(y)$ is the value in the vertical direction.

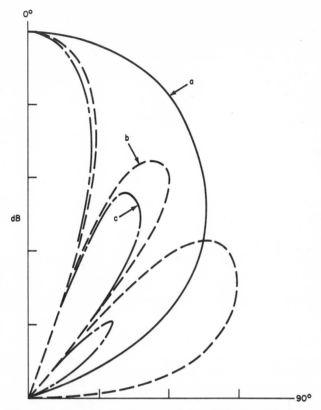

Fig. 4.12. Patterns of radiators consisting of (a) a line of 3 points with half-wavelength spacing and shaded according to 1-2-1 (the binomial coefficients for a power of 2), and with the pattern function $p(\theta) = \cos^2 (\tfrac{1}{2}\pi \sin \theta)$, (b) a line of 6 uniform points with half-wavelength spacing and pattern function

$$p(\theta) = \frac{\sin[6(\tfrac{1}{2}\pi) \sin \theta]}{6 \sin [\tfrac{1}{2}\pi \sin \theta]} ,$$

(c) a line of 8 points with half-wavelength spacing and shaded according to 1-3-4-4-4-4-3-1 (see Fig. 4.11), and with a pattern function equal to the product of (a) and (b).

If $f(x)$ and $f(y)$ were Gaussian functions of the form $e^{-kr^2}$, where $k$ is a constant and $r$ is the radial distance, this would result in an array with circular symmetry of source strength. For a Trott shading function, only approximately circular symmetry is obtained.

From the replicated-line design approach, the width of the uniform pressure volume would be assumed to correspond at least approximately to the width of the array area that was unshaded or had the maximum and constant shading

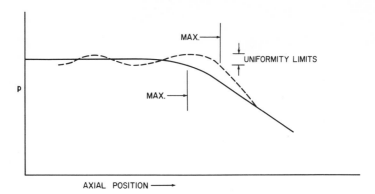

Fig. 4.13. Typical pressure on the axis of a circular piston that has a far-field directivity pattern with no side lobes (solid line) and with small side lobes (dashed line).

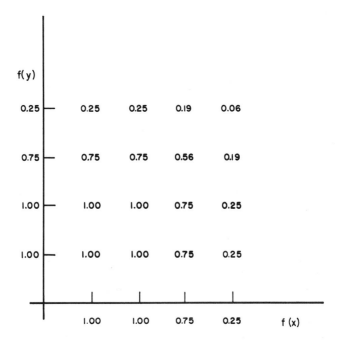

Fig. 4.14. One quadrant of a plane array in which the source strength of each element is proportional to the product $[f(x)] [f(y)]$.

coefficient of 1.00. Experience has shown that if a uniformity criterion of ±1 dB is used, the uniform-pressure region extends outward to the 0.80 shading coefficient position. The width of the unshaded region is given in units of element spacing $d$ by $(m - n)$, provided that $n$ is not too large. For $n = 7$, the smallest binomial coefficient is 1/35th of the largest. For $n = 10$, the smallest is 1/252nd of the largest. These small coefficients make negligible contributions to the constant shading function in the center; consequently, the width of the unshaded region is given by $(m - n)$ or $(m - 10)$, whichever is larger. It does not necessarily follow that $n$ never is larger than 10. The contour of the shading function as it decreases from 1.0 to zero determines how completely the edge diffraction, or second term in Eq. (4.10) is canceled out. Lysanov[18] has shown that for a straightedge, this contour is all important. The contour of the shading function outside of the constant region in the center is a function of $n$ alone (see Fig. 4.11 for example), and the small peripheral binomial coefficients for large values of $n$ can affect the contour.

The depth of the uniform-pressure region generally is greater than the width for any practical case of the Trott array; therefore, the region depth requirement does not affect the design. Trott has found experimentally that the depth is approximately $r^2/\lambda$, where $r$ is as shown in Fig. 4.15.

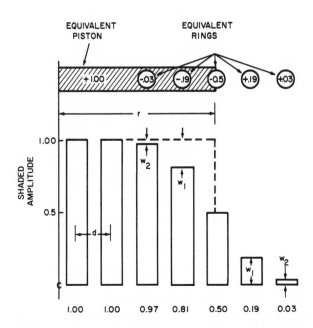

Fig. 4.15. Element shading for $m = 9$ and $n = 5$ and equivalent uniform piston and concentric ring configuration. Numbers in rings are proportional to ring source strength density.

It has been assumed in the concept and design theory up to this point that the element spacing is equal to a half-wavelength. Trott determined the useful bandwidth of an array, as well as the optimal values of $m$ and $n$, by calculating the sound pressure at the center of the array. It was assumed that the maximum variation in sound pressure amplitude in the near field of a circular radiator was on the axis or in the center near the radiator. This assumption is supported by the theory of Stenzel[13] and Lysanov.[18] Trott used the mathematical model illustrated by the drawing in Fig. 4.15 as the basis for his calculation. The array was assumed to be equivalent to a uniform piston radiator with a radius equal to the distance from the center to the element position with a shading value of 0.50, plus a series of concentric ring sources superimposed on this piston. The source strength of the ring was selected so that, where the ring and piston overlapped, the total source strength density was equal to the shading coefficient. For the inner rings, this requires a negative inner ring source strength. In this computational approach, the rings are intended to cancel the edge diffraction from the piston, as was suggested by Eq. (4.10). Trott shows that the normalized pressure at the center for an array where $n$ is odd, $r$ is the piston radius, and $w_n$ is the source strength density of the $n$-th rings, is

$$p = \sin kr + j(\cos \tfrac{1}{2}kd - \cos kr - 4w_1 \sin \tfrac{1}{2}kd \sin kd$$

$$-4w_2 \sin \tfrac{1}{2}kd \sin 2kd - 4w_3 \sin \tfrac{1}{2}kd \sin 3kd - \ldots). \quad (4.12)$$

For $n$ even, $r$ is taken as the radius to the point half way between the elements with the shading value 0.50 on either side, and the pressure is

$$p = \sin kr + j[1 - \cos kr - 4w_1 \sin \tfrac{1}{2}kd \sin (\tfrac{1}{2}kd)$$

$$-4w_2 \sin \tfrac{1}{2}kd \sin 3(\tfrac{1}{2}kd)$$

$$-4w_3 \sin \tfrac{1}{2}kd \sin 5(\tfrac{1}{2}kd) - \ldots]. \quad (4.13)$$

Figure 4.16 shows plots of $p$ computed with Eq. (4.12) for $n = 5$ and several values of $m$. The plot is symmetrical about the idealized value $d = 0.5\lambda$. From curves as in Fig. 4.16, Trott selected optimum values of $m$ and $n$. Figure 4.16 shows, for example, that, among the curves plotted, $m = 9$ gives the maximum bandwidth, if a uniformity limit of $\pm 1$ dB is acceptable.

A more direct approach is possible if one has access to a large computer. The near field of an array can be computed on a point-by-point basis for a variety of values of $m$ and $n$. This has been done,[19] and Fig. 4.17 is typical of some of the results. The computations show that pressure amplitude uniformity within $\pm 5\%$ is attainable over half the width of the array at the low end of the frequency range. Phase measurements generally show phase uniformity within $\pm 5°$ over an area greater than that for amplitude uniformity.

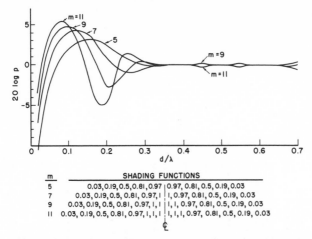

| m | SHADING FUNCTIONS |
|---|---|
| 5 | 0.03, 0.19, 0.5, 0.81, 0.97 $\mid$ 0.97, 0.81, 0.5, 0.19, 0.03 |
| 7 | 0.03, 0.19, 0.5, 0.81, 0.97, 1 $\mid$ 1, 0.97, 0.81, 0.5, 0.19, 0.03 |
| 9 | 0.03, 0.19, 0.5, 0.81, 0.97, 1, 1 $\mid$ 1, 1, 0.97, 0.81, 0.5, 0.19, 0.03 |
| 11 | 0.03, 0.19, 0.5, 0.81, 0.97, 1, 1, 1 $\mid$ 1, 1, 1, 0.97, 0.81, 0.5, 0.19, 0.03 |

Fig. 4.16. Relative sound pressure level at the center of shaded circular-symmetry area arrays, computed from Eq. (4.14).

Trott has determined from experience that (1) the width and height of an array should be twice that of the transducer to be immersed in the near sound field and calibrated, (2) the minimum number of elements is set by the 0.8λ spacing requirement at the highest frequency, (3) the minimum or cutoff shading coefficient, below which peripheral elements can be deleted, is 0.03, and (4) the source strength of the elements half way from the center to the edge should be between 0.94 and 0.98, and the edge of the uniform plane-wave region varies from the position of these elements to those of 0.80 source strength, depending on how "uniformity" and "edge" are defined.

The sequence of steps in selecting a shading function is illustrated by the following example. Suppose it is desired to obtain a uniform plane-wave area 12λ by 12λ. From the upper frequency limit criterion that the element spacing should be $d = 0.8\lambda$, the constant-pressure region or constant-shading function dimension is obtained: $12\lambda/0.8\lambda = 15d$. The total width then will be twice the constant-pressure region, or $30d$. The total width also is given by $m + n$. Thus

$$m + n = 30, \qquad (4.14)$$

and

$$m - n = 15. \qquad (4.15)$$

From these equations, $m$ should be 22 or 23, and $n \geqslant 7$. These actually are rules of thumb, and various combinations near these numbers should be examined as in Figs. 4.16 or 4.17.

axial dist. H= 250.0000 CM OR 10.000 WAVELENGTHS 6 kcps $\lambda$ = 25 cm.
PRESSURE TIMES 10000.000

| | | | | | | | | | | | | | | | | | | | | | | | | |
|---|---|---|---|---|---|---|---|---|---|---|---|---|---|---|---|---|---|---|---|---|---|---|---|---|
| 0 | 0 | 0 | 0 | 0 | 1 | 2 | 2 | 3 | 4 | 4 | 4 | 5 | 5 | 5 | 5 | 5 | 5 | 5 | 5 | 5 | 5 | 5 | 5 | 5 |
| 0 | 0 | 0 | 1 | 2 | 3 | 5 | 7 | 9 | 10 | 11 | 12 | 12 | 12 | 12 | 12 | 12 | 12 | 12 | 12 | 12 | 12 | 12 | 12 | 12 |
| 0 | 0 | 1 | 2 | 5 | 8 | 12 | 17 | 21 | 24 | 27 | 28 | 29 | 29 | 29 | 29 | 29 | 29 | 29 | 29 | 29 | 29 | 29 | 29 | 29 |
| 0 | 1 | 2 | 5 | 10 | 17 | 26 | 35 | 43 | 50 | 55 | 58 | 60 | 60 | 61 | 61 | 61 | 61 | 61 | 61 | 61 | 61 | 61 | 61 | 61 |
| 0 | 2 | 5 | 10 | 19 | 31 | 47 | 63 | 79 | 91 | 101 | 106 | 109 | 110 | 110 | 110 | 110 | 110 | 110 | 110 | 110 | 110 | 110 | 110 | 110 |
| 1 | 3 | 8 | 17 | 31 | 51 | 76 | 103 | 128 | 149 | 164 | 173 | 178 | 179 | 180 | 180 | 180 | 180 | 180 | 180 | 180 | 180 | 180 | 180 | 180 |
| 2 | 5 | 12 | 26 | 47 | 76 | 113 | 153 | 190 | 221 | 243 | 256 | 263 | 265 | 266 | 266 | 266 | 266 | 266 | 266 | 266 | 266 | 266 | 266 | 266 |
| 2 | 7 | 17 | 35 | 63 | 103 | 153 | 206 | 256 | 297 | 327 | 345 | 354 | 358 | 359 | 359 | 358 | 358 | 358 | 359 | 358 | 358 | 358 | 359 | 358 |
| 3 | 9 | 21 | 43 | 79 | 128 | 190 | 256 | 318 | 370 | 407 | 429 | 441 | 445 | 446 | 446 | 446 | 446 | 446 | 446 | 446 | 446 | 446 | 446 | 446 |
| 4 | 10 | 24 | 50 | 91 | 149 | 221 | 297 | 370 | 430 | 473 | 499 | 512 | 517 | 519 | 518 | 518 | 518 | 518 | 518 | 518 | 518 | 518 | 518 | 518 |
| 4 | 11 | 27 | 55 | 101 | 164 | 243 | 327 | 407 | 473 | 520 | 549 | 563 | 569 | 570 | 570 | 570 | 570 | 570 | 570 | 570 | 570 | 570 | 570 | 570 |
| 4 | 12 | 28 | 58 | 106 | 173 | 256 | 345 | 429 | 499 | 549 | 579 | 594 | 600 | 602 | 602 | 601 | 601 | 601 | 602 | 601 | 601 | 601 | 602 | 601 |
| 5 | 12 | 29 | 60 | 109 | 178 | 263 | 354 | 441 | 512 | 563 | 594 | 610 | 616 | 618 | 618 | 617 | 617 | 617 | 617 | 617 | 617 | 617 | 617 | 617 |
| 5 | 12 | 29 | 60 | 110 | 179 | 265 | 358 | 445 | 517 | 569 | 600 | 616 | 622 | 624 | 624 | 623 | 623 | 623 | 623 | 623 | 623 | 623 | 623 | 623 |
| 5 | 12 | 29 | 61 | 110 | 180 | 266 | 359 | 446 | 519 | 570 | 602 | 618 | 624 | 626 | 625 | 625 | 625 | 625 | 625 | 625 | 625 | 625 | 625 | 625 |
| 5 | 12 | 29 | 61 | 110 | 180 | 266 | 359 | 446 | 518 | 570 | 602 | 618 | 624 | 625 | 625 | 625 | 625 | 625 | 625 | 625 | 625 | 625 | 625 | 625 |
| 5 | 12 | 29 | 61 | 110 | 180 | 266 | 358 | 446 | 518 | 570 | 601 | 617 | 623 | 625 | 625 | 625 | 625 | 625 | 625 | 625 | 624 | 625 | 625 | 624 |
| 5 | 12 | 29 | 61 | 110 | 180 | 266 | 358 | 446 | 518 | 570 | 601 | 617 | 623 | 625 | 625 | 625 | 625 | 624 | 625 | 625 | 624 | 625 | 625 | 624 |
| 5 | 12 | 29 | 61 | 110 | 180 | 266 | 358 | 446 | 518 | 570 | 601 | 617 | 623 | 625 | 625 | 625 | 624 | 624 | 625 | 624 | 624 | 624 | 625 | 624 |
| 5 | 12 | 29 | 61 | 110 | 180 | 266 | 359 | 446 | 518 | 570 | 602 | 617 | 623 | 625 | 625 | 625 | 625 | 625 | 625 | 625 | 624 | 625 | 625 | 624 |
| 5 | 12 | 29 | 61 | 110 | 180 | 266 | 358 | 446 | 518 | 570 | 601 | 617 | 623 | 625 | 625 | 625 | 625 | 624 | 625 | 625 | 624 | 625 | 625 | 624 |
| 5 | 12 | 29 | 61 | 110 | 180 | 266 | 358 | 446 | 518 | 570 | 601 | 617 | 623 | 625 | 625 | 624 | 624 | 624 | 624 | 624 | 624 | 624 | 624 | 624 |
| 5 | 12 | 29 | 61 | 110 | 180 | 266 | 358 | 446 | 518 | 570 | 601 | 617 | 623 | 625 | 625 | 625 | 625 | 624 | 625 | 625 | 624 | 625 | 625 | 624 |
| 5 | 12 | 29 | 61 | 110 | 180 | 266 | 359 | 446 | 518 | 570 | 602 | 617 | 623 | 625 | 625 | 625 | 625 | 625 | 625 | 625 | 624 | 625 | 625 | 625 |
| 5 | 12 | 29 | 61 | 110 | 180 | 266 | 358 | 446 | 518 | 570 | 601 | 617 | 623 | 625 | 625 | 624 | 624 | 624 | 624 | 624 | 624 | 624 | 625 | 624 |

Boundary of Region of ±5% Uniformity

Fig. 4.17a. Computed relative pressure in one quadrant of a plane in the near field of the NRL Seneca Lake array. (From reference 19.)

axial dist. H= 250.0000 CM OR    10.000   WAVELENGTHS  
PHASE ANGLE

6 Kc, 8" Spacing  
N = 26, M = 36  
50 x 50 Array

Boundary of Region of Uniformity within 5°

| 253 | 223 | 208 | 195 | 184 | 176 | 171 | 168 | 167 | 166 | 167 | 168 | 169 | 169 | 170 | 170 | 169 | 169 | 170 | 170 | 169 | 170 | 170 | 169 |
|---|---|---|---|---|---|---|---|---|---|---|---|---|---|---|---|---|---|---|---|---|---|---|---|
| 208 | 183 | 166 | 153 | 142 | 135 | 130 | 126 | 125 | 125 | 125 | 126 | 127 | 128 | 128 | 128 | 128 | 128 | 128 | 128 | 128 | 128 | 128 | 128 |
| 195 | 170 | 153 | 139 | 129 | 121 | 116 | 113 | 112 | 111 | 112 | 113 | 114 | 114 | 114 | 114 | 114 | 114 | 114 | 114 | 114 | 114 | 114 | 114 |
| 184 | 160 | 142 | 129 | 119 | 111 | 106 | 103 | 102 | 101 | 102 | 103 | 104 | 104 | 104 | 104 | 104 | 104 | 104 | 104 | 104 | 104 | 104 | 104 |
| 176 | 152 | 135 | 121 | 111 | 103 | 98 | 95 | 94 | 93 | 94 | 95 | 96 | 96 | 96 | 96 | 96 | 96 | 96 | 96 | 96 | 96 | 96 | 96 |
| 171 | 147 | 130 | 116 | 106 | 98 | 93 | 90 | 89 | 88 | 89 | 90 | 91 | 91 | 91 | 91 | 91 | 91 | 91 | 91 | 91 | 91 | 91 | 91 |
| 168 | 144 | 126 | 113 | 103 | 95 | 90 | 87 | 86 | 85 | 86 | 87 | 88 | 88 | 88 | 88 | 88 | 88 | 88 | 88 | 88 | 88 | 88 | 88 |
| 167 | 143 | 125 | 112 | 101 | 94 | 88 | 85 | 84 | 84 | 84 | 85 | 86 | 87 | 87 | 87 | 87 | 87 | 87 | 87 | 87 | 87 | 87 | 87 |
| 166 | 143 | 125 | 111 | 101 | 93 | 88 | 85 | 84 | 83 | 84 | 85 | 86 | 86 | 86 | 86 | 86 | 86 | 86 | 86 | 86 | 86 | 86 | 86 |
| 167 | 143 | 125 | 112 | 102 | 94 | 89 | 86 | 84 | 84 | 85 | 85 | 86 | 86 | 87 | 87 | 87 | 87 | 87 | 87 | 87 | 87 | 87 | 87 |
| 168 | 144 | 126 | 113 | 102 | 95 | 90 | 86 | 85 | 85 | 85 | 86 | 87 | 88 | 88 | 88 | 88 | 88 | 88 | 88 | 88 | 88 | 88 | 88 |
| 169 | 145 | 127 | 113 | 103 | 95 | 90 | 87 | 85 | 86 | 86 | 87 | 87 | 88 | 88 | 88 | 88 | 88 | 89 | 88 | 88 | 88 | 88 | 88 |
| 169 | 145 | 127 | 114 | 104 | 96 | 91 | 88 | 86 | 86 | 86 | 87 | 88 | 89 | 89 | 89 | 89 | 89 | 89 | 89 | 89 | 89 | 89 | 89 |
| 169 | 145 | 128 | 114 | 104 | 96 | 91 | 88 | 87 | 86 | 87 | 87 | 88 | 89 | 89 | 89 | 89 | 89 | 89 | 89 | 89 | 89 | 89 | 89 |
| 170 | 146 | 128 | 114 | 104 | 96 | 91 | 88 | 87 | 86 | 87 | 88 | 89 | 89 | 89 | 89 | 90 | 89 | 89 | 90 | 90 | 90 | 90 | 89 |
| 170 | 146 | 128 | 114 | 104 | 96 | 91 | 88 | 87 | 86 | 87 | 88 | 89 | 90 | 90 | 90 | 90 | 90 | 90 | 90 | 90 | 90 | 90 | 90 |
| 169 | 146 | 128 | 114 | 104 | 96 | 91 | 88 | 88 | 86 | 88 | 88 | 89 | 89 | 89 | 89 | 89 | 89 | 89 | 89 | 89 | 89 | 89 | 89 |
| 169 | 146 | 128 | 114 | 104 | 96 | 91 | 88 | 88 | 87 | 88 | 88 | 89 | 90 | 89 | 89 | 89 | 90 | 89 | 89 | 89 | 89 | 89 | 89 |
| 170 | 146 | 128 | 114 | 104 | 96 | 91 | 90 | 88 | 87 | 88 | 88 | 89 | 90 | 90 | 90 | 90 | 90 | 90 | 90 | 90 | 90 | 90 | 90 |
| 170 | 146 | 128 | 114 | 104 | 96 | 91 | 89 | 88 | 87 | 88 | 89 | 89 | 90 | 90 | 90 | 90 | 90 | 90 | 90 | 90 | 90 | 90 | 90 |
| 169 | 146 | 128 | 114 | 104 | 96 | 91 | 89 | 88 | 88 | 88 | 89 | 89 | 90 | 90 | 90 | 89 | 89 | 89 | 89 | 89 | 89 | 89 | 89 |
| 170 | 146 | 128 | 114 | 104 | 96 | 91 | 89 | 88 | 88 | 88 | 89 | 89 | 90 | 90 | 90 | 90 | 90 | 90 | 90 | 90 | 90 | 90 | 90 |
| 170 | 146 | 128 | 114 | 104 | 96 | 91 | 89 | 88 | 88 | 88 | 89 | 89 | 90 | 90 | 90 | 90 | 90 | 90 | 90 | 90 | 90 | 90 | 90 |
| 169 | 146 | 128 | 114 | 104 | 96 | 91 | 89 | 88 | 88 | 88 | 89 | 89 | 89 | 89 | 89 | 89 | 89 | 89 | 89 | 89 | 89 | 89 | 89 |

Fig. 4.17b. Computed relative phase of sound pressure in one quadrant of a plane in the near field of the NRL Seneca Lake array. (From reference 19.)

The shading functions are conveniently available from tables of the partial sums of the binomial probability distribution for $r$ occurrences in $n$ independent trials when the probability in any single trial is ½.

The $n$ in these tables corresponds to the binomial power $n$ used in array design. The $r$ corresponds to the shading function term, with the largest $r$ corresponding to the smallest term. For example, from pages 199 and 200 of reference 20 for a probability of 0.50, and $n - 5$, the five terms are given as 0.03125, 0.1875, 0.5000, 0.8125, and 0.9687. When these numbers are rounded off to two significant figures, the results are as shown in Fig. 4.16. As noted previously, this part of the shading function is independent of $m$.

Figure 4.18 shows the first near-field array designed by Trott, the USRD type H33-6. It consisted of 140 capped PZT-4 ceramic cylinders, each ½ in. in diameter, ½ in. long, and 1/8 in. wall thickness. The cylinders were spaced 10 cm apart in oil-filled tygon plastic tubes, also spaced 10 cm apart. The elements are electrically connected in parallel, and shading is provided by series-connected capacitors functioning as voltage dividers. The acoustical resonance frequency is 70 kHz—well above the 4-12 kHz range in which the array is used. The ceramic elements thus function as electrical capacitors and mechanical springs. The array is 112 cm square and mounted between wire screens for electrical shielding. The four corner elements of the square were deleted. The shading is based on $m = 9$ and $n = 5$, selected on the basis of Fig. 4.16. Figure 4.19 is a sound field contour map of the measured relative pressure amplitude in the near field at the center frequency. The width of the uniform pressure region is 60 to 70 cm, whereas the unshaded dimensions of the array, given by $(m - n)$, is only four spaces or 40 cm. Part of this extended field is due to the somewhat arbitrary definition of uniformity. The element shaded by 0.97 is within 0.5 dB of 1.00 and one would for this reason expect uniformity within ±0.5 dB to extend beyond the unshaded element positions. The width of the region uniform within ±1 dB extends to about the position of the 0.80 shaded element. A second reason for the extended uniform field is the effect illustrated by Fig. 4.13—that is, the deliberate inclusion of small far-field pattern side lobes or small near-field pressure undulations.

Figure 4.20 and Table 4.1 show calibration data obtained with the H33-6 array and with conventional far-field techniques. The near-field data actually appear more consistent and reasonable than the far-field data. Both Baker and Trott came to have more confidence in their near-field measurements than they did in far-field measurements.

Figure 4.21 shows Trott's second array, USRD type H33-10. It consisted of 21 vertical and parallel lines. Each line was 10 ft long with 26 elements 4½ in. apart.

The shading was based on $m = 11$ and $n = 5$. Vertical shading is designed into the elements in each line, and horizontal shading is applied to the complete lines. The separation between lines is adjustable, and this provides some adjustment of the frequency range for transducers, such as a horizontal line, that are wide but

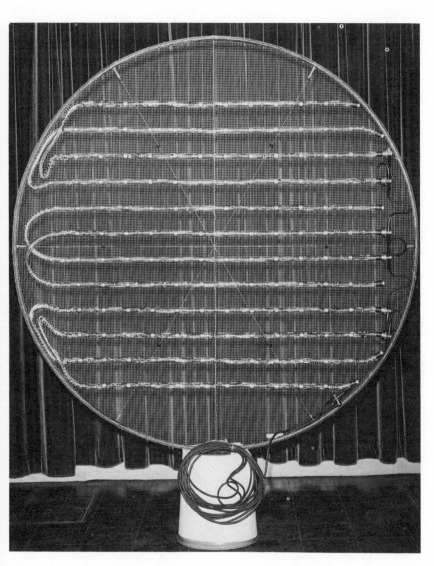

Fig. 4.18.  Trott near-field array type H33-6.

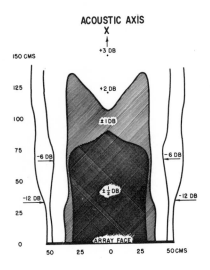

Fig. 4.19. Near sound field of the H33-6 array at 8 kHz.

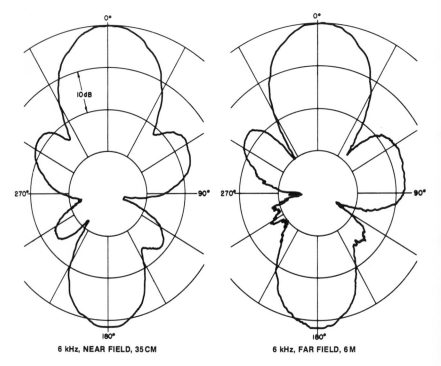

6 kHz, NEAR FIELD, 35 CM                    6 kHz, FAR FIELD, 6 M

Fig. 4.20. Directivity patterns measured on the same transducer by far-field and near-field methods.

Table 4.1.  Free-field voltage sensitivity (in dB *re* 1 V/μbar) of cylindrical transducer measured through beam-forming network.

| Freq. (kHz) | Measured in far field | | Measured in near field | |
|:---:|:---:|:---:|:---:|:---:|
| | Meas. 1 | Meas. 2 | Meas. 1 | Meas. 2 |
| 6 | −120.5 | −119.7 | −121.1 | −121.0 |
| 7 | −117.1 | −115.8 | −116.9 | −116.9 |
| 8 | −112.0 | −110.8 | −111.8 | −112.0 |
| 9 | −106.9 | −105.3 | −106.3 | −106.5 |
| 10 | −101.1 | −99.6 | −100.6 | 101.1 |
| 11 | −95.0 | −93.2 | −94.4 | −95.3 |
| 12 | −89.1 | −87.6 | −88.9 | −89.7 |
| 13 | −95.7 | −94.7 | −97.0 | −97.2 |

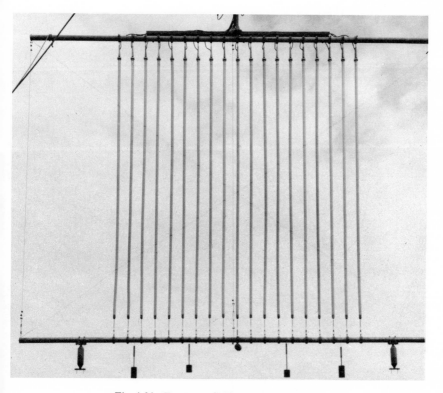

Fig. 4.21.  Trott near-field array type H33-10.

not high. The useful frequency range is 1.5 to 10 kHz. The near-field pressure is uniform 5 ft in the vertical direction, and 4 to 14 ft in the horizontal direction, depending on the line separation. Some design details of the elements and lines are shown in Figs. 4.22 and 4.23. Where the shading coefficients were near to 1.00 and very large series capacitors would be needed, shading was accomplished instead by removing part of the electrodes on the ceramic elements. (More design detail is available in reference 17.)

Figure 4.24 shows a very large near-field array designed for calibrating large sonar transducers at the Lake Seneca Facility of the Naval Research Laboratory.

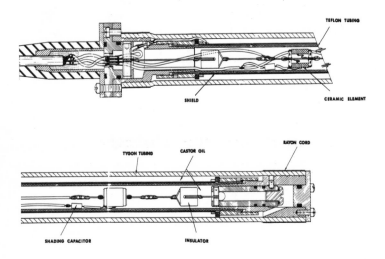

Fig. 4.22. Construction details of near-field array line transducer type H33-10.

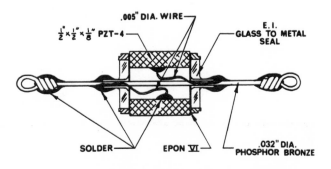

Fig. 4.23. Construction details of element type H33-10.

This array, designed by Hanish[19] after the technique of Trott, contains 2500 elements in a 50 × 50 configuration, with 8-in. spacing covering an area 33 ft square. A shading function based on $m = 37$ and $n = 49$ was used. The uniform-pressure region has been measured as approximately 19 ft in diameter and 40 ft in axial depth at 3.5 kHz. The useful frequency range is 1 to 6 kHz.

Fig. 4.24. Hanish near-field array for the NRL Lake Seneca Facility.

## 4.6  Calibration Methodology

The DRL method requires the use of a calibrated probe hydrophone for a direct measurement of the pressure amplitude and phase. These are inserted into Eq. (4.4) as $p(Q)$ in the form $|p|e^{-j\theta}$, where $\theta$ is the phase angle in radians. The phase angle is measured against an arbitrary reference signal. To avoid errors caused by instability in the electronic oscillator that generates the transducer signal, the reference phase signal should be the input signal into the transducer. In addition to $|p|e^{j\theta}$, various dimensions and angles must be measured to obtain $\beta$ and $r$ in Eq. (4.4). The value of $r$ cannot be approximated as a constant in a phase term like $e^{-jkr}$. The speed of sound and the frequency must be known to obtain the wave number $k = \omega/c$. The computation with Eq. (4.4) yields the far-field transmitted sound pressure in absolute terms so that the source level or transmitting response can be determined, or in relative terms so that a directivity pattern can be drawn. (Source level is a measure of the output pressure of a sonar projector at the distance one meter without reference to a projector input parameter like voltage or current.)

The electroacoustic system used in the DRL method can be linear, passive, and reciprocal. Theoretically, the scanning probe could be a calibrated projector and the unknown transducer could be the hydrophone. Equation (4.4) could be modified to yield a free-field voltage response. This technique is not used because of practical difficulties in obtaining and using a calibrated probe projector. In any case, it would be easier to verify that the unknown transducer is reciprocal in some other independent measurement, and then compute the free-field voltage sensitivity from the transmitting current response and the spherical-wave reciprocity parameter.

The methodology for the use of the Trott array is essentially the same as that for conventional measurements discussed in Sections 2.2.1 and 2.2.2. The free-field voltage sensitivity $M_s$ of an unknown transducer is obtained by a simple comparison calibration. The Trott array is used as a projector. The unknown and a calibrated standard hydrophone are immersed, in turn, in the uniform plane progressive wave in the near field of the array. Then,

$$M_x = \left(\frac{M_H}{e_H}\right)e_x, \qquad (4.16)$$

where $M_H$ is the free-field voltage sensitivity of the standard, and $e_H$ and $e_x$ are the open-circuit output voltages of the standard and the unknown, respectively. If the unknown transducer is large and the standard hydrophone is small, $e_H$ should be measured at several positions in the array near field and an average used. Repetitive averaging can be avoided by establishing a near-field plane-wave transmitting current response $S_A$ of the Trott array by probing the near field with a standard hydrophone of sensitivity $M_H$.

$$S_A = \frac{\left(\frac{e_H}{M_H}\right)}{i_A},$$ (4.17)

where $i_A$ is the input current to the array. Then, if the array is used as a standard projector,

$$M_x = \frac{e_x}{i_A S_A}.$$ (4.18)

If the unknown transducer is reciprocal, its transmitting current response $S_x$ can be obtained by measuring $M_x$ and computing $S_x$ from the conventional spherical-wave reciprocity relation $M_x/S_x = J_s = 2d\lambda/\rho c$ (see Fig. 3.70). As in conventional reciprocity measurements, the reciprocity check discussed in Section 2.3 can be used to determine whether the unknown transducer is reciprocal. That is, the unknown can be driven with current $i_x$ and the array output voltage $e_A$ measured. Then, if $e_A/i_x = e_x/i_A$, both transducers are reciprocal.

If a nonreciprocal source is being calibrated, the transmitting current response $S_x$ is obtained from Trott's equation[17]

$$S_x = \frac{e_A}{i_x S_A J_s}.$$ (4.19)

The product $S_A J_s$ is equivalent to an array receiving sensitivity that can be mathematically defined as $M_A = S_A J_s$. Equation (4.19) then would become

$$S_x = \frac{\left(\frac{e_A}{M_A}\right)}{i_x}$$ (4.20)

and have the same form as Eq. (4.17). The array then would be used as a standard hydrophone with sensitivity $M_A$. Trott stopped short of this step because the verbal definition of $M_A$ is awkard and might cause confusion rather than clarification. The verbal definition of $M_A$ is: The ratio of the open-circuit output voltage of the array to the far-field sound pressure, apparent at one meter, emanating from a source located within the plane-wave near-field region of the array.

From the foregoing it is evident that after the Trott array is designed and built, $S_A$ is measured, and $S_A J_s$ or $M_A$ is computed, the calibration methodology is the same as for conventional far-field measurements. This is a major advantage of the Trott array method.

An option of the Trott array technique is available for unknown transducers of negligible width—that is, points or lines. If the Trott array is reduced to a single shaded line, it will transmit uniform cylindrical waves in the near field. The pressure in the near field will be uniform along a line parallel to the shaded line, and will decrease at the rate 3 dB per double-distance in the direction of the axis of the line projector. A small or "point" hydrophone or a line hydrophone oriented parallel to the shaded line projector will be subject to uniform sound pressure. This arrangement will discriminate against interfering reflections from the top and bottom, if the line is vertical, more than it will against reflections from boundaries in the sideways direction. Directivity patterns cannot be measured with the single line projector, so the technique is limited to sensitivity measurements on point or line hydrophones. The near-field transmitting current response $S_L$ of the shaded line is measured by probing the near field with a calibrated hydrophone. Unlike $S_A$, $S_L$ is a function of the distance from the projector, and a reference distance must be specified. Departures from the reference distance must be accounted for by a 3-dB-per-double-distance correction. Except for the distance specification, Eqs. (4.16), (4.17), and (4.18) can be used, if $S_L$ and $i_L$ are substituted for $S_A$ and $i_A$. Point and line transducers usually are reciprocal and their transmitting responses can be obtained from the computation $S_x = M_x/J_s$.

### 4.7  Applications and Limitations

The near-field method of calibrating, testing, and evaluating transducers has various limitations. The usefulness of the method in general and the choice between the DRL technique or Trott array in particular depends to a large extent on the applications of the measurements and the relative importance of the limitations. Research and development measurements in a laboratory, quality control measurements in a factory, and post-repair measurements in shipyards, for example, have quite different requirements. The factors affecting the choice of a near-field method are discussed in the paragraphs that follow.

The practice of both the DRL and Trott array methods includes certain approximations. One, that points separated by 0.8λ or less approximate a continuous plane, is common to both methods. Others apply to only one of the two methods.

The assumption that the pressure and pressure gradient are related by Eq. (4.2) has been cited as the weakest link in the DRL method. It may be the reason for some of the errors in pattern measurements at angles well off the main beam. More important, the method itself provides no clue as to the magnitude of any errors due to the approximation of Eq. (4.2).

The Trott array method also contains approximations like the assumption of circular symmetry. However, the Trott array design can be tested by probing and mapping the near field. The magnitude of errors due to approximations or design and construction imperfections therefore can be measured. For example, the 33-ft lines used in the array shown in Fig. 4.24 were designed originally as three 11-ft lines connected together. Even though the connecting flanges were small and designed to be acoustically invisible, they perturbed the sound field. The reason never was ascertained, but a change to single continuous 33-ft lines removed the perturbation.

The near-field method was developed primarily to save space, and this is the major and general advantage of the method. The need to save space arises from two requirements. The first, discussed in Sections 3.2 and 4.1, relates to minimizing interference from the boundaries of small bodies of water. The second relates to the importance of maintaining a known relative orientation and spacing between the projector and the hydrophone in any electroacoustic measurement. At large and deep inland lakes or ocean sites, floating platforms must be used to support the transducers. If full advantage of the potentially good free-field conditions is to be realized, the transducers must be fairly far from the surface. In practice, this usually means depths of 100 ft or more. Then, if projector-to-hydrophone separations of 100 ft or more are used, it becomes very difficult to maintain a fixed orientation of hydrophone with respect to projector. The instability of the platform and the medium and the nonrigidity of mechanical linkages can cause significant errors in the relative positions of the projector and hydrophone. These errors are minimized by suspending the projector and hydrophone together as one integrated unit. The shorter the projector-to-hydrophone separation is, the more feasible and effective such a suspension becomes. For this, a near-field method and arrangement then has an obvious application.

Both near-field methods save considerable amounts of space. The DRL method has a small advantage in this respect over the Trott array. The integrating surface in the DRL method can be wrapped closely around the unknown transducer, whereas the Trott array is a plane surface about twice the width of the unknown transducer. There is no theoretical reason why Trott arrays must be plane, but this is as far as the current theory and practice have been carried.

The DRL method pays for its space-saving advantage with less configurational flexibility. That is, transducers of different shapes require different integrating surfaces, if the surface is to be wrapped closely around the transducer. A Trott array accommodates any transducer shape. The integrating surface of the DRL method has been likened to a raincoat; that of the Trott array method, to an umbrella.

The near-field method is most useful for calibrating large transducers in the 1 to 10 kHz frequency range. The high-frequency limit is set by the 0.8λ separation of Trott array elements or DRL probe positions. Also, the array elements or DRL probe hydrophone must be small enough so that they are acoustically invisible (maximum dimensions of about 0.1λ). The near-field technique could be used at low ultrasonic frequencies, but there is little advantage at these frequencies over other methods.

There is no low-frequency limit to the method itself. Below 1 kHz, however, directional transducers become gigantic, and both the DRL scanning mechanism and the Trott array would have to be correspondingly large. However, with wavelengths of 5 ft and longer, the probe or array element position separations become large and need not be very exact. This, in turn, would allow more flexibility in the scanning system or array design.

The DRL probe scanning arrangement probably is more easily adjusted to different dimensions than the Trott array is, and therefore has more flexible frequency limitations.

The Trott array produces a direct read-out in essentially real time. It is compatible with conventional measurements. Once the array itself is available, no other special equipment or personnel training is necessary.

The measurements and computations of the DRL method are sequential. The output thus is not immediately available. However, the sequential technique provides a point-by-point examination of the sound field that is useful for diagnostic purposes.

The DRL method is very specialized in that it is completely different from conventional techniques and requires special procedures and personnel. Where flexibility is important, this is a disadvantage. Where measurements and transducer configurations are repetitive, flexibility is not important, and no disadvantage obtains.

Scanning by the DRL probe requires more complicated mechanical engineering than the mere rotation of the unknown transducer. Such scanning presents some mechanical engineering problems when it must be remotely controlled, as in a closed high-pressure tank or at the end of a long suspension.

The DRL method requires initial major investments in the mechanical design and construction of the probe scanning system, a modest amount of electronic signal-generating and measuring equipment, and the programming and use of an electronic computer. All are matters of relatively conventional mechanical and electronic engineering, and computer technology.

The Trott array also requires a modest amount of conventional electronic equipment. But this would already be available in a conventional calibration facility. The main investment is in the design and construction of the array itself, which is an uncommon and sophisticated transducer engineering task.

In summary, the DRL method has the advantages of minimum space, frequency range flexibility, applicability to repetitive measurements, capability for sound field diagnosis, and conventional engineering. The Trott array has the advantages of direct read-out, transducer configuration flexibility, testing of theoretical approximations, compatibility with conventional measurements, and suitability for remote control.

# REFERENCES

1.  M. Lax and H. Feshbach, "On the Radiation Problem at High Frequencies," J. Acoust. Soc. Am. 19, 682 (1947).

2.  P. M. Morse and H. Feshbach, *Methods of Theoretical Physics* (McGraw-Hill Book Co., Inc., New York, 1953), Part I, Chap. 7.

3.  B. B. Baker and E. T. Copson, *The Mathematical Theory of Huygens' Principle* (Clarendon Press, Oxford, 1950), 2nd ed., pp. 20-38.

4.  J. Pachner, "On the Dependence of Directivity Patterns on the Distance from the Emitter," J. Acoust. Soc. Am. 28, 86 (1956).

5.  C. W. Horton and G. S. Innis, Jr., "The Computation of Far-Field Radiation Patterns from Measurements Made Near the Source," J. Acoust. Soc. Am. 33, 877 (1961).

6.  C. W. Horton, "Acoustic Impedance of an Outgoing Cylindrical Wave," J. Acoust. Soc. Am. 34, 1663 (1962).

7.  D. D. Baker, "Determination of Far-Field Characteristics of Large Underwater Sound Transducers from Near-Field Measurements," J. Acoust. Soc. Am. 34, 1737 (1962).

8.  W. J. Trott, "Transducer Calibration from Near-Field Data," Navy Underwater Sound Reference Laboratory Research Report No. 55, 6 Oct 1961 [AD-265 449].

9.  W. J. Trott and R. J. Bobber, "Transducer Calibration from Near-Field Data," Paper K33, Fourth International Congress on Acoustics, Copenhagen (1962).

10. A. O. Williams, Jr., "The Piston Source at High Frequencies," J. Acoust. Soc. Am. 23, 1 (1951).

11. H. Seki, A. Granato, and R. Truell, "Diffraction Effects in the Ultrasonic Field of a Piston Source and Their Importance in the Accurate Measurement of Attenuation," J. Acoust. Soc. Am. 28, 230 (1956).

12. Lord Rayleigh, *Theory of Sound* (McMillan & Co. Ltd., London, 1926), 2nd ed., Sec. 283.

13. H. Stenzel, *Leitfaden zur Berechnung von Schallvorgängen* (Julius-Springer Verlag, Berlin, 1939). English translation by A. R. Stickley, *Handbook for the Calculation of Sound Propagation Phenomena*, Naval Research Laboratory Translation No. 130, Part 2, Sec. 4.

14. K. von Haselberg and J. Krautkrämer, "Ein ultraschall Strahler für die Werkstoffprüfung mit verbessertem Nahfeld," Acustica 9, 359 (1959).

15. J. D. Kraus, *Antennas* (McGraw-Hill Book Co., Inc., New Yrok, 1950).

16. W. J. Trott, "Underwater-Sound-Transducer Calibration from Nearfield Data," J. Acoust. Soc. Am. 36, 1557 (1964).

17. W. J. Trott and I. D. Groves, "Application of the Near-Field Array Technique to Sonar Evaluation," Naval Research Laboratory Report 6734, 20 May 1968 [AD-669 433].

18. Yu.P. Lysanov, "The Edge Effect in a Large Radiator," Sov. Phys–Acoust. 10, 165 (1964); translated from Akusticheskii Zhurnal 10, 202 (1964).

19. S. Hanish, M. A. Blizard, and R. A. Matzner, "Design of a Plane-Wave, Near-Field Calibration Array," Naval Research Laboratory Memorandum Report 1565, 2 Sep 1964.

20. National Bureau of Standards, Applied Mathematics Series 6, *Tables of the Binomial Probability Distribution* (U.S. Government Printing Office, Washington, 1950).

# Chapter V

# MEASUREMENT TRANSDUCERS

## 5.1 Introduction

To select the right transducers for a measurement, the user must know the basic characteristics of the various available types and the advantages and limitations of each. After the general type has been chosen, he must know how this particular type of transducer will operate under the conditions that it will be subjected to. Too often a novice will attribute characteristics to a transducer that are not warranted. A calibrated standard hydrophone, for example, cannot be compared with other calibrated measuring instruments like thermometers, clocks, voltmeters, or barometers in either accuracy or stability. Often, the ranges of frequency, hydrostatic pressure, and temperature in which a hydrophone is used are quite large. A calibration is valid only within specified ranges of these variables, and the sensitivity usually cannot be extrapolated. Failure to understand the directional characteristics of transducers also is common among novices, who often will assume that a transducer is omnidirectional.

Measurement transducers consist of (1) standard hydrophones, (2) sound sources or projectors, and (3) other specialized transducers.

The primary requirements of a standard are stability and linearity. The sensitivity of an ideal standard hydrophone would be independent of time, frequency, and the environmental conditions—particularly hydrostatic pressure and temperature. A sensitivity that is independent of direction or orientation sometimes is desirable, but at other times, it is not. In practice, a period of one year, a frequency bandwidth of 2 decades, and stability within ±1 dB for pressures to a few thousand psi and temperatures between 0 and 40°C are possible. The linearity of standard hydrophones is limited more by associated amplifiers and transformers than by the electroacoustic generator.

The function of a projector usually is merely to produce a useful and controllable sound field in the medium. In calibration measurements, as in commercial audio engineering, high fidelity is desirable. That is, the transmitting response should be uniform in a wide band of frequencies. Efficiency is of secondary importance. Stability over a period of one measurement—say only a few days—is necessary.

227

Special measurement transducers are those designed to meet some special purpose. Pressure-gradient hydrophones or dipole projectors, for example, have patterns that are particularly useful in some measurements (see Section 2.12). When very high sensitivity or response is needed, it can be obtained at the expense of the wide bandwidth by using resonant transducers. High projector response also can be obtained, if linearity is sacrificed. A very important class of specialized transducers are those known to conform to the electroacoustic reciprocity theorem (see Section 2.3).

Since the Fessenden oscillator[1] produced continuous acoustic signals early in this century, thousands of underwater sound transducers have been invented, sometimes discarded, and sometimes reinvented. The widely ranging requirements for transducers in underwater acoustics and the development of new materials have prompted myriad designs through the years.

Practically all the measurement transducers in common use today are of the piezoelectric crystal or ceramic, magnetostrictive, and moving-coil types. Variable-reluctance, electrostatic, hydrostatic, mechanical and electrical motor, spark, pneumatic, electrokinetic, and electronic transducers all have been used for generating or receiving sound in water, but rarely are they used as standards, and they are not considered as such here.

## 5.2 Sensitivity and Response versus Frequency

The principal difference between measurement transducers and others used for navigation, communication, target location, and so forth is in the response or sensitivity-versus-frequency characteristic. Very wide band response is of major importance in measurement transducers. Some hydrophones have bandwidths of as much as 4 decades! The term bandwidth does not have a precise meaning when applied to measurement transducers, as it does in connection with filters. It generally means the useful frequency range.

The useful frequency range is determined by (a) the response or sensitivity level, (b) the electrical impedance of the transducers, (c) the mechanical limitations of the transducer, and (d) the contour of the response or sensitivity-versus-frequency curve. Limitations (a) and (b) are related to each other and to the conditions of measurement—particularly the acoustic and electrical noise levels. Consequently, these limitations are flexible, and there are no simple rules for minimum useful response, maximum useful impedance, and so forth. It can be noted, however, that a free-field voltage sensitivity of −120 dB referred to one volt per microbar is very low, and a sensitivity of −140 dB usually is too low to be useful in conventional electroacoustic measurements.

A satisfactory response level alone does not insure the usefulness of a projector. Piezoelectric projectors in particular are limited at low frequencies by the high electric impedance. The voltage necessary to drive a current of a few milliamperes through a small crystal array, for example, may be so high that arcing occurs.

In other projectors, the elastic or linear limits of the electroacoustic material or such mechanical parts as springs may be exceeded at signal levels necessary to produce useful pressure levels.

Limitation (d) is one that can be examined in detail. The theoretical sensitivities and responses of measurement transducers generally are known functions or frequency. That is, the general contour of the sensitivity-versus-frequency curve (or response) is predictable; however, the fine structure of the curve is affected by spurious resonances, reflections, and diffraction effects, and by real conditions that fail to approximate theoretical assumptions closely. Rigid boundaries is one common example of the latter.

The analog circuits shown in Fig. 5.1 can be used to analyze hydrophone sensitivity as a function of frequency for simple and idealized cases. Several important simplifying assumptions are used. It is assumed that the vibrating elements are equivalent, mechanically, to a single damped spring and mass. In practice this means that in an array all the elements are identical, and that all dimensions of the elements are small in comparison with a wavelength of sound in the element material and in water. The latter is a "lumped-parameter," as opposed to a "distributed-parameter," assumption. It is assumed also that the transducer is small enough so that the radiation, or water load, impedance can be neglected—that is, the characteristics of the medium do not influence the vibratory motion. At low frequencies, the radiation impedance consists of a resistance and mass. Neither of these is a constant, and they cannot be combined with the constant $R$ and $m$ in Fig. 5.1.

The analog circuit of a piezoelectric hydrophone is shown in Fig. 5.1a and of a moving-coil or magnetostrictive hydrophone in Fig. 5.1b. The two circuits are different because of the inherent difference between the two transduction principles.

It is evident from Fig. 5.1a that for piezoelectric hydrophones,

$$\frac{e_{oc}}{p} = \frac{\phi A}{j\omega C_e \phi^2 Z_m + 1}.$$                                  (5.1)

At all frequencies except perhaps near resonance, $\omega C_e \phi^2 Z_m \gg 1$, and the sensitivity is inversely proportional to $\omega Z_m$. Figure 5.2a is a plot of Eq. (5.1). At low frequencies, where $1/j\omega C \gg (R + j\omega m)$, the sensitivity is constant. At the resonant frequency, where $j\omega m = 1/j\omega C$, the sensitivity peaks. Above resonance, where $j\omega m \gg (R + 1/j\omega C)$, the sensitivity rapidly falls off with a slope inversely proportional to the square of the frequency. About an octave above resonance, the assumption of a lumped-parameter system no longer is valid, and a distributed-parameter or transmission-line analysis must be used. Above resonance, the curves go through a series of resonances and antiresonances, and for this reason hydrophones are not suitable for use as standards above resonance.

From consideration of reciprocity, it can be shown that the transmitting current response curve will have the same contour as the free-field voltage sensitivity

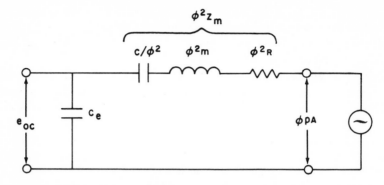

Fig. 5.1a. Analog circuit of a small piezoelectric hydrophone; $e_{oc}$ is the open-circuit voltage, $p$ is the acoustic pressure, $C_e$ is the electrical blocked capacitance, $C$ is the short-circuit compliance, $m$ is the effective mass, $R$ is the mechanical resistance, $\phi$ is the electromechanical voltage/force conversion factor, $Z_m$ is the mechanical impedance, and $A$ is the diaphragm area.

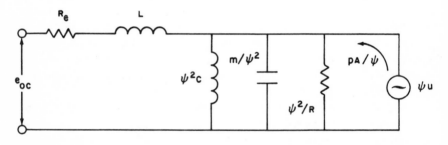

Fig. 5.1b. The analog circuit of a small moving-coil or magnetostrictive hydrophone; $e_{oc}$ is the open-circuit voltage, $p$ is the acoustic pressure, $u$ is the diaphragm velocity, $R_e$ is the electrical resistance, $L$ is the blocked inductance, $C$ is the open-circuit compliance, $m$ is the effective mass, $R$ is the mechanical resistance, $\psi$ is the electromechanical voltage/velocity conversion factor, and $A$ is the diaphragm area.

except that it will have a 6-dB-per-octave greater slope, or be proportional to an additional power of frequency. Consequently, a typical transmitting response curve for a piezoelectric projector will look like the dashed line of Fig. 5.2a.

It is evident also from Fig. 5.1b that

$$\frac{e_{oc}}{p} = \frac{\psi A}{\left(\dfrac{1}{j\omega C}\right) + j\omega m + R} = \frac{\psi A}{Z_m}. \tag{5.2}$$

Thus, for moving-coil and magnetostrictive hydrophones, the sensitivity $e_{oc}/p$ is inversely proportional to the mechanical impedance. Figure 5.2b is a plot of

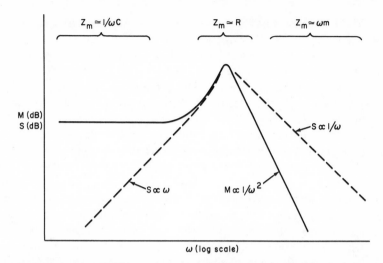

Fig. 5.2a. Piezoelectric transducer; free-field voltage sensitivity $M = e_{oc}/p$ (solid line) and transmitting current response $S$ (dashed line) as a function of angular frequency.

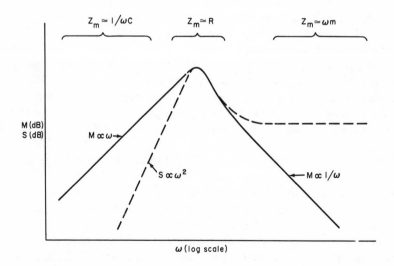

Fig. 5.2b. Moving-coil and magnetostrictive transducer; free-field voltage sensitivity $M$ (solid line) and transmitting current response $S$ (dashed line) as a function of angular frequency.

Eq. (5.2). Comparing Figs. 5.2a and 5.2b shows that the curves in the latter have an additional 6-dB-per-octave slope.

From Fig. 5.1, it can be seen that the best way to obtain a frequency-independent sensitivity—that is, one with a flat curve—is to use a piezoelectric element below its resonant frequency. This is one reason why wide-range hydrophones contain small piezoelectric generators with high resonant frequencies.

From Fig. 5.2, it would seem evident also that the best way to obtain a frequency-independent transmitting current response would be to use a moving-coil or magnetostrictive transducer above its resonant frequency. This is a valid conclusion for a moving coil, but not for a magnetostrictive transducer. In these curves, it has been assumed that the transducer elements are of dimensions small in comparison with a wavelength in water. Thus, to obtain the flat response characteristic, one needs a projector that is small and that resonates at low frequencies. Moving-coil transducers can be built with diaphragms a few inches in diameter and with resonant frequencies of about 100 Hz, where the wavelength in water is 50 ft. Magnetostrictive transducers, like piezoelectric transducers, are what Woollett[2] calls "body force" transducers, in which the electromechanical forces are generated throughout the material. Consequently, such transducers resonate at frequencies that are inversely proportional to the transducer size. Despite various design innovations, it still is not possible to build resonant magnetostrictive transducers that are very small and also resonate at very low frequencies.

At ultrasonic frequencies, piezoelectric or magnetostrictive projectors are most feasible. Comparing piezoelectric and magnetostrictive transducer transmitting current response curves below resonance in Figs. 5.2a and 5.2b shows that the piezoelectric type is the more nearly constant with frequency. Consequently, in practice, moving-coil projectors are used at audio frequencies and piezoelectric at ultrasonic frequencies.

The electrical impedance of a piezoelectric transducer decreases, and the impedance of a moving-coil or magnetostrictive transducer increases, with increasing frequency. Therefore, the slope of the transmitting voltage response curve of the piezoelectric projector will be greater than in Fig. 5.2a, and the slope of the moving-coil or magnetostrictive curve will be less than in Fig. 5.2b. See, for example, Fig. 5.31.

Real calibration curves seldom look like the idealized curves in Fig. 5.2. The dashed lines in Fig. 5.3 illustrate some of the more common effects on the free-field voltage sensitivity of a piezoelectric hydrophone. The resonant peak is damped by the electrical, mechanical, or acoustical resistance. Spurious resonances may appear. At some very low frequency, the capacitive reactance of the crystals or ceramics will become larger than the resistivity of, or the leakage resistance around, the crystal. The time constant of the RC circuit will be shorter than the fundamental period of the signal, and the charge on the electrodes will leak off faster than the instantaneous signal amplitude changes. This causes a 6-dB-per-octave roll-off of the sensitivity.

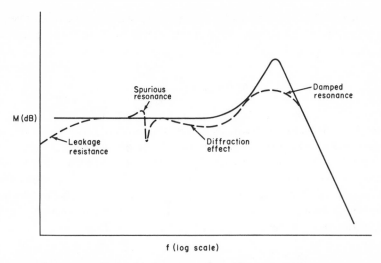

Fig. 5.3. Typical effects of resonant damping, diffraction, spurious resonances, and leakage resistance across the piezoelectric element on hydrophone sensitivity.

Spurious resonances and various resistances can be controlled to some extent by good design. A more complicated effect over which a designer has little control is the diffraction, also illustrated in Fig. 5.3.

A diffraction constant $D$ was defined in Section 2.2.3 and by Eq. (2.4) as the ratio of the average blocked pressure $p_b$ acting on a hydrophone to the free-field pressure $p_f$. That is,

$$D = \frac{p_b}{p_f}. \tag{5.3}$$

The term "diffraction" is used in a very broad sense in the definition of $D$. It pertains to all types of wave and signal interference associated with a transducer. This includes the conventional reflection and scattering of waves by an obstacle. It also includes interference when there is no obstacle. For example, a transducer could consist of two probes, each so small as not to disturb a passing wave. The diffraction constant for each individual probe would be one, but the diffraction constant for the combination could be anything from 0 to 1 because the signals at the two probes could be out of phase with each other. The diffraction constant is determined by the same phenomena that shape the receiving directivity pattern, and it is a function of the angle of incidence of the oncoming sound wave. As with patterns, there is a reciprocal relationship between the diffraction constants for the receiving and transmitting conditions. It has been shown[3] that for the transmitting case, $D$ is the ratio of the pressure produced by a transducer at a remote point in a free field to the pressure produced at the same point when a simple or very small spherical source with the same volume velocity is substituted for the transducer. The relationship between $D$ and other radiation parameters is given by[3]

$$D^2 = \frac{RR_\theta 4\pi}{k^2 \rho c}, \qquad (5.4)$$

where $R$ is the radiation resistance, $R_\theta$ is the directivity factor, $k$ is the wave number, and $\rho c$ is the specific characteristic impedance of water.

The values of $D$ for some common but idealized transducer shapes as calculated by Henriquez[4] are shown in Fig. 5.4. The value of $D$ for other shapes can be inferred from these curves. For example, the curve for a cylinder of finite length would fall between the curves for the infinite cylinder and the ring. For a piston of any shape in a rigid baffle, $D$ is 2, or +6 dB.

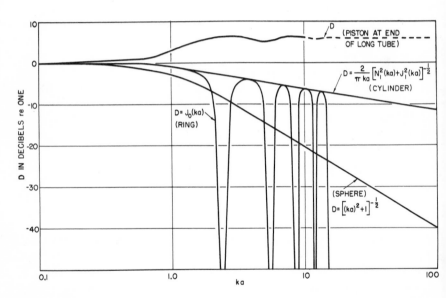

Fig. 5.4. Diffraction constants; $a$ is the radius of ring, sphere, cylinder, or piston; plane wavefront is parallel to long axis of cylinder or face of piston, and perpendicular to plane of ring; $k = 2\pi f/c$, where $f$ is the frequency in Hz and $c$ is the speed of sound.

The designer has relatively little control over the diffraction constant because the directivity pattern usually is specified. Since the diffraction constant and directivity pattern depend on the same interference phenomena, specifying one fixes the other.

## 5.3 Piezoelectric Transducers

The term piezoelectric is used for both the true single crystal like Rochelle salt, quartz, tourmaline, ammonium dihydrogen phosphate (ADP), and lithium sulfate, where the piezoelectric effect is inherent in the asymmetry of the natural crystal structure, and for polarized polycrystalline ceramics where the piezoelectric properties are produced in manufacture. All piezoelectric materials have certain properties aside from stability that affect their suitability as an electro-acoustic element in a measurement transducer. These properties include the piezoelectric constants, dielectric constant, resistivity, and the fact that the crystals and ceramics are anisotropic.

Two types of piezoelectric constants are used to describe the relationship of an electrical parameter such as charge density or electrical field and a mechanical parameter such as stress or strain. Since the material is anisotropic, the direction of the electrical and mechanical parameters are specified by subscripts.

The $g_{ij}$ constant is the quotient (mechanical strain)/(applied electric charge density) or (electric field/applied mechanical stress). The subscript $i$ specifies the direction normal to the electrodes, or direction of electrical field. The subscript $j$ specifies the direction of induced strain or applied stress.

The $d_{ij}$ constant is the quotient (strain)/(applied electrical field) or (charge density)/(applied stress). The subscripts have the same meaning as for the $g$ constants.

The subscripts 1, 2, and 3 pertain to the three mutually perpendicular directions. Subscripts 4, 5, and 6 pertain to shear motions about the 1, 2, and 3 axes, respectively. Subscript $h$ pertains to a hydrostatic or simultaneous 3-dimensional stress or strain.

The $g$ and $d$ constants are related by the dielectric constant:

$$d_{ij} = \epsilon\epsilon_0 g_{ij}, \qquad (5.5)$$

where $\epsilon_0$ is the dielectric constant of free space and $\epsilon$ is the dielectric constant of the material relative to $\epsilon_0$.

The (electrical field)/(stress) definition of $g$ is seen to be similar to the voltage/pressure definition of free-field voltage sensitivity. Consequently, the $g$ constant is proportional to hydrophone sensitivity and serves as the most useful criterion of a piezoelectric material for use in measurement hydrophones.

Of particular importance is the fact that $g$ and $d$ constants for different directions can differ in both magnitude and sign (or polarity). To illustrate, the $d_{21}$, $d_{22}$, and $d_{23}$ constants for lithium sulfate are +1.5, +16.0, and −4.0 (each times $10^{-12}$ C/N), respectively. The signs indicate the polarity or direction of the induced electric field. Now, if the stress were the same in all three directions, the resulting electric field in the "2" direction would be proportional to the arithmetic sum of the constants or $13.5 \times 10^{-12}$ C/N. Thus, the sensitivity for a three-dimensional stress would be less than for the 2 direction only. In this case, the hydrostatic modulus or $d_{2h}$ is only a little smaller than $d_{22}$ and quite useful. Lithium sulfate is considered a volume expander, therefore, even though the sign of $d_{23}$ is opposite to that of $d_{21}$ and $d_{22}$. In other crystals like ADP, there is a much larger cancelling effect. Because of such loss by cancellation, it is necessary to shield some surfaces of some crystals from the sound pressure. This shielding usually is provided by thin layers of an acoustically soft or "pressure-release" material. The failure of such shielding is one cause of the variability in hydrophone sensitivity.

Piezoelectric moduli and other design date are readily available in pamphlet form from one of the principal manufacturers, the Piezoelectric Division of the Clevite Corporation, Bedford, Ohio.

### 5.3.1 Piezoelectric crystals

Piezoelectric crystals have been used extensively in the past for both hydrophones and projectors. Although they have been largely replaced by the various ceramics, they still are needed where extreme stability with time is the prime requirement.

There are many excellent books on the molecular and phenomenological aspects of piezoelectric crystals,[5-8] and no attempt will be made here to discuss the theory in detail. It is sufficient for the designer of an experiment to know the strengths and frailties of crystals as transducer elements.

The crystals that have been used in underwater transducers are ADP (ammonium dihydrogen phosphate), lithium sulfate, Rochelle salt, quartz, and tourmaline. Of these, lithium sulfate and ADP still are used in standard transducers. Since these two types serve to illustrate two different general methods of crystal transducer design, they are chosen for discussion. Lithium sulfate and tourmaline crystals in the form of disks or plates are "volume expanders" or have useful $g_h$ and $d_h$ constants, and do not require pressure-release material on the edge faces. As noted in Section 5.3, the sensitivity of lithium sulfate is reduced only by approximately 20% when the acoustic pressure is admitted to all of the crystal faces. On the other hand, ADP, Rochelle salt, and quartz crystals require acoustic shielding in the form of pressure-release material (Corprene, air-cell rubber, paper, etc.) on some sides. Since a material normally cannot be dynamically soft and statically hard, the use of soft or pressure-release shielding limits the magnitude of hydrostatic pressure that can be applied.

Figure 5.5 shows a typical stack of crystals. The computed open-circuit voltage sensitivity $M$ of the stack is obtained from the general relationship $M = gL$, where $L$ is the dimension between electrodes across which the electrical voltage is measured. If the electrodes in Fig. 5.5 are connected in parallel, then $L$ is the thickness of the individual crystal. If they are connected in series, $L$ is the thickness of the whole 4-crystal stack. The choice of parallel or series connections must be made before the stack is assembled, because the polarity of the individual crystals is different for the two cases. When they are connected in parallel, the sensitivity of the whole stack is the same as for only one of the four crystals. The advantage of the high sensitivity of the series arrangement is offset by a much higher impedance. That is, when the crystals are viewed as parallel plate capacitors, the series arrangement has only 1/16 the capacitance, or 16 times the impedance, of the parallel arrangement. In hydrophones with small piezoelectric generators and closely associated preamplifiers, the higher impedance may increase the hydrophone voltage coupling loss (see Section 3.6), resulting in lower end-of-cable sensitivity, thus increasing the effective preamplifier noise (see Fig. 5.19) and producing lower signal-to-noise ratios. Thus, there is a trade-off between sensitivity and electrical impedance in crystal transducers. In practice, crystals usually are connected in parallel.

The resistivity of the crystalline material itself must be high for the same reason that the leakage resistance discussed in Section 5.2 and illustrated in Fig. 5.3 must be high. The resistivity of lithium sulfate is very high, which, combined with its good hydrostatic pressure response, makes it a good material for hydrophones used at low frequencies and high hydrostatic pressures.

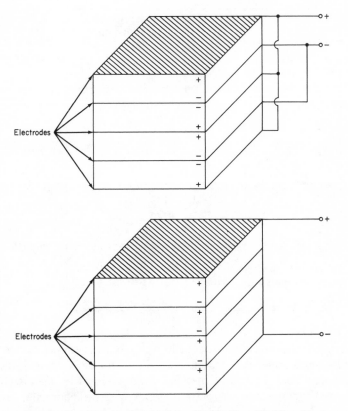

Fig. 5.5. Crystal stack assembled for electrical parallel (above) and series (below) connections.

Very-wide-frequency-range hydrophones have very small crystal stacks to avoid resonances and minimize diffraction effects; consequently, the electrical impedance is high. A disadvantage of crystals is that small quantities of moisture will shunt the crystal impedance and cause a low-frequency drop in sensitivity. Lithium sulfate and ADP are hygroscopic and if they are exposed to much moisture for any length of time, they will be irreversibly changed. Also, temperatures above 125°C will destroy ADP, and 75°C is the limit for lithium sulfate.

A preamplifier usually is an integral part of a wide-band crystal hydrophone because of the high electrical impedance of the crystal. A crystal hydrophone then consists of the basic crystal generator, a mounting, housing, acoustic window and fluid coupling for the crystal to the window, preamplifier and case, and cabling. The interaction of these components upon each other and the acoustic field are factors in designing a measurement. Some of the fundamental parameters of lithium sulfate and ADP are shown in Table 5.1.

Table 5.1. Properties of Piezoelectric Crystals and Ceramics

| Piezoelectric Material | Relative Dielectric Constant $\epsilon/\epsilon_0$ | $d$ Constant (m/V) (multiply by $10^{-12}$) | Resistivity (ohm-meter) |
|---|---|---|---|
| lithium sulfate | 10 | $+16.0\ (d_{22})$ <br> $+13.5\ (d_{2h})$ | $>10^{10}$ |
| ADP | 15 | $+48.0\ (d_{36})$ | $>10^8$ |
| barium titanate | 1200 | $-58\ (d_{31})$ <br> $+149\ (d_{33})$ <br> $+242\ (d_{15})$ | $>10^{10}$ |
| lead zirconate titanate (several different compositions) | 1300 to 3400 | $-125$ to $-275\ (d_{31})$ <br> $+300$ to $+600\ (d_{33})$ <br> $+500$ to $+750\ (d_{15})$ | $>10^{10}$ |

Crystal projectors consist essentially of a mosaic of crystal elements that is generally much larger than that in hydrophones for the same frequency range. The size and configuration of the mosaic are governed by the directivity and source level requirements. The electrical series or parallel connections among the crystals depend on the competing requirements of response and impedance, and the kind of crystal used. In addition to the response and impedance requirements, hydrostatic pressure requirements and cost affect the choice of kind of crystal. A large number of crystals are used in a projector mosaic and piezoelectric crystals are expensive. A lithium sulfate disk the size of a 25-cent piece costs $30 to $40; a similar piece of ADP costs less than $10 (1967 prices).

## 5.3.2 Ferroelectric ceramics

Ceramics that have such electrical properties as fields, polarity, and so forth, that are analogous to the magnetic properties of ferromagnetic materials are called ferroelectric ceramics. The ceramics came into general use for transducers in the early 1950's and have rapidly replaced crystals in many applications. High dielectric and piezoelectric constants, variety of shapes available, low cost, and inherent ruggedness are reasons for the popularity of this material.

Of the several kinds of ceramic, barium titanate and lead zirconate titanate are the most popular. Some types of lead metaniobate have characteristics that make it peculiarly suited to broad-band, high-pressure transducers, and it is incorporated in some transducers of this type.

The theory of designing ferroceramic transducers is similar to that for crystal transducers. The practice is somewhat different because (1) the dielectric constant of ceramics is larger by a factor of about 100 than that of crystals and this fact eliminates some of the problems of very high electric impedance; and (2) ceramics can be manufactured in practically any shape, which gives the designer considerably more flexibility than was possible with crystals. Transducers have been made from plates, cylinders, spheres, mosaics, staves, and sections of various geometric shapes. Cylinders and spheres are helpful not only in obtaining desired directivity patterns, but they also act as mechanical transformers. For example, the circumferential stress in a cylinder wall is higher than the radial pressure by the ratio of the cylinder outside radius to the wall thickness. Some of the fundamental parameters of ferroelectric ceramics are shown in Table 5.1.

The $d_{32}$ and $g_{32}$ constants in ceramics always are the same as the $d_{31}$ and $g_{31}$, respectively. It is evident then from the values in Table 5.1 that the ceramics will have low hydrostatic moduli. That is, the sum $d_{31} + d_{31} + d_{33}$ will be smaller than either $d_{31}$ or $d_{33}$. Consequently, when ceramics are used in a plate or disk configuration, acoustic shielding is necessary or at least desirable. Lead metaniobate is an exception. It has a useful hydrostatic modulus and needs no shielding.

The effective hydrostatic modulus becomes a matter of design in a cylindrical shell configuration. The mechanical transformer function of the cylinder itself, the mechanical transformer action of end caps on the cylinder, and whether or not the sound pressure is allowed to act in the inner wall of the cylinder all affect the sensitivity.[9] Properly designed capped thin-walled cylinders do provide good sensitivity. On the other hand, with certain ratios of wall thickness to diameter, the effective wall thickness modulus ($d_{33}$) can be exactly equal and opposite to the effective combined circumferential $(d_{31})$ and longitudinal $(d_{32})$ moduli, resulting in zero sensitivity. In typical cases, this ratio varies from 0.3 to 0.4.

Considerable work has been done on the characteristics of ceramics under the various environmental conditions encountered in underwater acoustic measurements. The ceramics are not as predictable as the crystals, because of variations in composition and manufacture, but with careful control and selection, ceramic transducers that are stable within prescribed time, temperature, and pressure limits have been constructed.

## 5.4 Magnetostrictive Transducers

The possible application of magnetostriction in underwater sound transducers probably was recognized first by G. W. Pierce and his associates at Harvard in the 1920's.

Magnetostrictive transducers were used extensively in World War II. A comprehensive report on the fundamentals and design of magnetostrictive transducers of that period is contained in the National Defense Research Committee's report on magnetostriction transducers.[10] A general treatment of the subject also is available in other literature.[11,12]

Magnetostrictive transducers have several drawbacks that limit their usefulness for measurement applications. One, the contour of the calibration curves, already has been discussed in Section 5.2. Others include inherent nonlinearity, hysteresis, and the need for a biasing magnetic field. The principal advantages are low electrical impedance and good mechanical strength.

Unlike the piezoelectric effect, the magnetostriction effect is nonpolarized. That is, the mechanical displacement is independent of the direction of the magnetic field in the metal. Nickel, for example, will shorten when it contains a magnetic field regardless of the polarity of the field.

Figure 5.6 illustrates both the inherent nonlinearity and the need for a bias field, if frequency doubling is to be avoided.

Two types of magnetostrictive transducers remain as measurement transducers in some places and so will be mentioned briefly. One is a thick-walled cylinder comprised of a laminated stack of annular nickel rings and a toroidally wound coil.[13,14] This usually is referred to as a "ring stack." Remanent magnetism provides the magnetic bias.

The other type is a thin-walled tube transducer developed at the Navy Underwater Sound Laboratory, New London, Conn.[10] The inside of the tube contains a permanent bar magnet and a coil of wire wound around a wood dowel.

In the magnetostrictive tubes or cylinders, as in the piezoelectric counterparts, the stress in the wall is increased over the sound pressure in the water by the ratio of the tube radius to wall thickness. A disadvantage is that although the tube theoretically is omnidirectional in one plane, this is not easy to achieve in practice because of the problems of housing and sealing the nickel tube or cylinder, the magnet, the coil, and so forth.

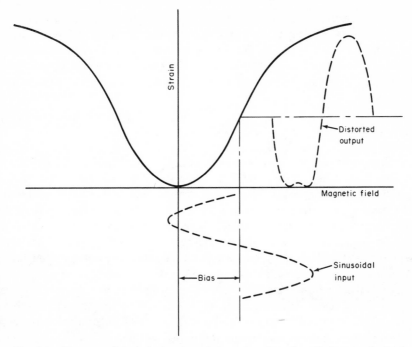

Fig. 5.6. Magnetostrictively induced strain as a function of applied magnetic field.

The tube types have been used on Navy ships for checking alignment of sonar systems. They have been replaced recently by ceramic.

## 5.5 Moving-Coil Transducers

The moving-coil or electrodynamic transducer for underwater use is similar in principle to the air loudspeaker, and, like the loudspeaker, is used primarily as a wide-band sound source. The Rice-Kellogg[15] method, in which the frequency range above resonance is used to obtain high fidelity or a flat transmitting current response, is applicable in both media.

From the well-known equations for the transduction of energy with moving-coil transducers, the definition of mechanical impedance, and the radiation of sound from a small diaphragm moving with uniform velocity, we can see why the transmitting current response is constant above resonance:

$$F = BLi, \tag{5.6}$$

$$F = j\omega m u, \tag{5.7}$$

$$p \propto \omega u, \tag{5.8}$$

where $i$ is electrical current, $F$ is force, $B$ is magnetic flux, $L$ is the length of wire that moves at right angles across the magnetic lines of force of flux density $B$, $\omega$ is angular frequency, $m$ is the combined mass of coil, diaphragm, and water load, $u$ is the linear velocity of the coil and diaphragm, and $p$ is the radiated sound pressure. Combining the three equations produces

$$p \propto \omega u = \omega\left(\frac{F}{j\omega m}\right) = \frac{BLi}{jm} \propto i. \qquad (5.9)$$

These equations are valid only when both the mechanical and acoustical impedances are mass controlled and the diaphragm is small in comparison with a wavelength. The mechanical impedance is mass controlled at frequencies above the basic spring-mass resonance and below the flexure mode resonances of the diaphragm. The acoustical or radiation impedance is predominantly a mass reactance at frequencies where the diaphragm is very small in comparison with a wavelength in water. More detail on the application of the Rice-Kellogg technique to underwater sound transducers is given by Sims.[16]

Large diaphragm volume displacements are needed to radiate acoustic power at low frequencies. With inherently stiff piezoelectric or magnetostrictive transducers, this is difficult to do without resorting to very large transducers where large radiation area can compensate for limited small linear displacements. In a moving-coil transducer, the stiffness is all in the diaphragm spring suspension, which can be made almost arbitrarily compliant. This enhances the usefulness of the moving-coil transducer at low frequencies, but it also makes it mechanically fragile. Consequently, moving-coil transducers have automatic compensating systems for equalizing the gas pressure inside the transducer with the hydrostatic pressure on the outside. For modest depths (down to about 100 feet), a collapsible bag arrangement is used (see Fig. 5.37). For greater depths, a Scuba-type mechanism can be used. Even with a properly operating compensation system, moving-coil transducers are relatively fragile instruments.

Moving-coil projectors are used in the audio-frequency range and typically have transmitting current responses of about 50-60 dB referred to one microbar at one meter per ampere. As hydrophones, moving-coil transducers have limited usefulness, because the electrical impedance is rising and the free-field voltage sensitivity is dropping as the frequency is increased. They generally are not used as receivers except in reciprocity calibration measurements where they serve as reciprocal transducers. In the latter application, the basic resonant frequency should be avoided because the transducers sometimes are nonlinear at resonance.

## 5.6 Typical Hydrophone Designs

There is no single typical design for a broad-frequency-band hydrophone. Nor is there a single widely used standard hydrophone comparable to the Western

Electric type 650AA microphone. A good microphone is used only in the audio-frequency range. It seldom is used in a hostile environment or at other than atmospheric pressure. A good hydrophone, on the other hand, would be usable in the infrasonic-, audio-, and ultrasonic-frequency ranges. It would be immune to the effects of high hydrostatic pressure, near-freezing temperatures, corrosion and electrolysis, nibbling fish, and the less-than-delicate handling by sailors, stevedores, and ship riggers. There are many hydrophone designs to meet a great variety of needs in underwater acoustics.[17-21] Four representative or typical designs are discussed in the sections that follow.

### 5.6.1 Type M115B and DT-99/PQM-1A

The M115B, shown in Fig. 5.7, is a commercial hydrophone developed and manufactured by Massa Division, Dynamics Corporation of America. It has been manufactured and widely used since the early 1950's for many types of research, development, engineering, and calibration measurements. The electroacoustic generator consists of two stacks of ADP crystals, each snugly fitted inside a metal cylindrical sleeve. The metal sleeve and the Corprene between the crystal and the metal constitute the acoustic shielding of the sides of the crystal stack discussed in Section 5.3. The ends of the two crystal stacks, which are exposed to the castor oil and to the sound field, form in effect a short 4-point line hydrophone. Castor oil is used in most such hydrophones because the oil is acoustically similar to water but also is a dielectric. The preamplifier is a cathode-follower type that functions as an impedance-matching device rather than as an amplifier. That is, the input impedance of a cathode follower is high and the output impedance is low. Thus, the high-impedance electroacoustic generator is matched to the relatively low-impedance hydrophone cable. The voltage amplification of a cathode follower is less than one—that is, it has a loss rather than a gain. A typical sensitivity curve and patterns are shown in Figs. 5.8 and 5.9. The principal drawback of the M115B design has been that with time, or high hydrostatic pressure, or both, the castor oil leaks into the Corprene and destroys the shielding effect. This results in lowered sensitivity at low frequencies. A newer version designated M115C contains a sealed vinyl cartridge designed to overcome this deficiency. Another version of the M115B is the Navy type DT-99/PQM-1A that is used with a Navy noise-measuring set. The DT-99/PQM-1A contains an electroacoustic generator element larger than, but similar in design to, that in the M115B.

### 5.6.2 Type H23

The H23 hydrophone was developed in 1963 by the Navy Underwater Sound Reference Laboratory as a general-purpose laboratory standard.

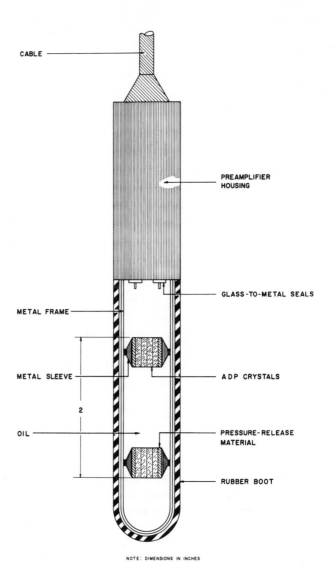

CABLE

PREAMPLIFIER
HOUSING

GLASS-TO-METAL SEALS

METAL FRAME

METAL SLEEVE

ADP CRYSTALS

2

OIL

PRESSURE-RELEASE
MATERIAL

RUBBER BOOT

NOTE: DIMENSIONS IN INCHES

Fig. 5.7. Massa type M115B hydrophone.

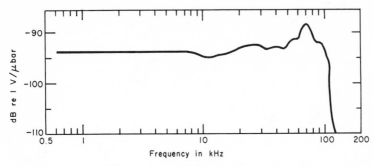

Fig. 5.8. Typical free-field voltage sensitivity of Massa type M115B hydrophone.

The hydrophone and typical calibration curves are shown in Figs. 5.10 through 5.12. Eight lithium sulfate crystals are used as the electroacoustic generator. The crystal is not shielded acoustically with Corprene or other pressure-release material, and the hydrostatic pressure limit of 2500 psig therefore is fixed only by the mechanics of the preamplifier housing.

The crystals float on rubber mounts to eliminate mechanical coupling to the housing. The boot is butyl rubber because the permeability to water is an order of magnitude lower in butyl than in other elastomers suitable for this purpose. The coupling fluid is castor oil.

The useful frequency range of the H23 can be extended beyond the 150-kHz frequency shown, but orientation becomes critical because of the vertical directivity. The transistorized preamplifier provides 10 dB gain.

### 5.6.3 Types LC32 and BC32

The LC32 hydrophone was developed and is manufactured by the Atlantic Research Corporation. The hydrophone and typical calibration curves are shown in Figs. 5.13 through 5.15. Like the M115B, it is a commercial hydrophone, and along with a preceding model, the BC32, it has been widely used for a variety of applications for many years. The generator is a stack of ceramic rings. The ceramic is lead zirconate titanate in the LC32 and barium titanate in the older BC32. The rings are bonded to a thin neoprene protective coating and no coupling fluid is used. Also, there is no preamplifier. The LC32 is easy to use and relatively inexpensive. As a price for simplicity and low cost, it is less sensitive than the M115B and H23, and less stable with pressure and temperature. At frequencies above about 50 kHz, the LC32 can be used also as a projector.

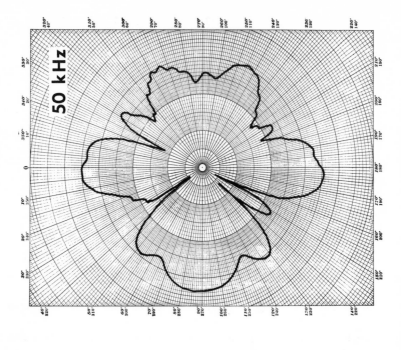

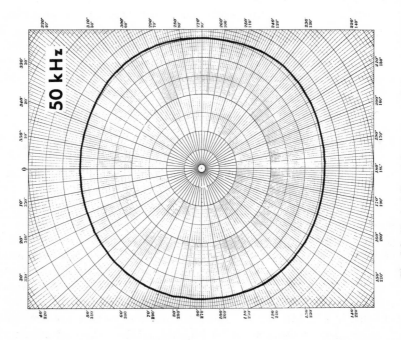

Fig. 5.9. Typical directivity patterns of Massa type M115B hydrophone (horizontal plane, left; vertical plane, right).

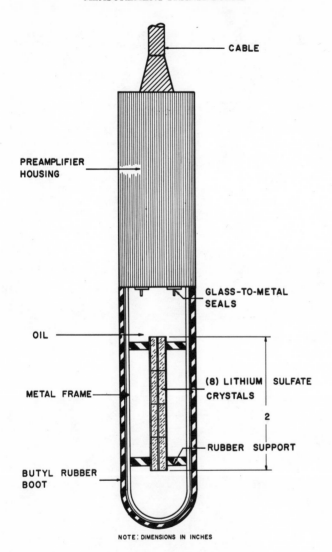

CABLE

PREAMPLIFIER
HOUSING

GLASS-TO-METAL
SEALS

OIL

(8) LITHIUM SULFATE
CRYSTALS

METAL FRAME

2

RUBBER SUPPORT

BUTYL RUBBER
BOOT

NOTE: DIMENSIONS IN INCHES

Fig. 5.10. USRD type H23 hydrophone.

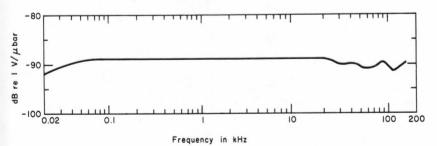

Fig. 5.11. Typical free-field voltage sensitivity of USRD type H23 hydrophone.

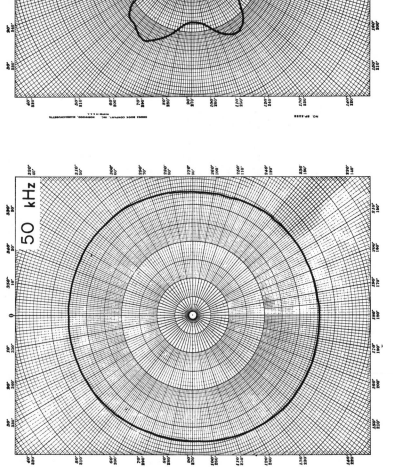

Fig. 5.12.  Typical directivity patterns of USRD type H23 hydrophone (horizontal plane, left; vertical plane, right).

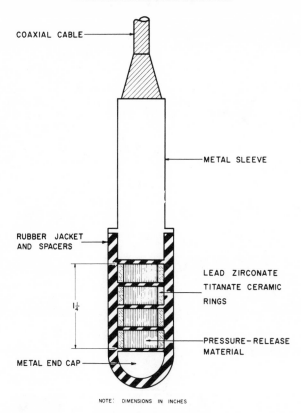

Fig. 5.13. Atlantic Research Corporation type LC32 hydrophone.

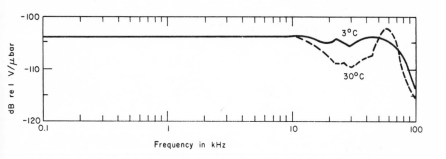

Fig. 5.14. Typical free-field voltage sensitivity of Atlantic Research Corporation type LC32 hydrophone.

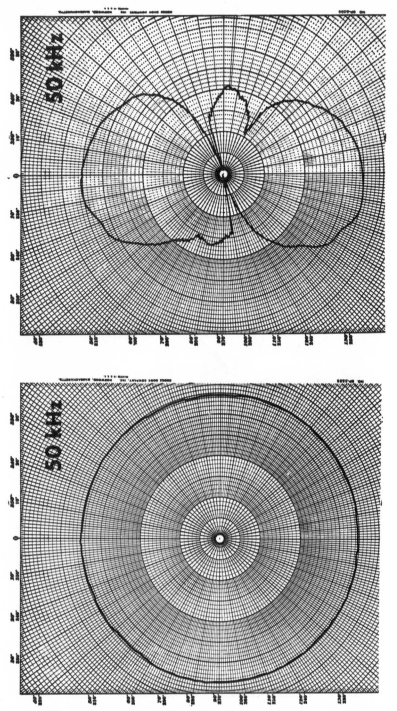

Fig. 5.15. Typical directivity patterns of Atlantic Research Corporation type LC32 hydrophone (horizontal plane, left; vertical plane, right).

### 5.6.4 Types F36, F37, and TR-205/WQM

The F36 was developed in 1965 by the Navy Underwater Sound Reference Laboratory as a versatile, general-purpose hydrophone. It is versatile in the sense that it is stable enough for a laboratory standard, rugged enough for shipboard use, and it can be used also as a reciprocal transducer or projector at high audio and low ultrasonic frequencies. The transducer and typical calibration curves are shown in Figs. 5.16 to 5.18.

The F36 is designed to be suspended by its electrical cable. Horizontal orientation is not critical because it is omnidirectional in the horizontal plane. The generator consists of a line of lead zirconate titanate ceramic elements in the form of glass-capped cylinders that require no pressure-release material. The space between the cylinders and the rubber boot is filled with castor oil. The dimensions of the cylinder and end caps, and the properties of materials are chosen to give a broad bandwidth with constant sensitivity.

The F37 is a higher frequency version of the F36. The TR-205/WQM is a version of the F36 used by the Navy on board ships for the specific purpose of monitoring the performance of the ship's sonar system. In this application, the TR-205/WQM is suspended by its cable over the side of the ship to the same depth as the sonar transducer on the bottom of the ship. Signals then are transmitted between the sonar transducer and the TR-205/WQM. These hydrophones have hooks on the bottom for attaching a heavy weight that helps to hold the instrument steady in ship over-the-side measurements.

### 5.7 Noise-Measuring Hydrophones

The special feature of the noise-measuring hydrophone is the low self noise requirement. An informal index of the quality of a noise hydrophone has been the self noise per hertz in decibels referred to the noise at Knudsen sea state zero. Sea state zero formerly was the lowest noise field that the hydrophone would be expected to measure. With modern techniques for extracting signals buried in noise, however, it is possible to measure signals far below the sea state noise level.

For nonresonant piezoelectric sensitive elements, the self noise of the radiation resistance, mechanical resistance, and electrical resistance is not significant in comparison with the noise of the preamplifier. The threshold or equivalent noise pressure then is dependent on the capacitance and sensitivity of the piezoelectric element as related to the preamplifier noise under the input load conditions presented by the element.

The inherent noise voltage of a typical transistor preamplifier is given in Fig. 5.19. This preamplifier, when used in a standard noise hydrophone, will result in the equivalent noise pressure shown in Fig. 5.20 along with the noise in Knudsen sea state zero.

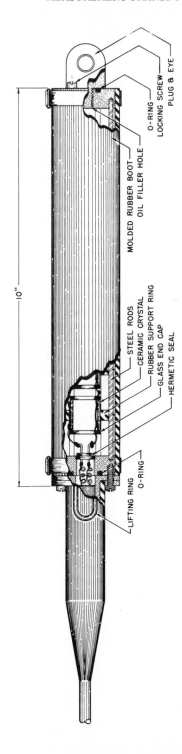

Fig. 5.16. USRD type F36 and Navy type TR-205/WQM hydrophone and projector.

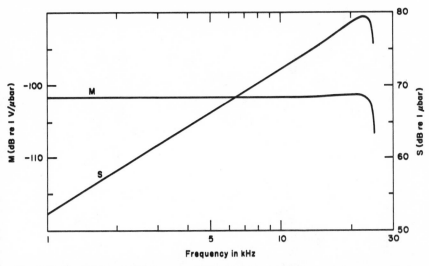

Fig. 5.17. Typical free-field voltage sensitivity $M$ and transmitting current response $S$ of USRD type F36 hydrophone and projector (also Navy type TR-205/WQM).

The DT-99/PQM-1A hydrophone (see Section 5.6.1) is an example of a noise-measuring hydrophone. The original ADP crystals have been replaced with a ceramic element that provides better vertical directivity and improves the long-time stability. A later version of the hydrophone, type DT-268, also contains a transistorized preamplifier.

## 5.8  Piezoelectric Projector Design

Piezoelectric measurement projectors are designed for operation below resonance in the stiffness-controlled frequency range of the piezoelectric motor elements. Usable levels of sound pressure can be transmitted by nonresonant ceramic projectors at frequencies above about 1 kHz, and by nonresonant crystal projectors at frequencies above about 5 kHz. Below these frequencies, the amount of ceramic or crystal becomes too great to be practical or economical, or the driving voltage becomes so high that arcing and electrical breakdown occur. An exception to this is ceramic projectors enclosed in small chambers where the load impedance on the projector is primarily the compliance of the chamber. The pressure produced per volt then is constant with frequency. This exception is discussed in Section 5.9.5.

For most laboratory or tank measurements, it is desirable to have unidirectional projectors to discriminate against reflections from side, top, and bottom boundaries. In field measurements, omnidirectional projectors are needed because orientation is less precise and controllable than in a laboratory.

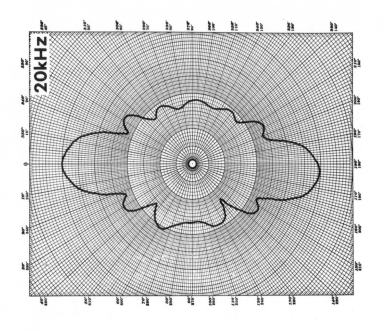

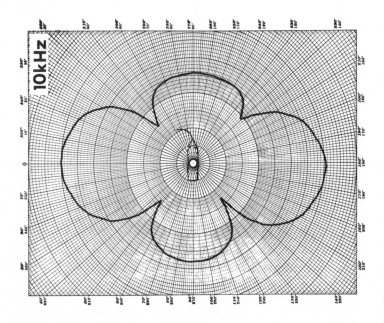

Fig. 5.18.  Typical vertical directivity patterns of USRD type F36 hydrophone and projector (also Navy type TR-205/WQM).  The transducer is omnidirectional within ±0.5 dB in the horizontal plane.

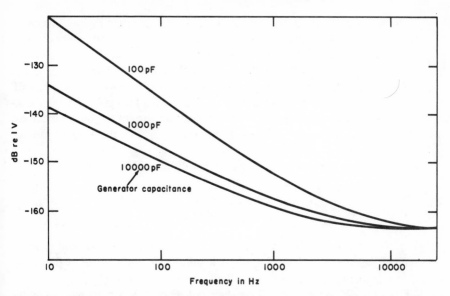

Fig. 5.19. Typical transistor preamplifier equivalent input noise in decibels referred to one volt for a bandwidth of one Hertz.

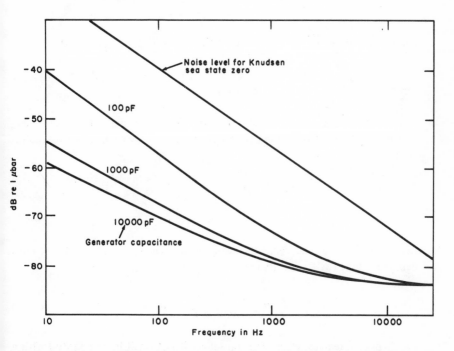

Fig. 5.20. Equivalent noise pressure of a piezoelectric element generator connected to the preamplifier of Fig. 5.19. A typical element sensitivity of –80 dB re 1 V/μbar is used. The noise pressure is stated in decibels referred to one microbar in a one Hertz bandwidth. ·

The major projector design problems are anomalies caused by spurious resonances in the housing and mounting of the elements, and flexural modes of vibration in the ceramic. At the low frequencies where the dimensions of the projector are small in comparison with a wavelength in water and the simple source concept applies, the transmitting voltage response is a curve with the slope 12 dB per octave. This derives from the constant displacement per volt of the stiffness-controlled piezoelectric element. The transmitting current response curve has a 6-dB-per-octave slope. Transformers are used to modify these slopes in some transducers.

The acoustic pressure produced at radial distance $r$ from a simple source is

$$|p| = \frac{\omega \rho U}{4 \pi r}, \tag{5.10}$$

where $U$ is the rms volume velocity, $p$ is the rms sound pressure, and $\omega$ is the angular frequency; also, $U = \omega \xi A$, where $\xi$ is the linear displacement of the radiating face or diaphragm and $A$ is the radiating area.

From the definition of the $d$ constant in Section 5.3, $\xi = de$, where $e$ is the applied voltage. Thus,

$$U = \omega \xi A = \omega deA. \tag{5.11}$$

Then the magnitude of the pressure per volt is

$$\frac{p}{e} = \frac{\omega^2 \rho dA}{4 \pi r} \propto \omega^2. \tag{5.12}$$

The transmitting current response has the slope 6 dB per octave in the low-frequency region because the impedance is almost entirely a capacitive reactance; that is,

$$\frac{p}{e} = \frac{P}{\dfrac{i}{j \omega C}}, \tag{5.13}$$

where $C$ is the electrical capacitance of the free element, and $i$ is the current. Then, from Eqs. (5.12) and (5.13),

$$\frac{p}{i} = \frac{\omega^2 \rho dA}{4 \pi r} \frac{1}{\omega C} \propto \omega. \tag{5.14}$$

At high frequencies, where the transducer is not small in comparison with a wavelength, the simple source concept does not apply. The transmitting response then becomes dependent on the radiation impedance and directivity factor.

Both of these parameters are in turn dependent on the transducer configuration, and relate to the diffraction constant according to Eq. (5.4). The transmitting response is subject to the effects shown in Fig. 5.4 in the same way that the receiving sensitivity is.

Ceramic is the preferred material for piezoelectric projectors in the high-audio and low-ultrasonic frequency range. Ceramics have higher dielectric constants or lower electrical impedances than do crystals; they also are less expensive and provide more flexibility in design. The superior stability of crystals is not as important in projectors as it is in standard hydrophones. Crystals are used in projectors for frequencies above 100 kHz, because the vibrational modes are predictable with good accuracy and resonances are higher than for ceramics of equal dimensions. This is important when maximum bandwidth is required. Also, cross-coupling between vibrational modes usually is less troublesome.

When transformers are used to step down the high electrical impedance of the crystals, the transformer is considered an integral part of the transducer. These transformers must transfer energy into crystals, which have a mostly reactive electrical impedance, without distortion, over many octaves. Such transformers are not commonly available and must be designed for the particular transducer.

If a piezoelectric transducer is to be used at hydrostatic pressures above a few hundred pounds per square inch, designers have a special problem with acoustic shielding to prevent the sound pressure from impinging on certain parts of the piezoelectric motor. There are three general design choices for acoustic shielding: (1) Use volume expander materials like lithium sulfate or lead metaniobate to eliminate the need for shielding. (2) Use the impedance mismatch principle wherein very low or very high acoustic impedance baffles shield part of the piezoelectric elements from the sound pressure. (3) Use cylindrical or spherical configurations that expose only one face to the sound pressure.

Choice (1) is suitable for small hydrophone generators, but less so for projectors. The high electrical and mechanical impedance of lithium sulfate is a disadvantage. Lead metaniobate has a useable hydrostatic modulus, but it is inferior to lead zirconate titanate in most other respects.

The low-impedance option (2) is not feasible because low-impedance or pressure-release materials like Corprene and cellular rubber lose their air content under high pressure. Further, such a material would need to have a built-in high-pass filter characteristic. That is, it should have a high static but a low dynamic acoustic impedance. High-impedance baffles can be obtained from high-density materials such as tungsten, and they are used in some special cases. However, this option has the disadvantages of high volume, high weight, and high cost.

Thin-walled lead zirconate titanate cylinders sealed and capped at each end are commonly used for high-pressure hydrophones (see Section 5.6.4). For projectors, large cylinders are needed, but are difficult to fabricate with the degree of uniformity and symmetry necessary to sustain high differential stress across the wall thickness. Barrel-stave-type construction has been used with some success. Thick-walled cylinders approach the critical wall-thickness-to-diameter ratios that nullify the signals as explained in Section 5.3.2. Designing end caps that will seal the cylinder and yet allow the cylinder to vibrate radially is a further complication. Admission of the oil or other acoustic coupling mediums and the high hydrostatic pressure to the inside of the cylinder alleviates the mechanical stress; however, such a design stiffens the whole cylinder and requires a low-pass acoustic filter between the inside and outside of the cylinder.

One solution to these several problems, particularly for omnidirectional radiation, is a ceramic air-filled spherical shell that is strong enough to sustain the external pressure. The technology of fabricating large spheres either as one piece or as a spherical mosaic of small, flat, fitted pieces is advancing rapidly. Having a large radiating area per unit volume, such spheres are feasible for low-audio-frequency projectors.

Another possibility is to use the shell as a Helmholtz resonator[22] to enhance the low-frequency response. Figure 5.21 shows the response of one such experimental transducer designed by C. C. Sims.

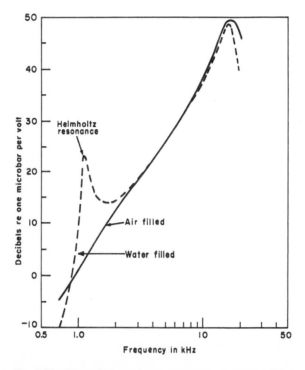

Fig. 5.21. Transmitting voltage response at one meter, 4-in. o.d. PZT-4 ceramic sphere.

## 5.9 Typical Piezoelectric Projector Designs

Since 1945, the development in the United States of wide-range projectors for measurement applications has been confined largely to the Navy Underwater Sound Reference Laboratory (USRL), now the Underwater Sound Reference Division of the Naval Research Laboratory. During World War II, the Bell Telephone Laboratories pioneered the development of moving-coil and piezoelectric projectors using some of the technology developed in the audio engineering and communications business. This work was done under contract to the Underwater Sound Reference Laboratory, a Columbia University Division of War Research activity. In 1945, all of this work was turned over to the Navy. The Brush Development Company (now part of the Clevite Corporation) was the principal source of such piezoelectric crystals as Rochelle salt and ADP during World War II, and also developed some wide-range crystal projectors. The projector development essentially ceased after World War II, although the company continued as a primary source of crystals and ceramics.

All the typical designs shown in the following sections are those developed at the USRL. Some of these transducers have been manufactured under contract for the USRL and are available from the manufacturer as USRL-developed, but commercially manufactured, projectors. For the most part, these USRL projectors (and USRL hydrophones) are borrowed by naval activities and contractors from the USRL, or now the USRD of the Naval Research Laboratory, under a formal and continuing loan program. Some 1000 measurement hydrophones and projectors are in use throughout the Navy.

All the typical projectors shown here are relatively modern. The older World War II types have been replaced and are described elsewhere in the literature.[23]

### 5.9.1 Type F27

The USRD type F27 transducer was designed as a wide-range unidirectional projector for underwater sound calibration measurements in the frequency range 1 to 40 kHz, and for stable operation in the temperature range 1 to 35°C at hydrostatic pressures to 5000 psig. It can be used also as a hydrophone and as the reciprocal transducer in a reciprocity calibration.

The piezoelectric motor consists of 55 1-in.-diameter lead metaniobate disks 0.22 in. thick, each of which is cemented to a 1-in.-diameter, ½-in.-thick tungsten backing plate. The 55 elements are arranged in a circular array that is approximately 9 in. in diameter. The design is shown in Fig. 5.22. The tungsten backing plates are molded in butyl rubber that supports the individual elements and provides a water seal for the rear of the transducer. The front acoustic window also is butyl. The transducer is filled with castor oil.

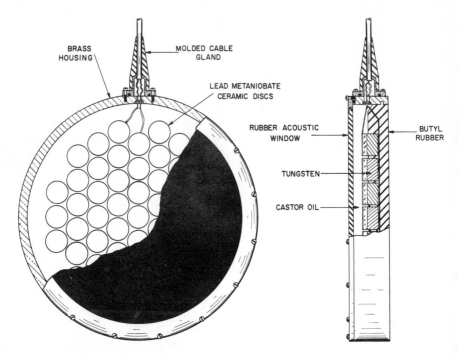

Fig. 5.22. USRD type F27 reversible transducer for the high-audio and low-ultrasonic range.

A typical transmitting current response is shown in Fig. 5.23. The transducer has been tested statically to 5000 psig, but at this writing there is no way of calibrating it acoustically at that pressure. The transducer is stable in the frequency range 1 to 20 kHz at all pressures to 1000 psig and at temperatures from 3 to 25°C. In the frequency range 20 to 35 kHz, the sensitivity varies by 1 dB in the same temperature and pressure ranges.

The directivity of the F27 is approximately that expected from unbaffled 9-in.-diameter uniform piston radiators, except for the backward radiation shown in Fig. 5.24. The transducer resonates well above 40 kHz but is not very useful at higher frequencies because the beam pattern becomes too sharp. Also, at the high frequencies any transducer consisting of a mosaic of elements resolves into ar array of point radiators, and high side lobes appear in the pattern.

### 5.9.2  Type F30

The USRD type F30 transducer was designed as a wide-range unidirectional projector for underwater sound calibration measurements in the frequency range 10 to 150 kHz, and for stable operation in the temperature range 0 to 35°C at pressures to 3500 psig. Like the F27, it can be used also as a hydrophone and a reciprocal transducer.

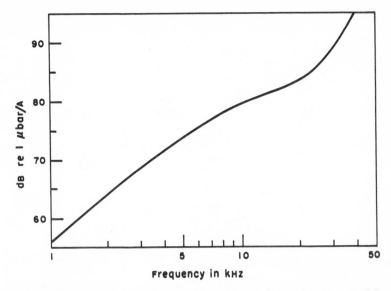

Fig. 5.23. Typical transmitting current response, USRD type F27 transducer.

The piezoelectric motor is a rectangular array 2 in. high and 1-1/2 in. wide, consisting of twelve 1/2 × 1/2 × 1/16-in. lithium sulfate crystals cemented to 1/2-in. tungsten cubes. The array is supported by rubber pads in a steel housing field with castor oil. The design is shown in Fig. 5.25.

A transformer having a turns ratio 30:1 reduces the output impedance to a nominal 100 ohms at 20 kHz. The electrical circuit of the transducer is shown in Fig. 5.26. The resistances in the circuit serve to stabilize the impedance.

A typical transmitting current response is shown in Fig. 5.27. The response changes less than ±0.5 dB with pressures to 1000 psig. From static tests and theoretical considerations, no greater change is expected with pressures to 3500 psig. In the frequency range 25 to 150 kHz, the response varies less than ±0.6 dB in the temperature range 3 to 25°C.

The directivity pattern is broader in the horizontal plane than it is in the vertical plane because of the rectangular shape of the array. Typical patterns are shown in Fig. 5.28.

### 5.9.3  Type F33

The types F27 and F30 projectors described in the preceding sections are similar in design. The major difference is in the sizes chosen to accommodate the different frequency ranges. Exceptional bandwidth can be achieved by combining two piezoelectric motors into one projector. Such a combination is the distinguishing feature of the USRD type F33 transducer, which contains a

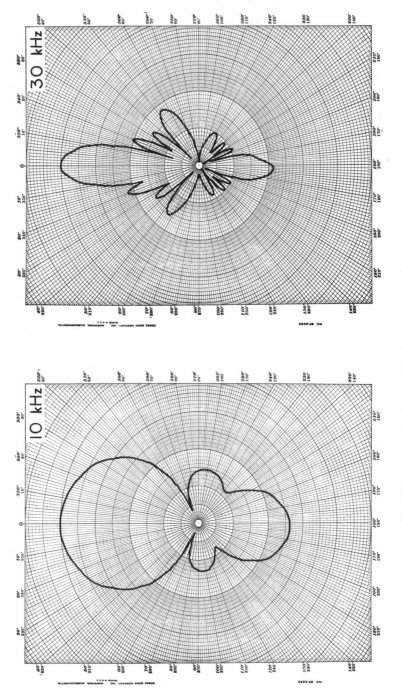

Fig. 5.24. Typical directivity patterns, USRD type F27 transducer.

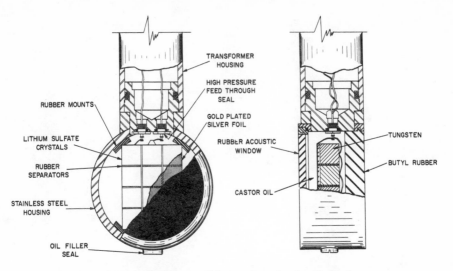

Fig. 5.25.  USRD type F30 reversible transducer for the ultrasonic range.

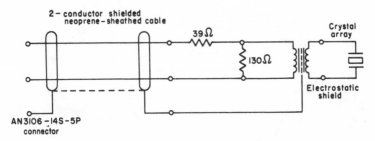

Fig. 5.26.  Schematic circuit diagram, type F30 transducer.

Fig. 5.27.  Typical transmitting current response, USRD type F30 transducer.

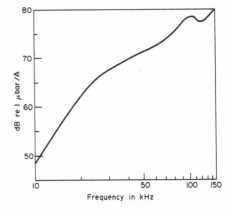

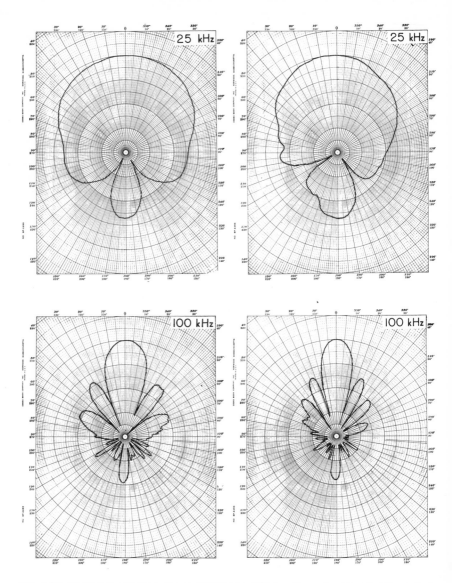

Fig. 5.28. Typical directivity patterns, USRD type F30 transducer (horizontal, left; vertical, right)

piezoelectric motor consisting of two sections—one the size of the F30 motor, and one approximately the size of the F27 motor. The frequency range of the F33, consequently, is 1 to 150 kHz.

The dual array is shown in Fig. 5.29. The smaller, inner array is composed of twelve 0.5-in.-diameter by 0.10-in.-thick lead zirconate titanate elements cemented to Kennametal disks. This array is approximately 1.5 in. wide and 2 in. high; it is useful in the frequency range 5 to 150 kHz.

The larger array is constructed from 64 modified barium titanate ceramic plates 1 in. long by 0.75 in. wide by 0.250 in. thick. Each plate is cemented to a steel backing embedded in butyl rubber to form an array approximately 8 in. wide by 8.5 in. high. When the two arrays are driven simultaneously, the transducer is useful in the frequency range 1 to 50 kHz. Normally, the transducer is calibrated electrically unbalanced, with the shield and the low-output lead connected to ground.

The transducer is provided with 100 ft of vinyl-sheathed cable. The leads to each array section are individually shielded, as shown in the circuitry of Fig. 5.30. A 1-ft length of cable provided with mating connectors serves to connect the inner and the outer sections in parallel. The entire transducer than can be driven by a signal applied to pins A and B of the AN adapter. The shields are accessible at pin E.

Fig. 5.29. Piezoelectric ceramic element arrays, USRD type F33 transducer.

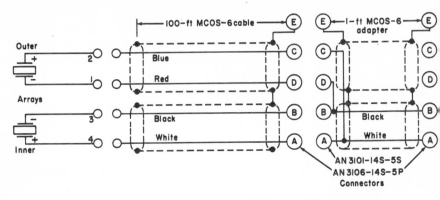

Fig. 5.30. Schematic diagram of cable, USRD type F33 transducer.

Pressure-release Corprene is used between the individual ceramic elements. Both sections are sealed in transparent polyurethane; castor oil provides the coupling medium between the polyurethane potting material and the butyl-rubber acoustic window.

Typical transmitting current and voltage responses of both sections in parallel and of the inner section alone are shown in Fig. 5.31. Some compromises were made in the design to keep the cost within reasonable limits. The high pressure limit is only 500 psig, but the response is stable to 500 psig and in the temperature range 5 to 30°C.

Typical directivity patterns are shown in Fig. 5.32.

### 5.9.4 Type E8

The USRD type E8 transducer was developed in 1950 as a calibration transducer for the frequency range 150-2000 kHz.[24] It is used as a projector, hydrophone, and reciprocal transducer. The design and typical calibration curves are shown in Figs. 5.33 and 5.34.

The piezoelectric element is a 2-cm-diameter lithium sulfate disk cemented to a Corprene disk. A pulse transformer with an impedance ratio 20:1 approximately matches the impedance of the crystal to that of the coaxial cable and attached transmitting or receiving circuit. The coupling fluid is castor oil. The acoustic window is natural gum rubber. This rubber is not particularly durable, but it has less attenuation at magahertz frequencies than do neoprene or butyl rubber. The selection of fluid and elastomer materials becomes particularly important at megahertz frequencies because of attenuation. The attenuation in small volumes of water itself becomes measurable at these frequencies.

At the high frequencies, there is little need for high pressure capability. The maximum hydrostatic pressure for the E8 is only 50 psig. The temperature range is 5 to 35°C.

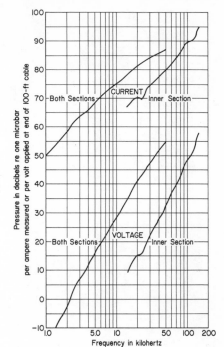

Fig. 5.31. Typical transmitting responses at 1 m, USRD type F33 transducer.

The directivity, shown in Fig. 5.35, is very close to that of a theoretical baffled piston 2 cm in diameter. Above about 500 kHz, the beam becomes very narrow, and precision rigging is required.

The millimeter wavelengths at these high frequencies present many problems in measurement transducer design. Consider, for example, how one can build an omnidirectional hydrophone that is small in comparison with a wavelength if the wavelength is only one millimeter! If one seeks an omnidirectional pattern in only one plane by resorting to a ceramic cylinder that is not small in comparison with a wavelength, it still is necessary to fabricate the cylinder and to mount it with a degree of dimensional accuracy and symmetry compatible with the millimeter wavelength. The narrow beam of the E8 at megahertz frequencies illustrates a second problem. High transmitted power requires a large transmitting area. But a large transmitting area results in extremely narrow beams. Thus, high signal levels and even moderate beamwidths are incompatible at millimeter wavelengths.

### 5.9.5 Type G23

The USRD type G23 is typical of transducers designed as projectors for small high-pressure tanks and the infrasonic- and audio-frequency range below 1 kHz.

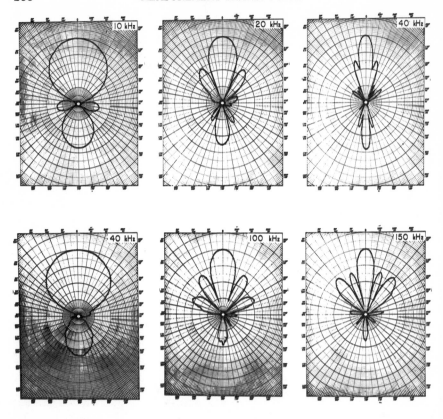

Fig. 5.32. Typical directivity patterns in the horizontal plane, USRD type F33 transducer. Top row, both sections in parallel; bottom row, inner section only.

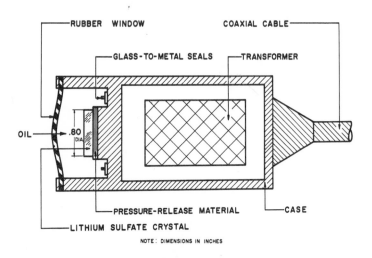

Fig. 5.33. USRD type E8 transducer.

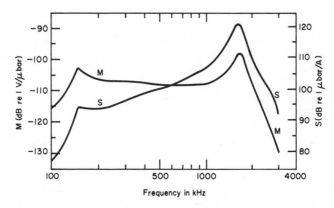

Fig. 5.34. Typical free-field voltage sensitivity $M$ and transmitting current response $S$ of USRD type E8 transducer.

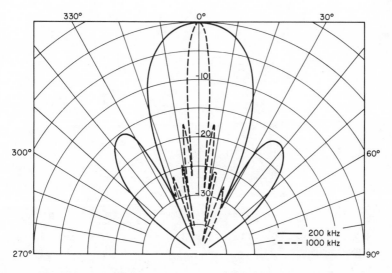

Fig. 5.35. Directivity, USRD type E8 transducer, in planes that include the axis.

Moving-coil transducers are not used at pressures above 1000 psi because of the hazards of using high-pressure gas in the compensating system. Also, the maximum static differential pressure on the diaphragm (±1 psi) remains constant as the static pressure increases, thus the compensating system must become increasingly sensitive and, consequently, increasingly complicated and large.

Fortunately, the methods used for calibrating transducers at high pressures and low frequencies involve small tanks or chambers (see Sections 2.2.3, 2.3.6, 2.3.7, and 2.5.1). The radiation load on the projector is essentially the bulk compliance of the water in the tank. Then, the sound pressure is proportional to the volume displacement of the projector. Where the tank is small, as with a coupler described in Section 2.3.7, a small stack expander of piezoelectric material like lithium sulfate or lead metaniobate can be used. For larger tanks with volumes of several cubic feet, the amount of crystal or ceramic becomes so large that the cost becomes prohibitive. In such cases the type G23 shown in Fig. 5.36 is used.

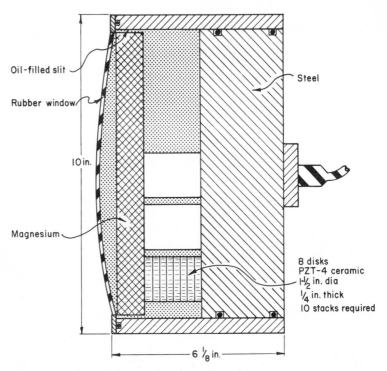

Fig. 5.36. Section through USRD type G23 transducer. PZT-4 ceramic is lead zirconate titanate.

In the G23, ten parallel stacks of lead zirconate titanate ceramic disks drive forward against a relatively light magnesium front plate or diaphragm, and backward against a heavy steel backing plate. The hydrostatic pressure is distributed throughout the transducer by filling all voids with silicone oil. Most of the volume displacement is provided by the magnesium front plate, and the displacement is proportional to the voltage applied to the ceramic. The sound pressure in the oil inside the transducer will be opposite in phase to the sound pressure on the outside or in the tank. For this reason, the oil-filled slits at the periphery of the front plate must have a high acoustic impedance to avoid shunting the sound pressure in the tank. This same problem is discussed in connection with the type J9 in Section 5.10.

The G23 is used in a tank 11 in. in diameter and 5 ft long. In this tank, sound pressures of 63 to 78 dB referred to one microbar are produced in the frequency range 0.3 to 600 Hz when the projector is driven with a nominal 500 volts. The low-frequency response is limited acoustically by the acoustic impedance of the peripheral slit that functions as a low-pass filter around the front plate and electrically by the problem of driving a capacitive load with almost a direct-current signal.

The G23 is used to 1000 psig, but similar designs have been built for pressures to 10,000 psig.

### 5.10  Type J9 Moving-Coil Projector Design

Unlike the case of piezoelectric transducers, one moving-coil projector design concept can be used for all measurement applications where a moving-coil transducer is desirable or useful. This design is exemplified by the USRD type J9 designed by C. C. Sims.[16]

The USRD type J9 was developed in 1958 as a projector and reciprocal transducer for the frequency range 40 Hz to 20 kHz. The design and a typical transmitting response are shown in Figs. 5.37 and 5.38.

A lightweight, but stiff, 2-1/4-in.-diameter diaphragm is supported by a rubber suspension system that permits large linear movement of the diaphragm.

When the transducer is submerged, water enters the rear compensation chamber and compresses the butyl rubber bag until the internal air pressure is equal to the external water pressure. The diaphragm does not then undergo any static displacement when the depth is changed. This compensation system works to an 80-ft depth. Beyond that, a Scuba-type compensation system must be used. The compliance of the air inside the transducer is one of the factors in the fundamental and highly damped resonance below 200 Hz. The change in this compliance with static pressure causes the response below 200 Hz to be a function of the depth.

The peak in the response at 20 kHz is due to a flexure resonance in the diaphragm. At still higher frequencies, other resonances cause wild fluctuations in the response curve. The J9, as with all moving-coil transducers, is not very efficient—less than 1%. The maximum input power is 20 W at frequencies above 200 Hz. The USRD type J11 is a larger version of the J9 with a 4-in.-diameter diaphragm and a narrower bandwidth. The J11 is a few dB more sensitive, but, more important, it can accept 200 W of power. It is feasible also to use either the J9 or J11 in clusters of 2 or more units to obtain higher level signals.

The J9 is omnidirectional at low and mid-audio frequencies. At the high audio frequencies, it has a very wide beamwidth typical of a 2-in.-diameter piston.

Prior to the development of the J9, all moving-coil transducers for use in water were designed with one seemingly unavoidable defect: The spring suspension at the periphery of the diaphragm had to have large mechanical compliance to permit large diaphragm displacement. Ordinarily this meant that the acoustic

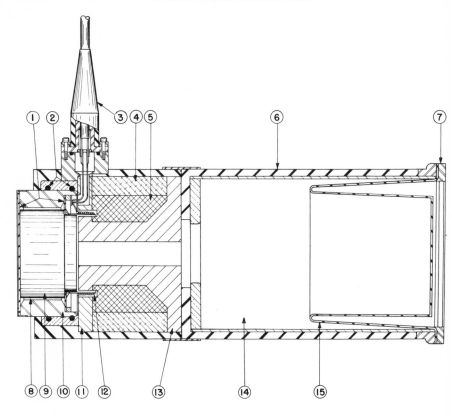

Fig. 5.37. Assembly drawing, USRD type J9 transducer; 1, rubber seals; 2, rubber O-rings; 3, cable gland; 4, magnet; 5, lead; 6, rubber jacket; 7, grille; 8, slit filled with silicone oil; 9, magnesium diaphragm; 10, diaphragm housing; 11, front pole piece; 12, coil; 13, back pole piece; 14, compensating air chamber; 15, rubber compensating bag. Over-all length, 11 in.; diameter, 4-1/2 in.

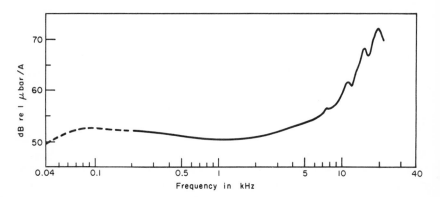

Fig. 5.38. Typical transmitting current response of USRD type J9 transducer. Response below 0.2 kHz is a function of depth.

impedance of the transducer also was low at the diaphragm periphery as viewed from the water. Under such conditions, the sound pressure generated in front of the diaphragm was shunted, or could not be sustained, by the low acoustic impedance at the periphery. In the J9, the shunt is avoided by the dual rubber suspension on the front and back of the diaphragm and the silicone-oil-filled slit between the two rubber suspensions.

## 5.11 Reciprocal Transducers

The theoretical requirements for a reciprocal transducer are given in Section 2.3. In practice, any ordinary piezoelectric or moving-coil transducer probably is reciprocal if it is reversible, passive, and used with signal levels in the linear range. For a transducer to be reversible, it usually is sufficient that it have no pre-amplifier or other nonreversible electrical circuit. The passive requirement eliminates transducers that require any kind of bias current or voltage.

The linearity requirement limits signal levels to a restricted range of values. That is, the transducer should not be over-driven. This is particularly true of moving-coil transducers at and near resonance.

Methods for testing for reciprocity are explained in Section 2.3.

All of the projectors described in Sections 5.9 and 5.10 are used both as projectors and reciprocal transducers.

## 5.12 Doublet Transducers

Doublet transducer is a general term for velocity and pressure-gradient hydrophones and doublet or dipole projectors. This type of transducer functions as two, small, closely spaced transducers operating 180° out of phase. In practice, the two transducers usually are the opposite sides or ends of a single element oscillating in a translational mode. Doublet transducers find more use in air (in the ribbon microphone, for example[25]) than they do in water. One reason for this is the shorter wavelengths, larger pressure gradients, and larger particle velocities in air.

The distinguishing and most useful feature of a doublet is its directivity pattern. If the two transducers are both very small in comparison with a wavelength in water and are separated by a distance also small in comparison with a wavelength, then the doublet has a figure-eight or cosine directivity pattern.[26] That is, the pressure at an angle $\theta$ is proportional to $\cos \theta$ as shown in Fig. 5.39. The pattern is essentially independent of frequency in the range where the initial assumptions about the dimensions are valid. Some theoretical discussions refer to pressure-gradient hydrophones of $n$ orders when the directivity pattern is given by the function $\cos^n \theta$. Thus, a pressure-gradient hydrophone of the zero order is omnidirectional. In practice, the term pressure-gradient means first-order pressure-gradient unless otherwise defined.

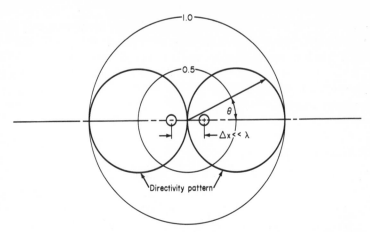

Fig. 5.39. Theoretical model of a doublet transducer as two out-of-phase point sources separated by a distance $\Delta x$, with a directivity pattern as a function of $\cos \theta$.

The use of a doublet transducer is the only practical method of obtaining even a modest degree of narrow-beam directivity at low and mid-audio frequencies without resorting to very large transducers.

The terms velocity and pressure-gradient hydrophones usually are used interchangeably; however, there are distinctions that can be made between the two types. These distinctions relate to the predicted calibration curve and are thereby helpful to those who use or calibrate such hydrophones.

Most velocity and pressure-gradient hydrophones consist of some type of element that vibrates under the influence of the pressure gradient or in the manner of the particle velocity in the water medium.

The relationship among the pressure, particle velocity, and pressure gradient in a plane progressive wave is given by

$$p = \rho c u, \tag{5.15}$$

$$\frac{\partial p_i}{\partial x} = -j\omega\rho u = -j\left(\frac{\omega}{c}\right)p, \tag{5.16}$$

where $p$ is the rms pressure, $u$ is the rms particle velocity, $p_i$ is the instantaneous pressure, $\partial p_i/\partial x$ is the pressure gradient at point $x$ and in the direction of the $x$ coordinate, $\omega$ is the angular frequency, $\rho$ is the density, and $c$ is the speed of sound.

From these equations, it is evident that, given a constant pressure $p$ as a function of frequency $\omega$, the particle velocity $u$ also will be constant, but the pressure gradient $\partial p_i/\partial x$ will be proportional to the frequency. It should be noted also from Eq. (5.16) that the velocity and pressure gradient are $90°$ out of phase.

Thus, if we define a velocity hydrophone as one wherein the voltage output of the hydrophone is proportional to $u$, the free-field voltage sensitivity of a velocity hydrophone will be constant or the frequency calibration curve will be flat. On the other hand, if a pressure-gradient hydrophone is defined as one where the voltage output is proportional to the pressure gradient, the free-field voltage sensitivity of such a hydrophone will be proportional to frequency, or the frequency calibration curve will have a 6-dB-per-octave slope.

Since the slope of a hydrophone's sensitivity curve depends on both the transduction principle used and on the mechanical impedance of the vibrating element, the same hydrophone usually will be a pressure-gradient hydrophone below, and a velocity hydrophone above, the resonant frequency. The definitions then describe, not the hydrophone design, but the idealized sensitivity-versus-frequency curve. In practice, the same hydrophone seldom is used at frequencies both below and above the resonant frequency. Consequently, the terminology usually is unambiguous and helpful.

The velocity of the vibrating element and the pressure gradient driving it are not necessarily the same as the particle velocity and pressure gradient in the plane progressive wave. A major design objective is somehow acoustically to amplify the wave velocity or pressure gradient so as to increase the hydrophone sensitivity at off-resonance frequencies.

Velocity and pressure-gradient hydrophones are calibrated in terms of the plane-wave sound pressure just as are pressure hydrophones. When in some special cases the plane-wave velocity is used as a reference, the calibration curve is adjusted by adding $20 \log \rho c$ or 103.5 dB.

### 5.12.1 Velocity hydrophones

A typical wide-range velocity hydrophone operates on the electric generator transduction principle in which a voltage $e$ is generated when a wire (usually a coil) of length $L$ cuts a magnetic field of flux density $B$ with a velocity $u_c$ according to the equation.

$$e = BLu_c. \tag{5.17}$$

One type is similar to that of a moving-coil transducer except that the sound pressure acts on opposite sides or ends of the coil so that the driving pressure is the instantaneous pressure difference $\Delta p_i$. The pressure difference is the pressure gradient in the sound field multiplied by the acoustic path difference $\Delta x$ between the two sides or ends of the coil exposed to the sound field, and by $\cos \theta$ as shown in Fig. 5.39. Thus,

$$\Delta p_i = \frac{\partial p_i}{\partial x} \Delta x \cos \theta. \tag{5.18}$$

Substituting Eq. (5.16) into (5.18) produces

$$\Delta p_i = -j\left(\frac{\omega}{c}\right)p\Delta x \cos \theta.$$ (5.19)

The effective path difference $\Delta x$ has been found experimentally to approximate closely the physical dimension around whatever baffle surrounds the coil.

The quotient $\Delta p_i/u_c$ depends on the specific acoustic impedance of the coil and its suspension. The compliance of the coil suspension is made very high so that the coil mass and suspension compliance resonate below the frequency range of interest—50 to 100 Hz, for example. Then the impedance is essentially the coil and water-load mass reactance $j\omega m$, and

$$\frac{\Delta p_i}{u_c} = \frac{j\omega m}{S_c},$$ (5.20)

where $S_c$ is the area of the coil facing the sound pressure.

Combining Eqs. (5.17), (5.19), and (5.20) gives the free-field voltage sensitivity $e/p$:

$$\left|\frac{e}{p}\right| = \frac{BLS_c\Delta x \cos \theta}{mc}.$$ (5.21)

Equation (5.21) shows that the sensitivity is independent of frequency and proportional to $\cos \theta$.

The first velocity hydrophone of this type probably was the Bell Telephone Laboratory (BTL) type 1A designed about 1942 for the Underwater Sound Reference Laboratory.[23] Its coil and magnet arrangement are shown in Fig. 5.40. The magnet was suspended from a light frame and assumed to be relatively motionless. A typical calibration curve is shown in Fig. 5.41. As with other transducers, spurious vibrations distort the curve. The type 1A has a very low sensitivity. Some more recent designs based on the mass-controlled moving-coil principle have higher sensitivities in the −110 to −120 dB range. Figure 5.42 shows another coil and magnetic field arrangement by B. B. Bauer at CBS Laboratories.[27]

The sound rays depicted by arrows in both Figs. 5.40 and 5.42 are not an accurate representation of the sound field around the hydrophone, but they do illustrate in a general way the extra acoustic path $\Delta x$.

Figure 5.43 shows a still different arrangement by Leslie, et al., at the Naval Ordnance Laboratory (NOL).[28] In the NOL hydrophone, the spherical shell and magnet vibrate while the coil is held stationary by the inertia of the internal mass that is approximately 3 times the mass of the displaced water. The mass of the shell plus the magnet is designed to be the same as the mass of the displaced water. Then the dynamic density of the hydrophone is the same as that of water, and the velocity of the sphere is the same as the plane-wave particle

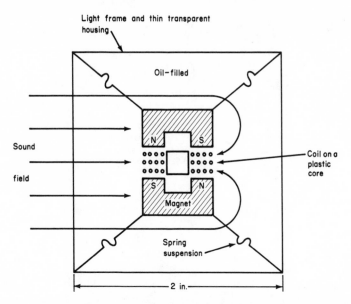

Fig. 5.40. Simplified horizontal cross-section of BTL type 1A hydrophone.

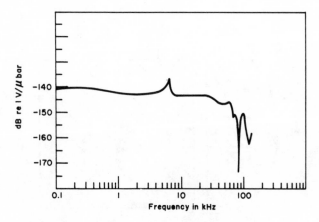

Fig. 5.41.  Free-field voltage sensitivity of BTL type 1A
hydrophone.

velocity in the plane of the center of the sphere.  Consequently, the sensitivity
derives directly from Eqs. (5.15) and (5.17):

$$\frac{e}{p} = \frac{BL}{\rho c}.$$  (5.22)

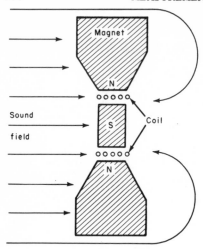

Fig. 5.42. Magnet and coil arrangement in CBS hydrophone.

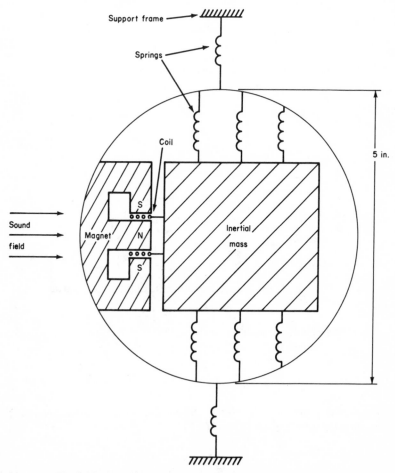

Fig. 5.43. Simplified drawing of NOL velocity hydrophone.

The resonant frequency of the internal mass and its suspension is put below the useful frequency range so that the impedance is mass controlled and the assumption of coil immobility due to inertia is valid.

### 5.12.2 Pressure-gradient hydrophones

A hydrophone developed by G. L. Boyer at the Navy David Taylor Model Basin (DTMB)[29] is shown in Fig. 5.44. The DTMB hydrophone is similar in design to the NOL velocity hydrophone shown in Fig. 5.43. Both have an average density the same as water so that they move with the same particle velocity as the displaced water, or, more strictly speaking, the average particle velocity over the 3-in. length of the hydrophone. Both have an internal mass in their electromechanical sensor and are typical of accelerometer designs. However, the DTMB hydrophone senses the vibration with a ceramic piezoelectric disk sandwiched between the outer housing and the internal mass. As a result of this feature, the free-field voltage sensitivity of the DTMB hydrophone is proportional to the pressure gradient rather than to the velocity.

The internal mass $m$ is not stationary. It exerts an inertial force $F$ on the ceramic disk which acts as a spring. The force $F$ is given by

$$F = m\left(\frac{du}{dt}\right) = m\omega u, \qquad (5.23)$$

where $u$ is the velocity of the mass.

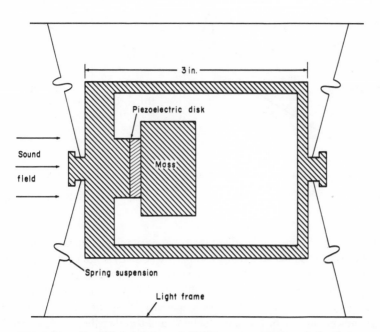

Fig. 5.44.  Simplified drawing of DTMB pressure-gradient hydrophone.

The ceramic is a very stiff spring of negligible mass, and the resonant frequency of the spring-mass is above the frequency range of interest. Then the internal mass, outer housing, and plane-wave particle velocities are all approximately the same. The voltage output $e$ of the piezoelectric disk is given by

$$e = gtSF, \tag{5.24}$$

where $g$ is the piezoelectric modulus, $t$ is the ceramic disk thickness, and $S$ is the disk area. From Eqs. (5.16), (5.23), and (5.24),

$$e = \left(\frac{gtSm}{\rho}\right)\left(\frac{\partial p_i}{\partial x}\right). \tag{5.25}$$

Thus, the output voltage is proportional to the pressure gradient, or, using Eqs. (5.15), (5.16), and (5.25), we obtain

$$\left|\frac{e}{p}\right| = \left(\frac{gtSm\omega}{\rho c}\right), \tag{5.26}$$

and the free-field voltage sensitivity is proportional to the frequency $\omega$. The sensitivity of the DTMB hydrophone is shown in Fig. 5.45.

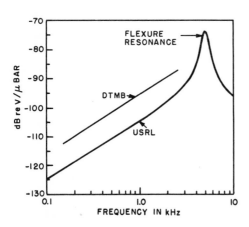

Fig. 5.45. Free-field voltage sensitivity, DTMB and USRL pressure-gradient hydrophones.

Another type of pressure-gradient hydrophone developed by C. C. Sims at the Navy Underwater Sound Reference Laboratory (USRL) is shown in Fig. 5.46. A thin lead zirconate titanate disk is cemented to a beryllium copper diaphragm surrounded by a tungsten collar. The difference in pressure on the two sides of the diaphragm drives the disk and diaphragm in a flexure or bending mode. The copper and ceramic are of the same thickness and together they form a bilaminar element. The ceramic disk diameter therefore is stretched on one half of the vibration cycle and compressed on the other half. The tungsten collar serves to hold the diaphragm edge immobile and provides a baffle to enlarge $\Delta x$.

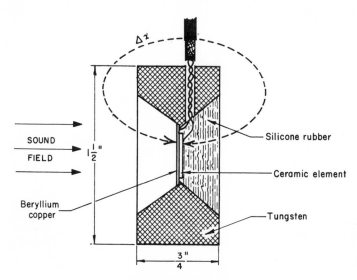

Fig. 5.46. USRL pressure-gradient hydrophone.

In the frequency range below the flexure resonance where the impedance of the bilaminar element is stiffness controlled, the voltage output of the piezoelectric disk is proportional to the bending pressure. The bending pressure $\Delta p$ is given by

$$\Delta p = \frac{\partial p_i}{\partial x} \Delta x. \qquad (5.27)$$

Thus, the voltage is proportional to the pressure gradient over the distance $\Delta x$. The free-field voltage sensitivity of the USRL hydrophone is shown in Fig. 5.45, and a typical directivity pattern in Fig. 5.47.

The pattern is typical of doublet transducers. A decibel scale is used. At $\pm 60°$, the sensitivity is 6 dB below that at $0°$, as would be expected from cos 60°.

Although less sensitive than the NOL type, the USRL design has the advantage of being small and requiring no fragile spring suspensions of any kind. The BTL and NOL types have spring suspensions on both the coil and magnet. The CBS type has a coil suspension, and the DTMB type, a housing suspension. All these suspensions must be carefully designed so that vibration is allowed in only one translational mode. Vibrations in the other two translational modes and any rotary motion is a source of error. The compliance of the magnet or housing suspension in the BTL, DTMB, and NOL types means that these hydrophones

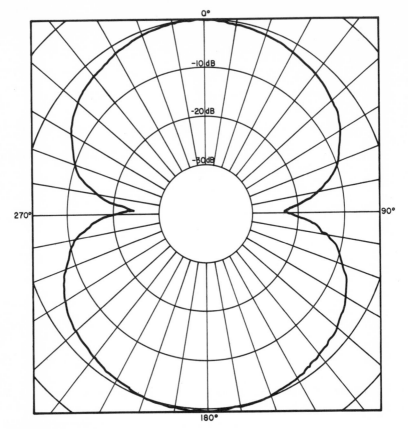

Fig. 5.47. Typical directivity in the horizontal plane at 4.0 kHz, USRL pressure-gradient hydrophone.

cannot be tipped or used to sense other than horizontal velocities or pressure gradients. The CBS and USRL hydrophones can be used in any orientation. The BTL hydrophone could have been designed without the compliant magnet suspension, the purpose of which was to isolate the magnet from mechanical vibration of the rigging.

The theoretical model of a doublet transducer shown in Fig. 5.39 as two closely spaced identical point transducers 180° out of phase can be physically approximated with two probe hydrophones electrically connected out of phase. This design, shown schematically in Fig. 5.48 is, of course, a pressure-gradient type. The electrical output is proportional to the phasor difference between the sound pressures at the two probes. This type requires that the two probes be electroacoustically identical, a difficult requirement to achieve in practice over a wide frequency range. It is easier to build a single-element hydrophone and, for

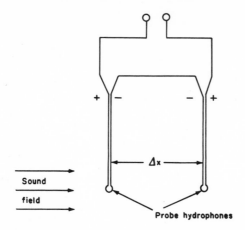

Fig. 5.48.  Two-pressure-probe pressure-gradient hydrophone.

this reason, the two-probe design has not found much use for wide-frequency-
range applications.


### 5.12.3  Doublet projectors

Doublet projectors are inherently low-response transducers because they have
built-in pressure cancellation.  That is, at one instant a positive pressure is being
generated at one end while a negative pressure is being generated at the same instant at the nearby other end.  Nevertheless, where the need for the cosine
directivity pattern outweighs the low response, they are used.

The NOL hydrophone in Fig. 5.43 has a relatively large area that serves as a
diaphragm, and it could be used as a projector.  It also has the low electrical
impedance that is necessary for a projector.  The DTMB hydrophone has the
large area, but the electrical impedance would be too high.

The projector counterpart of the two-probe pressure-gradient hydrophone
also can be used.  Two USRL type J9 transducers (see Section 5.10) set side by
side and electrically connected out of phase have been used as a quasi-doublet
projector to obtain discrimination against surface and bottom reflections in a
shallow lake.[30]  Two J9's are much too large to be a doublet transducer except
at the low audio frequencies; however, they provide a useful approximation to a
doublet projector up to several kilohertz.

# References

1. H. J. W. Fay, *Submarine Signal Log* (Raytheon Company, Submarine Signal Division, Portsmouth, R.I., 1963), Chap. V.

2. R. S. Woollett, "Transducer Comparison Methods Based on the Electromechanical Coupling-Coefficient Concept," 1957 Institute of Radio Engineers National Convention Record, Part 9, p. 23.

3. R. J. Bobber, "Diffraction Constants of Transducers," J. Acoust. Soc. Am. 37, 591 (1965).

4. T. A. Henriquez, "Diffraction Constants of Acoustic Transducers," J. Acoust. Soc. Am. 36, 267 (1964).

5. W. G. Cady, *Piezoelectricity* (McGraw-Hill Book Company, Inc., New York, 1946; new revised edition, Dover Publications, New York, 1964).

6. W. P. Mason, *Physical Acoustics* (Academic Press, New York, 1964), Vol. I, Part A.

7. W. P. Mason, *Piezoelectric Crystals and Their Application to Ultrasonics* (D. Van Nostrand Company, Inc., Princeton, N.J., 1950).

8. J. F. Nye, *Physical Properties of Crystals* (Clarendon Press, Oxford University Press, London and New York, 1957).

9. R. A. Langevin, "The Electro-Acoustic Sensitivity of Cylindrical Ceramic Tubes," J. Acoust. Soc. Am. 26, 421 (1954).

10. *Summary Technical Report of Division 6, NDRC,* Vol. 13, "The Design and Construction of Magnetostriction Transducers," Washington, D.C., 1946.

11. B. A. Wise, "Design of Nickel Magnetostriction Transducers," Development and Research Division, The International Nickel Company, New York, 1955. (Note: This is an INCO report written by B. A. Wise under contract to Battelle Memorial Institute.)

12. T. F. Hueter and R. H. Bolt, *Sonics* (John Wiley & Sons, Inc., New York, 1955), Chap. 5.

13. S. Butterworth and F. D. Smith, "The Equivalent Circuit of the Magnetostriction Oscillator," Proc. Phys. Soc. (London) 43, Part 2, 166 (1931).

14. L. Camp, "The Magnetostriction Radial Vibrator," J. Acoust. Soc. Am. 20, 289 (1948).

15. C. W. Rice and E. W. Kellogg, "Notes on the Development of a New Type of Hornless Loud Speaker," Trans. AIEE 44, 461 (1925).

16. C. C. Sims, "High-Fidelity Underwater Sound Transducers," Proc. IRE 47, 866 (1959).

17. I. D. Groves, "The USRL Infrasonic Hydrophone Type H11," Navy Underwater Sound Reference Laboratory Research Report No. 37, 3 Jan 1956 (AD-88 170).

18. I. D. Groves "The USRL Broadband Hydrophone Type H17," Navy Underwater Sound Reference Laboratory Research Report No. 59, 15 Feb 1962 (AD-271 910).

19. C. C. Sims, "Standard Calibration Hydrophone," J. Acoust. Soc. Am. 31, 1676 (1959).

20. C. C. Sims, "An Improved Noise-Measuring Hydrophone," Navy Underwater Sound Reference Laboratory Research Report No. 52, 18 Oct 1960 (AD-244 882).

21. C. C. Sims, "A Deep-Submergence Long-Life Hydrophone for Use in the Ocean at 2200 psi Pressure," Navy Underwater Sound Reference Laboratory Research Report No. 72, 3 Jun 1964 (AD-440 762).

22. L. E. Kinsler and A. R. Frey, *Fundamentals of Acoustics* (John Wiley and Sons, Inc., New York, 1962), 2nd ed., Chap. 8.

23. *Summary Technical Report of Division 6, NDRC,* Vol. 11, "A Manual of Calibration Measurements of Sonar Equipment" Washington, D.C., 1946.

24. R. J. Bobber, "The USRL Type E8 Transducer," Navy Underwater Sound Reference Laboratory Research Report No. 22, 16 Jan 1952 (AD-10 093; PB-164 145).

25. H. F. Olson, *Acoustical Engineering* (D. Van Nostrand Company, Inc., Princeton, N.J., 1957), p. 279.

26. Reference 25, p. 32

27.  B. B. Bauer, "Measurement of Particle Velocity in Underwater Sound," in *Lateral Line Detectors*, P. Cahn (ed.) (Indiana University Press, Bloomington, Ind., 1967), Chap. 27.

28.  C. B. Leslie, J. M. Kendall, and J. L. Jones, "Hydrophones for Measuring Particle Velocity," J. Acoust. Soc. Am. 28, 711 (1956).

29.  G. L. Boyer, "Instrumentation for Measuring Underwater Acoustic Intensity," J. Acoust. Soc. Am. 32, 1519(A) (1960); also, USN David Taylor Model Basin Preliminary Report "Acoustic Intensity Meter" by G. L. Boyer, Dec 1959.

30.  R. J. Bobber, "Near Field of a Dipole for Measurements in Shallow Lakes," J. Acoust. Soc. Am. 40, 1300 (1966).

# Chapter VI

# MEASUREMENTS ON AUXILIARY MATERIALS

## 6.1 Introduction

Acoustic windows and domes, baffles, reflectors, anechoic coatings, and bulk sound absorbers are important in the functioning, application, and testing of underwater electroacoustic transducers. The techniques and facilities for evaluating these auxiliary materials are very similar to those used in transducer calibration measurements. Because of this intimate relationship, a chapter on measurements to evaluate such materials is included in this book even though these measurements are acoustic rather than electroacoustic.

The word "material" is used to mean any one of or any combination of windows, reflectors, baffles, anechoic coatings, and bulk absorbing materials. In most of the measurements, however, we evaluate not the material itself but a particular sample whose dimensions, configuration, and means of support all influence the result. Sometimes, the particular sample is a complete hardware item—a sonar dome or transducer window, for example. At other times, it is a partly complete hardware item, like a section of an anechoic coating. As we shall see, only in the evaluation of "bulk absorbing materials," among the five types of material evaluations, is the result independent of the particular sample dimension or configuration, and even here "bulk absorption" must be carefully defined (see Section 6.5).

Windows, reflectors, baffles, and anechoic coatings constitute a complete set of materials insofar as their function is concerned. Ideal specimens of the four materials will, respectively, (1) transmit 100%, (2) reflect 100%, (3) transmit 0%, and (4) reflect 0% of the sound incident on them. Each of these four materials can be evaluated by measuring the percentage of sound transmitted through and reflected from the material when a sample is immersed in water. These two measured characteristics, called the "insertion loss" and "echo reduction," are defined by

$$\text{Insertion loss} \quad = 20 \log \frac{\text{Incident sound pressure}}{\text{Transmitted sound pressure}} \cdot$$

$$\text{Echo reduction} = 20 \log \frac{\text{Incident sound pressure}}{\text{Reflected sound pressure}} \cdot$$

Plane-wave propagation is assumed in both definitions. As defined, both characteristics are expressed in positive decibel units. These terms are preferred over similar terms such as transmission loss and reflection loss, because they are less ambiguous, they conflict less with terms used in architectural acoustics and electrical engineering, and the names relate directly to the measurement technique.

In some measurements, "absorption loss" is computed from the insertion loss and echo reduction by assigning all missing sound energy to absorption. This is not a good procedure if the material is not an absorber, which usually is true of windows, reflectors, and baffles, because in practice more sound energy may be scattered, diffracted, or refracted than is absorbed.

The measurement of insertion loss and echo reduction is very simple in theory, but can be very difficult in practice.

Evaluation measurements of a bulk absorbing material are complex in both theory and practice. The significant characteristics of a bulk absorber are the attenuation constant $a$ and the complex wave number $k$, which are the real and imaginary parts of the complex propagation constant $\gamma$, where $\gamma = a + jk$. These terms are defined and discussed in Section 6.4.

In most respects, the evaluation measurement theory of acoustic materials is analogous to the same theory for evaluating electrical resistors, capacitors, inductors, and cables.

## 6.2  Insertion Loss

Insertion loss is the reduction in the signal, in decibels, caused by inserting the material between the sound source and the receiver with diffraction and refraction effects absent. The insertion loss of the material is due to the combination of sound reflected from the material and sound absorbed in the material. In any practical window material and in most baffles, however, the absorption is negligible.

The measurements are of two general types. In the early stages of developing a sonar dome, a transducer rubber boot, a soundproof housing, and so forth, the best material usually is selected on the basis of measurements made on samples in the form of plane sheets. The sample is large enough for the insertion loss to be essentially independent of the lateral dimensions, though still dependent on the thickness. That is, the sample is intended to simulate an infinitely long and wide sample.

In the second type of measurement, the material is of the size and configuration in which it will be used. In the case of a sonar dome, the material is in its streamlined shape, complete with structural reinforcement, holes, flanges, and so forth. In the second type of measurement, the conditions under which the insertion loss is measured should be the same as the conditions of actual use. For example, measurements on a sonar dome should be made with the actual sonar transducer inside the dome. The insertion loss then depends on the shape, size, and mounting of the dome, the sonar transducer, and added hardware such as reinforcing structure and the flange needed to attach the dome to a ship. Ideally, the ship hull also should be in place, but this usually is impractical.

Data obtained from measurements on a sheet are subject to theoretical analysis and prediction. The results of hardware measurements usually are not.

### 6.2.1 Theoretical insertion loss

When plane waves impinge normally on a plate of a homogeneous non-absorbing material of uniform thickness, and water is on both sides of the plate, the theoretical insertion loss is given by

$$\text{Insertion loss} = 10 \log \left[ \frac{(1 - m^2)^2}{4m^2} (\sin^2 kx) + 1 \right], \qquad (6.1)$$

where $m$ is the ratio of the characteristic impedance $\rho c$ of the material to the characteristic impedance of water $(\rho_w c_w \simeq 1.5 \times 10^6 \text{ rayls})$, $k$ is the wave number, and $x$ is the thickness of the plate. Figure 6.1 shows insertion loss curves for steel and cork plotted from Eq. (6.1) and using $m = 26$ and $c = 5{,}000$ m/sec for steel and $m = 1/12$ and $c = 500$ m/sec for cork. Equation (6.1) remains unchanged if $1/m$ is substituted for $m$. Physically, this means a high-impedance material such as tin $(m = 12)$ can have the same insertion loss as a low-impedance material such as cork $(m = 1/12)$, where $m$ for one material is the reciprocal of $m$ for the other material, and $kx$ is the same in each case.

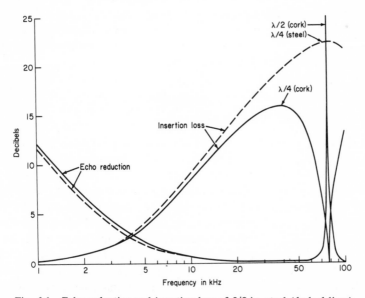

Fig. 6.1. Echo reduction and insertion loss of 5/8-in. steel (dashed lines) and 1/8-in. cork (solid lines) in water.

The insertion loss becomes zero whenever $kx = 0$, $\pi$, $2\pi$, $3\pi$, etc. Thus, any nonabsorbing material is transparent when the thickness is near a multiple of a half wavelength. The insertion loss also is zero when a perfect impedance match exists, or when $m = 1$. The maximum insertion loss occurs when $kx = \pi/2$, $3\pi/2$, $5\pi/2$, etc., or when the thickness is an odd multiple of a quarter wavelength.

It is well known that a layer of air is a very good baffle for underwater sound because $m = 1/3600$. A layer of air in the form of an independent baffle, however, is very difficult to achieve in practice. One approach is to use an air sandwich; that is, two sheets of metal or other stiff material, sealed at the edges, with air between. There are two practical problems with air sandwiches. They must either be pressure compensated or have supports between the plates to prevent the hydrostatic pressure from bending or even collapsing the metal plates. Second, the plates must be rigidly joined at the edges. Any supports and rigid edge joints act as acoustic short circuits; that is, the sound vibration will be transmitted through these rigid parts, bypassing the air layer. If the supports are closely spaced, as in a honeycomb, the sandwich acutally becomes a good acoustic window. When an air sandwich is evaluated as a baffle, therefore, it is necessary to qualify the measured insertion loss as applying only to the particular sample tested. Another baffle with the same metal-air-metal thickness dimension but different lateral dimensions, internal supports, or edges could have a different insertion loss.

A second approach to air baffles is to assume that cork, or a cork-neoprene mixture called Corprene, is essentially the same as air, acoustically. From the values of $m = 1/12$ for cork and $m = 1/3600$ for air, it can be seen that this may not be a very good assumption. In fact, cork has a better impedance match with water than does steel ($m = 26$). The slow speed of sound in cork is an advantage, however; a wavelength in cork is only one-tenth as long as a wavelength in steel, and consequently a cork baffle can be much thinner than an equivalent steel baffle.

### 6.2.2 Measurement of insertion loss

Insertion loss measurement is a straightforward procedure. A projector-to-hydrophone signal is measured before and after the insertion of the material between the two transducers, and the difference is noted. Although pulsed sound as described in Section 3 is preferred, a c-w (continuous-wave) signal can be used, and has some advantages at very low frequencies. Interference caused by reflections from the surface and bottom and from the rigging, and diffraction of sound around the sample are sources of error. The error introduced by such interference is minimized by keeping the distance from projector to hydrophone short. Rigging reflections are minimized by keeping frameworks as remote as possible and acoustically as transparent as possible. The measurement arrangement and the interfering signals are illustrated in Fig. 6.2.

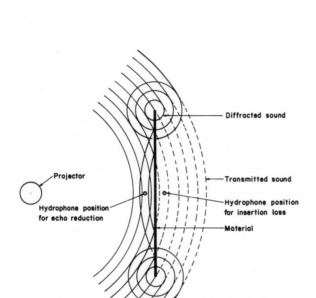

Fig. 6.2. Arrangement for measurement of insertion loss and echo reduction showing edge diffraction waves.

Plane-wave propagation was assumed in the definition of insertion loss, but, of course, spherical waves are used in practice. As in the calibration of hydrophones, if the hydrophone is small enough so that it intercepts an essentially plane-wave segment of a spherical wave, the measurement is valid.

Diffraction interference is minimized by using the largest possible sample size and by using asymmetrical geometry—that is, by using square or rectangular samples and by having the imaginary line connecting the projector and hydrophone asymmetrical with respect to the sample. The connecting line should not pass through the center of the sample. These two conditions destroy the coherence of the diffraction interference. That is, the infinite number of ray paths around the sample will, with a few exceptions, all be of different lengths. Consequently, the signals for each path measured at the hydrophone will not be in phase with each other. The result is a phasor sum that is lower than the sum for the symmetrical case.

A circular sample and a hydrophone position on the centerline of the sample is the worst arrangement because it produces the largest diffraction signal. Even if the sample is perfectly opaque, the intensity at the hydrophone position is the same as if the sample were not there! This corresponds to the bright spot behind a circular opaque obstacle that is well known in optics.

The intensity of the diffraction around the edge is proportional to the impedance mismatch between the sample material and water. Thus, the diffracted signal intensity is lower in measurements on window materials than on baffles. Moreover, since the signal level transmitted through a window is higher than that through a baffle, the ratio of diffracted signal level to transmitted signal level is much higher in baffle measurements than in window measurements. Window insertion-loss measurements have been made on samples as small as two wavelengths square. The insertion loss as a function of angle of incidence is measured by rotating the sample in its position between the projector and the hydrophone. Since the effective width, or width normal to the imaginary line joining the projector and hydrophone, becomes smaller as the sample begins to rotate, the diffraction becomes worse. Measurements at grazing angles, or angles of incidence near 90°, become difficult unless the sample is very large. Angles of incidence other than normal also give rise to shear and transverse waves in the sample. Then, measurements on small samples involve very complicated wave phenomena and are not very useful; measurements on the finished hardware item become very important.

### 6.3 Echo Reduction

Echo reduction is the important parameter of reflectors and anechoic coatings. It is a measure of how much the incident sound pressure level is reduced after reflection.

Echo reduction depends on the acoustical impedance mismatch at the reflecting boundary. The boundary acoustical impedance in turn depends on the material itself, its thickness, and usually on how the material is "backed up."

As with insertion loss, there are two general types of echo reduction measurements—those on sample sheets, and those on complete hardware items.

Anechoic coatings, unlike windows, baffles, and reflectors, sometimes are not made of a homogeneous material. Windows, baffles, or reflectors require only a good acoustical impedance match or mismatch with water. An anechoic coating has a more complicated function: It should make an otherwise good reflector appear to be acoustically transparent. First, the coating must have a good impedance match with the water so the sound energy will not be reflected. Second, after entering the coating, the sound energy must be absorbed, otherwise the sound will be reflected at some subsequent boundary such as the wall or ship hull to which the coating is attached. Thus, both the echo reduction and the insertion loss should be high.

It is difficult to make thin homogeneous anechoic coatings with absorbing characteristics that are independent of frequency. Anechoic coatings usually consist of a layer of rubber or rubber-like material mixed with either low-acoustic-impedance air voids or high-acoustic-impedance metal particles. The intent is to cause shear motions in the rubber rather than simple compression and elongation. The backing material is an integral part of the coating; for example, the thickness of the steel plate to which a coating usually is attached and the medium (air or water) behind the steel affect the anechoic characteristics. Because the coating is heterogeneous, it may be and usually is resonant. This results in large vibration amplitudes and large echo reduction in a narrow band of frequencies.

Reflectors are made simply of either a material having a very low acoustical impedance (cork, Corprene, or an air sandwich) or a very high acoustical impedance (steel, nickel, tungsten). In some special cases, various types of tuned or resonant spring-mass systems or quarter-wave stubs have been used to obtain high-impedance boundaries. Such devices are feasible only for a narrow band of frequencies.

If the angle of incidence is the variable, echo reduction needs further definition—specifying the reflection angle. Sometimes, specular reflection is of primary interest (a material for a tri-plane target simulator or an acoustic mirror); at other times, most of the sound may be reflected, but not necessarily as a specular reflection (a nonplanar surface). This ambiguity is present in all reflection measurements; consequently, the intended use of the material must be known and the appropriate kind of reflection must be measured. The terms "monostatic" and "bistatic" are used in this connection. Monostatic pertains to a measurement at one point; that is, the source and receiver are at the same point, or the angle of incidence and reflection are the same angle. Bistatic pertains to two points; that is, the source is at one angle and the receiver at another. Specular reflection is the special case of bistatic reflection when the angle of reflection is equal and opposite to the angle of incidence.

### 6.3.1 Theoretical echo reduction

As with insertion loss, theoretical echo reduction can be computed most easily for sound incident normally on a uniform plate of nonabsorbing material immersed in water. Other situations are more complex and are beyond the scope of this book.

The theoretical echo reduction for a nonabosrbing homogeneous material in a water medium is given by

$$\text{Echo reduction} = 10 \log \left[ \frac{4m^2}{(1 - m^2)^2 \sin^2 kx} + 1 \right], \tag{6.2}$$

where $m$ and $kx$ are the same as in Eq. (6.1). As in Eq. (6.1), $1/m$ can be substituted for $m$ without changing the equation. Echo reduction decreases gradually with increasing frequency until the thickness becomes a quarter wavelength and then increases until the thickness becomes a half wavelength. When the $kx$ term in Eq. (6.2) is $\pi/2$, $3\pi/2$, $5\pi/2$, etc., or when the thickness is an odd multiple of a quarter wavelength, the echo reduction is a minimum. For either large or small values of $m$ (that is, for $m \gg 1$ or $m \ll 1$), the echo reduction is close to zero, but theoretically never reaches zero. When $kx = 0$, $\pi$, $2\pi$, etc., the sine term in Eq. (6.2) is zero and the reduction becomes infinite for any finite value of $m$. This means that any nonabsorbing material is perfectly transparent when the thickness is a multiple of a half wavelength. The echo reduction is infinite also when $m = 1$, of course. These are the same conclusions inferred from Eq. (6.1).

Figure 6.1 shows the echo reduction of two typical reflector-type materials. The 1/8-in. cork becomes completely transparent at 78 kHz. The corresponding frequency for the 5/8-in. steel is 186 kHz. Again we see that cork is not equivalent to air as is sometimes assumed. A true layer of air is a good reflector; a 1/8-in. layer has an echo reduction of only 0.0004 dB at 1 kHz.

### 6.3.2 Measurement of echo reduction

Echo reduction usually is measured with the arrangement shown in Fig. 6.2. Both the incident sound and the reflected sound are measured by the probe hydrophone placed close to the material sample. Two techniques are used to separate the two measured signals. With a short pulse technique, the incident and reflected sounds can be separated by the time interval required for the pulse to travel the path from the hydrophone to the sample and back to the hydrophone. With an interferometer technique, the two signals are allowed to overlap, and are computed from the maximum and minimum signal levels that result from constructive and destructive interference.

As with the measurement of insertion loss, reflections and diffraction are the main measurement problems. The diffraction effects are more than the conventional diffraction "around" an obstacle. When plane waves impinge normally on a reflecting plate, the reflected sound is indistinguishable from the sound that would emanate from the plate if the plate were vibrating as a source. Thus, a probe near the plate is in the near field or Fresnel zone of the plate. The reflected sound can be considered to be the combination of two waves: (1) a plane wave of the same amplitude and phase as would be reflected from an infinitely large plate, and (2) a diffracted wave that appears to emanate from the edge of the plate, and which is similar to the diffracted wave that "goes around" the plate in an insertion-loss measurement.

When short pulses of sound are used and the incident and reflected sounds are separated in time, it is necessary also to separate the reflected and diffracted pulses. The two separation requirements have opposite effects on the selection of the sample-to-probe distance. Increasing this distance increases the reflected and incident pulse separation but decreases the reflected and diffracted pulse separation. Decreasing the distance has a reverse effect. In practice, the distance is kept as small as possible and minimum pulse lengths are used. The pulse length cannot be made shorter than about two cycles, however, which sets a low-frequency limit for the technique. Longer minimum pulse lengths are needed for resonant reflectors.   Short-pulse sound-reflection measurements in water generally are useful only when the sample is five or more wavelengths long and wide.

Diffraction effects are minimized by asymmetrical geometry as described in Section 6.2.2 for insertion-loss measurements.

Measuring the pulse reflected from a resonant coating is complicated by the fact that the coating acts like a notch filter. The fundamental or carrier frequency is attenuated much more at the resonance frequency of the coating than are the sideband frequencies in the pulse spectrum; consequently, the high echo reduction at resonance is masked by the lower echo reduction at the sideband frequencies. A very narrow-band wave analyzer at the output of the probe hydrophone is needed to obtain the true echo reduction near the resonance frequency.

At low frequencies (long wavelengths), where short pulses are not feasible, an interference technique can be used. A probe hydrophone is placed close to the sample where it will simultaneously receive the signal that arrives directly from a distant source and a signal that arrives after reflection from the sample. Either c-w or long-pulse signals are used. A long pulse is one that is long enough to cause overlapping of the direct and reflected signals but still short enough to "gate out" diffraction, surface reflection, and so forth. The probe measures the phasor sum of the incident and reflected sound pressures. By sweeping through a range of frequencies, the phase between the incident and reflected signals will change continually. The magnitude of the sum signal will oscillate between the in-phase and the out-of-phase conditions with a pattern similar to that produced by interference from surface reflections, standing waves, or crosstalk in transducer calibration measurements. We are, in fact, deliberately producing standing waves. The probe should be at least one quarter wavelength from the reflecting surface and preferably several wavelengths away. If the probe is too close, the frequency interval between peaks (or nulls) in the oscillation pattern is large, and the pattern is difficult to identify. Figure 6.3 shows an example in which the interfering signal or reflection is half the direct signal and illustrates how the relative amplitude of two interfering signals is found with the aid of Fig. 6.4 or Table 6.1. Since the direct signal alone can be obtained by merely removing the sample, the interference-to-direct signal ratio can be obtained either as a numeric ratio or in decibels from any of the three measured values in Fig. 6.3; that is, from (1) MAX (2) MIN, or (3) MAX + MIN. Since the depth of sharp nulls is subject to greater error than is the rounded maximums, the MAX measurement shown in the figures is most reliable. Table 6.1 is merely a tabulation of the same values presented graphically in Fig. 6.4 and is more suitable for small or precise values. The interference technique is similar in principle to the technique used in air acoustics to measure the acoustic impedance at a boundary terminating a tube.

In practice, the sound waves that impinge on the sample reflector are not plane. Normally, this does not affect the measurements unless it results in transverse wave motion. It may help to some extent because it introduces a shading effect. That is, considering the plate as a vibrating source, the vibration at the periphery will be slightly lower in amplitude than, and have a phase lag with

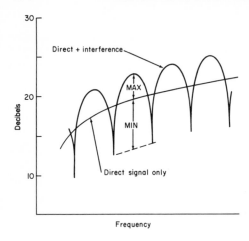

Fig. 6.3. Effect of interference on a direct signal. MAX = 3.5 dB. MIN = 6 dB. From Fig. 6.4 or Table 6.1, the ratio of interference signal level to direct signal level is 0.5, or 6 dB down.

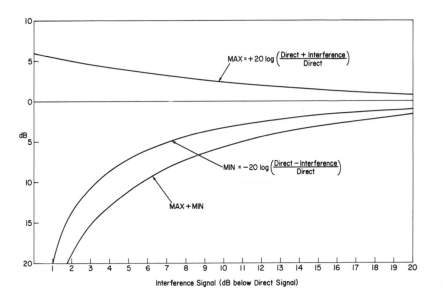

Fig. 6.4. Magnitude of interference signals.

respect to, the vibration at the center. Such shading reduces the near-field undulations caused by edge diffraction. The spreading loss of spherical waves does mean, however, that a distance loss correction must be applied to the measured ratio of reflected signal level to direct signal level. Whenever sound impinges on a material at angles other than normal incidence, transverse waves may be excited in the material. Such waves may interfere with the longitudinal waves that are presumed to carry all the sound energy. Consequently, the measurement

Table 6.1.  Magnitude of Interference

$D$ = Direct Signal                                    $I$ = Interference Signal

| $I/D$ | | Max $[(D+I)/D]$ | | Min $[(D-I)/D]$ | | Max-to-Min Spread |
|---|---|---|---|---|---|---|
| −dB | Ratio | +dB | Ratio | −dB | Ratio | dB |
| 0.0 | 1.000 | 6.0 | 2.000 | ∞ | 0.000 | ∞ |
| 0.5 | .944 | 5.8 | 1.944 | 25.0 | .056 | 30.8 |
| 1.0 | .891 | 5.5 | 1.891 | 19.9 | .109 | 25.4 |
| 1.5 | .841 | 5.3 | 1.841 | 16.0 | .159 | 21.3 |
| 2 | .794 | 5.1 | 1.794 | 13.7 | .206 | 18.8 |
| 3 | .708 | 4.7 | 1.708 | 10.7 | .292 | 15.4 |
| 4 | .631 | 4.3 | 1.631 | 8.7 | .369 | 13.0 |
| 5 | .562 | 3.9 | 1.562 | 7.2 | .438 | 11.2 |
| 6 | .501 | 3.5 | 1.501 | 6.1 | .499 | 9.6 |
| 7 | .447 | 3.2 | 1.447 | 5.1 | .553 | 8.3 |
| 8 | .398 | 2.9 | 1.398 | 4.4 | .602 | 7.3 |
| 9 | .355 | 2.6 | 1.355 | 3.8 | .645 | 6.4 |
| 10 | .316 | 2.4 | 1.316 | 3.3 | .684 | 5.7 |
| 12 | .251 | 2.0 | 1.251 | 2.5 | .749 | 4.5 |
| 14 | .200 | 1.6 | 1.200 | 1.9 | .800 | 3.5 |
| 16 | .159 | 1.3 | 1.159 | 1.5 | .841 | 2.8 |
| 18 | .126 | 1.0 | 1.126 | 1.2 | .874 | 2.2 |
| 20 | .100 | 0.8 | 1.100 | 0.9 | .900 | 1.7 |
| 25 | .056 | 0.5 | 1.056 | 0.5 | .944 | 1.0 |
| 30 | .032 | 0.3 | 1.032 | 0.3 | .968 | 0.6 |
| 35 | .018 | 0.2 | 1.018 | 0.2 | .982 | .4 |
| 40 | .010 | 0.1 | 1.012 | 0.1 | .990 | .2 |

conditions should duplicate as closely as possible the ideal plane longitudinal wave condition whenever transverse wave motion is likely.

## 6.4  Bulk Absorbing Materials.

Evaluation of bulk absorbing materials requires measurement techniques completely different from those used to evaluate windows, reflectors, baffles, and anechoic coatings.  The latter materials generally are in the form of a slab, plate, sheet, or layer. The dimensions, particularly the thickness, are chosen to meet some particular need and the evaluation results usually apply only to samples of these dimensions. An absorbing material, as the term is used here, is a material like wood, oil, rubber, soil, and so forth, whose sound absorption depends on its particle or molecular content or structure, and not on the dimensions or configuration of the material. When we evaluate an absorbing material, we evaluate the material itself; however, this does not mean that the dimensions or shape in which an absorbing material is used is unimportant. Wedges are used in anechoic rooms and tanks because the wedges form a boundary that increases the percentage of sound entering the wedge material rather than being reflected away. In solid materials, the configuration is important because the elastic behavior depends on the geometry of the applied stress and allowed strain. (See Section 6.5.)

One practical difference between an analysis of an anechoic coating and an absorbing material is that the coating is analyzed as a lumped-parameter system but the material is analyzed basically as a distributed system. Equivalent circuits can be used to represent coatings, but materials are studied as transmission lines, although short lines as special cases may reduce to a lumped-parameter system. An absorbing material can be treated as a lumped impedance to the extent that a short electrical cable is treated as a capacitor. The material must be both thin and homogeneous, if this treatment is to be used.

In the analysis of acoustic transmission lines and acoustic impedance that follows, the symbols $c$, $\lambda$, $\rho$, $s$, $C$, $p$, $\omega$, $t$, and $x$ will have their familiar definitions of speed, wavelength, density, stiffness, compliance, pressure, angular frequency, time, and distance, respectively. The symbol $k$ denotes the wave number and is equal to $\omega/c$ or $2\pi/\lambda$. The symbol $Z_0$ represents the characteristic impedance of the medium. When $c'$, $\lambda'$, $\rho'$, $s'$, $C'$, $k'$, and $Z_0'$ are used, the prime denotes that the parameters pertain to an absorbing medium. Such parameters are referred to as "complex" where the word carries the same connotation that it has in "complex number" or "complex impedance." The physical significance or meaning of the complex parameters is discussed in later paragraphs.

Stiffness as used here is the same as the plate elastic modulus. That is, it is the quotient of the stress (force/area) to the strain (displacement/thickness), where the stress is being extended normal to a plate and the strain exists and is measured only in the plate thickness direction. The stiffness then is related to the acoustic impedance per unit area $Z_a$ (pressure/volume velocity) by $Z_a = s/j\omega x$, where $x$ is the thickness. Thus, stiffness is the negative reactance of a sample of unit cross-sectional area and unit thickness. The elastic behavior of solids depends on which combination of three-dimensional stresses and strains are allowed. The stiffness of a solid, therefore, does not have a unique meaning. The different kinds of elastic moduli are discussed in Section 6.5.

Compliance is the reciprocal of stiffness. Stiffness is the older of the two terms and is familiar from classical physics and mechanics. Compliance is a newer term that is particularly convenient when electromechanical analogies are used. Compliance is directly analogous to electrical capacitance, whereas stiffness

is inversely related to capacitance.  All the relationships of electrical transmission line theory therefore can be used to describe an acoustic transmission
line when the following substitutions are made:

compliance → capacitance per unit length
density → inductance per unit length
admittance of complex compliance → open-circuit admittance per unit length
impedance of complex density → short-circuit impedance per unit length

A bulk absorbing material is characterized by its complex propagation constant
$\gamma = a + jk$, where $a$ is the attenuation constant.  In addition to $a$ and $k$, other
parameters are used by various authors—usually because they are useful in special
cases.  These other parameters include the loss factor $\eta$, the loss angle $\delta$, the complex stiffness or compliance, and the complex density.

### 6.4.1  The attenuation constant $a$

The attenuation constant $a$ is the signal loss of a plane wave per unit distance
in the medium.  The loss is expressed as the natural logarithm of the ratio of the
signal amplitudes at two points.  In mathematical terms,

$$ax = \ln \frac{p_1}{p_2} , \qquad (6.3)$$

where $x$ is the distance between the points at which $p_1$ and $p_2$ are measured.
The value of $a$ is measured in nepers/cm.  If a medium has a loss of 1 neper/cm,
the signal decreases by $1/e$ every centimeter.  The neper is similar to the bel in
being a logarithm of a ratio.  It differs in being based on natural rather than common logarithms, and is defined as the logarithm of a ratio of pressures, voltages,
or other parameters proportional to the square root of power, rather than to
power itself.  One neper equals 8.686 dB.
The attenuation constant is most useful in describing a medium when the
medium is considered to be distributed rather than lumped.  In practice, this
means that the dimension in the direction of wave propagation is larger than about
$\lambda/10$.  Consider a plane pressure wave in a lossless medium: The instantaneous
pressure $p_i$ at any time $t$ and any point $x$ is

$$p_i = p_0 e^{j(\omega t - kx)}, \qquad (6.4)$$

where $p_0$ is the pressure amplitude.  If the medium dissipates energy and the
ratio $p_1/p_2$ is independent of the initial amplitude, the pressure amplitude decreases exponentially with the distance $x$ and is

$$|p_i| = p_0 e^{-ax}. \qquad (6.5)$$

The complete expression for $p_i$ in an absorbing medium is, then,

$$p_i = p_0 e^{-ax} e^{j(wt - kx)},  \tag{6.6}$$

or

$$p_i = p_0 e^{-j[\omega t - (k - ja)x]}.  \tag{6.7}$$

Now we can define a complex wave number $k' = k - ja$ and substitute $k'$ into Eq. (6.7), making it look like Eq. (6.4):

$$p_i = p_0 e^{j(\omega t - k'x)}.  \tag{6.8}$$

Equations (6.4) and (6.8) illustrate the point that any equation applying to a lossless transmission line can be altered to apply to a lossy line by changing all the appropriate parameters from their real to their complex forms. By "appropriate" parameters we mean those whose values depend on the characteristics of the medium, such as $\rho$, $c$, $s$, $k$, $\lambda$, and $Z_0$. The parameters $\omega$, $x$, and $t$ are not included. To illustrate with other equations that will be used later, consider the expression for the input impedance $Z_i$ of a finite transmission line $x$ units long, where $Z_L$ is the terminating load impedance. If the line is lossless,

$$Z_i = Z_0 \left[ \frac{Z_L \cos kx + jZ_0 \sin kx}{Z_0 \cos kx + jZ_L \sin kx} \right].  \tag{6.9}$$

If it is lossy, change $Z_0$ and $k$ to their complex forms:

$$Z_i = Z_0' \left[ \frac{Z_L \cos (k - ja)x + jZ_0' \sin (k - ja)x}{Z_0' \cos (k - ja)x + jZ_L \sin (k - ja)x} \right].  \tag{6.10}$$

Rearranging Eq. (6.10) and using standard identities between circular trigonometric and hyperbolic functions produces

$$Z_i = Z_0' \left[ \frac{Z_L \cosh (a + jk)x + Z_0' \sinh (a + jk)x}{Z_0' \cosh (a + jk)x + Z_L \sinh (a + jk)x} \right],  \tag{6.11}$$

or

$$Z_i = Z_0' \left[ \frac{Z_L \cosh \gamma x + Z_0' \sinh \gamma x}{Z_0' \cosh \gamma x + Z_L \sinh \gamma x} \right],  \tag{6.12}$$

where $\gamma = a + jk$. Equation (6.12) is the standard expression for any one-dimensional transmission line. Note from the definitions of $k'$ and $\gamma$ that $\gamma = jk'$, and

$$c' = \frac{\omega}{k'} = \frac{\omega}{k - ja} = \frac{\omega c}{\omega - jac} = \frac{c}{1 - \dfrac{ja}{k}}  \tag{6.13}$$

### 6.4.2 The loss factor $\eta$

A material has two loss factors $\eta_e$ and $\eta_\rho$ that are inherent properties of the material regardless of the material dimensions, but which are most useful in absorption measurements when used to characterize the absorption of thin layers. When an elastic material dissipates energy as it undergoes compression and extension, there is a loss component to its mechanical impedance or admittance. The elastic loss factor $\eta_e$ is defined in terms of the imaginary part of elastic impedance or admittance—that is, the stiffness or compliance.

$$s' = s(1 + j\eta_s) \qquad (\eta_e = \eta_s) \qquad (6.14)$$

$$C' = C(1 - j\eta_c) \qquad (\eta_e = \eta_c). \qquad (6.15)$$

When the elastic loss factor is discussed in general terms, the subscript $e$ will be used. When it is used as specifically defined by Eq. (6.14) or (6.15), the subscript $s$ or $c$ will be used.

When a material in motion is subjected to a viscous drag, there is a loss component to its inertial impedance. The density loss factor $\eta_\rho$ is defined in terms of the imaginary part of this inertial impedance:

$$\rho' = \rho(1 - j\eta_\rho). \qquad (6.16)$$

From Eqs. (6.14), (6.15), and (6.16), it can be seen that all the loss factors are dimensionless ratios of acoustic resistance to reactance or conductance to susceptance. Thus, the loss factor is similar to the reciprocal of $Q$, where $Q$ has the conventional connotation of ratio of reactance to resistance or stored energy to dissipated energy.

It is evident also from Eqs. (6.14), (6.15), and (6.16) that the complex stiffness, compliance, and density correspond, respectively, to the shunt impedance, the shunt admittance, and the series impedance of a unit length of the acoustic transmission line—or thickness of the plate. This correspondence is shown in Fig. 6.5. The corresponding impedances or admittances of a plate $x$ units thick are given by

$$\frac{s'}{j\omega x} = \frac{x}{j\omega x} + \frac{s\eta_s}{\omega x}, \qquad (6.17)$$

$$j\omega C' x = (j\omega Cx) + (\omega Cx\eta_c), \qquad (6.18)$$

$$j\omega \rho' x = (j\omega \rho x) + (\omega \rho x \eta_\rho). \qquad (6.19)$$

The initial choice of positive or negative signs in Eqs. (6.14), (6.15), and (6.16) becomes evident from Eqs. (6.17), (6.18), and (6.19). The real part of the impedance or admittance must be positive!

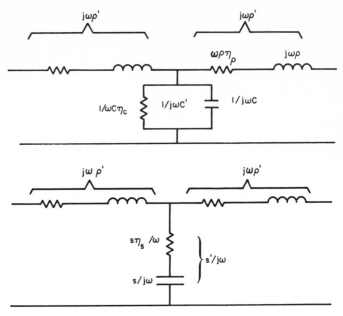

Fig. 6.5. Electrical analogs of unit-length acoustic transmission line with (a) shunt admittance and (b) shunt impedance.

An interesting fact is pointed out by Tamm.[1] If $\eta_c = \eta_\rho$ in the same material, then the imaginary part of the characteristic impedance disappears.

$$Z_0' = \left(\frac{\rho'}{C'}\right)^{\frac{1}{2}} = \left[\frac{\rho(1 - j\eta_\rho)}{C(1 - j\eta_c)}\right]^{\frac{1}{2}}. \tag{6.20}$$

If $\eta_\rho = \eta_c$, then,

$$Z_0' = \left(\frac{\rho}{C}\right)^{\frac{1}{2}} = Z_0. \tag{6.21}$$

This conclusion is the same as that for electrical transmission line theory wherein the characteristic impedance is a pure resistance if $R_{ss}/\omega L_{ss} = G_{oc}/\omega C_{oc}$ where $R_{ss}$ and $L_{ss}$ are the short-circuit resistance and inductance, and $G_{oc}$ and $C_{oc}$ are the open-circuit conductance and capacitance of a unit line.

Tamm actually made his point using $\eta_s$ rather than $\eta_c$. The same conclusion as made in Eq. (6.21) can be made when $\eta_\rho = \eta_s$, provided that $\eta_s$ is small—that is, if the loss component is a small part of the impedance or admittance.

### 6.4.3 The loss angle $\delta$

The loss angle $\delta$ is the complement of the phase angle of the impedance $Z_i$ defined for Eq. (6.9):

$$\tan \delta = \frac{R_i}{X_i}. \tag{6.22}$$

If the load or "backing" impedance $Z_L \rightarrow \infty$ and the plate thickness or acoustic line length is short ($x < \lambda/10$), the impedance $Z_i$ becomes stiffness controlled and

$$\tan \delta = \frac{R_i}{X_i} \simeq \frac{\left(\dfrac{s\eta_s}{j\omega}\right)}{\left(\dfrac{s}{j\omega}\right)} = \eta_s. \tag{6.23}$$

If the load or "backing" impedance is zero and the line is short, the impedance becomes inertia controlled, and

$$\tan \delta = \frac{R_i}{X_i} \simeq \frac{(\omega_\rho \eta_\rho)}{(\omega_\rho)} = \eta_\rho. \tag{6.24}$$

Thus, for small samples, arctan $\eta$ and the loss angle are the same.

### 6.4.4 Relationships among $a$, $\eta$, and $\delta$

Before discussing the measurement of $a$, $\eta$, and $\delta$, it is helpful to understand some relationships among these parameters. In many practical cases, when one parameter is known, the other two can be computed or at least approximated.

Starting with the usual expression for the speed of sound

$$c = \left(\frac{s}{\rho}\right)^{\frac{1}{2}} \quad \text{or} \quad c' = \left(\frac{s'}{\rho'}\right)^{\frac{1}{2}} \tag{6.25}$$

and using Eqs. (6.13), (6.14), and (6.16), we can derive

$$\left[\frac{\rho(1-j\eta_\rho)}{s(1+j\eta_s)}\right]^{\frac{1}{2}} = \frac{1 - \dfrac{ja}{k}}{c}. \tag{6.26}$$

After some algebraic manipulation, Eq. (6.26) can be reduced to

$$\frac{\eta_\rho + \eta_s}{1 - \eta_s \eta_\rho} = \frac{\dfrac{2a}{k}}{1 - \dfrac{a^2}{k^2}}. \tag{6.27}$$

Equation (6.27) also can be obtained by using compliance instead of stiffness, or $c' = (1/\rho' C')^{1/2}$, so the general elastic loss factor $\eta_e$ is used in Eqs. (6.29) and (6.30).

The factor $a/k$ appears regularly in absorption analysis. Cramer[2] gives it the symbol $r$ and the name "loss parameter":

$$r = \frac{a}{k} = \frac{ac}{\omega^2} = \frac{a\lambda}{2\pi}. \tag{6.28}$$

It can be seen that $r$ in the form $a\lambda/2\pi$ is the attenuation per radian length. In terms of $r$, Eq. (6.27) becomes

$$\frac{\eta_\rho + \eta_e}{1 - \eta_\rho \eta_e} = \frac{2r}{1 - r^2}. \tag{6.29}$$

Equation (6.29) is exact for all values of absorption. If the absorption is low enough for second-order terms to be neglected, Eq. (6.29) becomes

$$\eta_\rho + \eta_e = 2r = \frac{a\lambda}{\pi}. \tag{6.30}$$

Thus, r is the simple average of $\eta_\rho$ and $\eta_e$.

Most materials have either primarily elastic or viscous losses, but not both. If either $\eta_\rho$ or $\eta_e$ are zero, then Eq. (6.29) becomes

$$\eta = \frac{2r}{(1 - r^2)}. \tag{6.31}$$

If both the low-absorption approximation of Eq. (6.30) and the single-loss factor assumption of Eq. (6.31) are used,

$$\eta = 2r = \frac{a\lambda}{\pi}. \tag{6.32}$$

The loss angle $\delta$ is related to $\eta$ by Eq. (6.23) or (6.24). When $\eta < 0.5$, the approximation $\tan \delta \simeq \delta$ can be used with less than 10% error, and

$$\tan \delta \simeq \delta = \eta. \tag{6.33}$$

The validity of the "low absorption" approximations and the relationships among $r$, $\eta$, and $\delta$ are graphically illustrated in Fig. 6.6. Essentially, the curves are plots of Eqs. (6.31) and (6.32). Equation (6.30) cannot be plotted because it has three variables. The curves show that $2r \simeq \eta \simeq \delta$, when $r$ is less than about 0.3, or $\eta$ is less than about 0.6. The value $r = 0.3$ corresponds to an attenuation of 16.3 dB per wavelength. This is good attenuation. For a wavelength of 1 ft, or 30 cm, $r = 0.3$ corresponds to $a = 0.6$. It can be concluded that small values of the attenuation constant ($a < 0.1$) and loss factor ($\eta < 0.6$) are useful, and that the approximation $2r \simeq \eta \simeq \delta$ can be used in most practical cases.

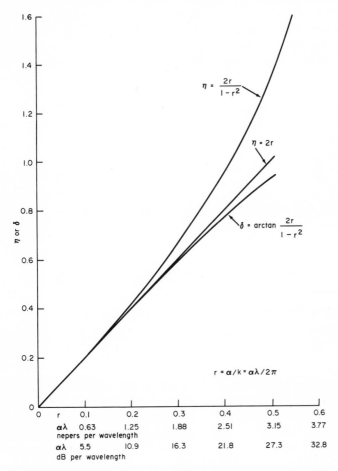

Fig. 6.6. The loss factor and loss angle as functions of attenuation per wavelength according to Eqs. (6.31) and (6.32).

### 6.4.5  Measurement of $a$, $\eta$, and $\delta$

If both a sound source and receiver can be immersed in a large sample of a homogeneous absorbing material, $a$ can be measured simply and directly from the signal attenuation under free-field conditions. That is, a transmission loss in a progressive wave between two points that exceeds the spherical spreading loss can be assigned to absorption. The free-field requirement limits this technique to very large samples, and for this reason the technique seldom is used.

It might appear that a simple insertion-loss measurement would yield a value for $a$. For example, if the insertion loss of a 5-cm-thick plate is 1.0 dB, one might conclude (erroneously) that $a = 0.2$ dB/cm or 0.023 neper/cm. The error here arises from the fact that the signal is reflected at both of the solid-water boundaries and, each time the sound trapped in the plate is reflected by the front or rear boundary, some sound escapes into the water. Consequently, we have a standing-wave condition inside the plate, and the transmitted wave consists of the phasor sum of many signals that have traversed the 5-cm thickness 1, 3, 5, 7, . . ., etc. times.

In practice, $a$, $\eta$, and $\delta$ usually are measured by a system referred to as an impedance tube, which is shown schematically in Fig. 6.7. The system is treated as a one-dimensional acoustic transmission line. Plane-wave propagation is assumed and attained in practice by using a rigid-walled tube with a diameter equal to a small fraction of a wavelength of sound in the water and material.

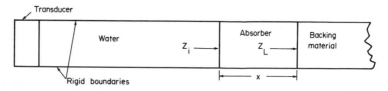

Fig. 6.7. Impedance tube arrangement for measuring attenuation parameters in an absorbing material.

The key parameter used to find $a$, $\eta$, or $\delta$ is $Z_i$, the complex acoustic impedance at the boundary between the water medium and the absorbing medium as seen from the water medium. Various impedance tube techniques have been used, mostly in air acoustics.[3,4] The most successful technique for evaluating underwater sound absorbers has been the pulsed-sound technique.[2,5] A short pulse of sound is reflected at the $Z_i$ boundary, and the complex reflection coefficient $A$ is measured. The magnitude of $A$ is the ratio of reflected-to-incident sound pressure. The phase of $A$ is the phase shift of the reflected sound. Then,

$$Z_i = Z_w \frac{(1+A)}{(1-A)}, \qquad (6.34)$$

where $Z_w$ is the specific acoustic impedance of the water. The magnitude of $A$ is relatively easy to measure. For example, an uncalibrated but linear probe hydrophone in the tube can measure both the incident and reflected pulses, and display both on an oscilloscope. The magnitude ratio is readily obtained from the display. The phase measurement is more difficult. The relative phase of the two pulses could be measured at the probe hydrophone output, but the phase shift at the water-material boundary can be computed only if the boundary position and the wavelength of sound in the water in the tube are precisely known.

Another method is to compare both the magnitude and phase of the signal reflected from the sample to those of the signal reflected from a perfect reflector, such as a very high- or very low-impedance boundary at the same location. From $Z_i$ and a knowledge of $x$ and $Z_L$ (the impedance at the boundary between the absorber and the backing material, as seen from the absorbing medium), $a$, $\eta$, or $\delta$ can be calculated. For example, $\eta_s$ can be found by making $x < \lambda/10$ and letting $Z_L \to \infty$. That is, we use a thin layer of absorber with a rigid backing. Then we have a condition analogous to the measurement of capacitance and conductance in a short length of open-circuited cable. The absorber acts like a lossy spring, and

$$Z_i = R_i + jX_i = \frac{s'}{j\omega x} = \frac{s}{j\omega x} + \frac{s\eta_s}{\omega x}, \qquad (6.35)$$

or

$$R_i = \frac{s\eta_s}{\omega x}, \qquad (6.36)$$

and

$$X_i = \frac{s}{\omega x}. \qquad (6.37)$$

Equations (6.36) and (6.37) can be solved for both $s$ and $\eta_s$.

If $\eta_\rho$ is desired, we let $x < \lambda/10$ and $Z_L \to 0$. That is, we use a thin layer with no backing, or with air backing. Then we have a case analogous to the use of a short-circuited cable and the measurement of inductance and resistance of the wire. The absorber acts like a mass subjected to some viscous drag, and

$$Z_i = R_i + jX_i = j\omega\rho'x = j\omega\rho x + \omega\rho\eta_\rho x, \qquad (6.38)$$

or,

$$R_i = \omega\rho\eta_\rho x, \qquad (6.39)$$

and

$$X_i = \omega\rho x. \qquad (6.40)$$

Equations (6.39) and (6.40) are solved for $\rho$ and $\eta_\rho$.

The loss angle $\delta$ is available directly from $Z_i$, according to Eq. (6.24).

To measure $a$, the backing is made very rigid, or it is assumed that $Z_L \to \infty$. Then Eq. (6.11) reduces to

$$Z_i = Z_0{}' \coth (a + jk)x, \qquad (6.41)$$

where $Z_0{}'$ is the complex specific impedance of the material. From Eqs. (6.13), (6.34), and (6.41), and neglecting inertial losses,

$$\frac{1}{\left(\dfrac{\rho}{\rho_w}\right)k_w x} \frac{1 + A}{1 - A} = j \frac{\coth (ax + jkx)}{(ax + jkx)}, \qquad (6.42)$$

where the $w$ subscript indicates the parameters of the water. All parameters in the left side of Eq. (6.42) are measured. The unknowns $a$ and $k$ cannot be obtained from transcendental equations like Eq. (6.42) by algebraic methods. However, Sabin[6,7] has developed charts from which $a$ and $k$ can be obtained from the magnitude and phase of the left side of Eq. (6.42) and subsequently he has used a computer to solve Eq. (6.42) automatically by successive approximations.[8]

Figure 6.8 is a plot of Eq. (6.41) and, in addition, a plot of Eq. (6.11) for the special case $Z_L = 0$. If $Z_i$ can be measured as a function of $x$ and plotted as in Fig. 6.8, a spiral curve should result; and the various relationships shown graphically in Fig. 6.8 can be found.

Generally, all the curves are spirals converging to a point corresponding to $Z_i = Z_0{}'$. That is, when $x$ is large, the absorber appears infinitely thick and $Z_i$ becomes the characteristic impedance. Both spirals converge to the $Z_i = Z_0{}'$ point because, in infinitely thick layers, the backing impedance does not affect $Z_i$. As $x$ becomes smaller, the $Z_L \to \infty$ curve for $Z_i$ unwinds along the spiral, oscillating in amplitude. These oscillations correspond to the tuned or resonant conditions where $x$ is equal to multiples of quarter or half wavelengths. As $x$ becomes small, the thin-layer or lumped-parameter condition is approached; $Z_i$ becomes $-js'/\omega x$, and the slope becomes $-1/\eta_s$. Similarly, the $Z_L = 0$ curve unwinds and approaches $Z_i \simeq +j\omega\rho x$ with the slope $+1/\eta_\rho$. The slope of the impedance vector $Z_i = Z_0{}'$ is $(\eta_s - \eta_\rho)/a = r$, according to Eq. (6.45). All the information needed to find $\eta_s$, $\eta_\rho$, $r$, $a$, $c'$, and $Z_0{}'$ is available from either curve. In practice, the curve for $Z_L \to \infty$ is the easier of the two to obtain because $-js'/\omega x$ is large, while $+j\omega\rho x$ is small. The use of the variable $x$ in these curves is based on the assumption that the frequency is constant. The variable should be $kx$. If the absorption is independent of, or changes slowly with frequency, a change in frequency or wavelength is equivalent to a change in $x$.

The characteristic impedance of a medium is given by

$$Z_0{}' = (\rho' s')^{\frac{1}{2}} = [\rho(1 - j\eta_\rho)s(1 + j\eta_s)]^{\frac{1}{2}} \qquad (6.43)$$

$$Z_0{}' = (\rho s)^{\frac{1}{2}}[1 + j(\eta_s - \eta_\rho) + \eta_\rho \eta_s]^{\frac{1}{2}}. \qquad (6.44)$$

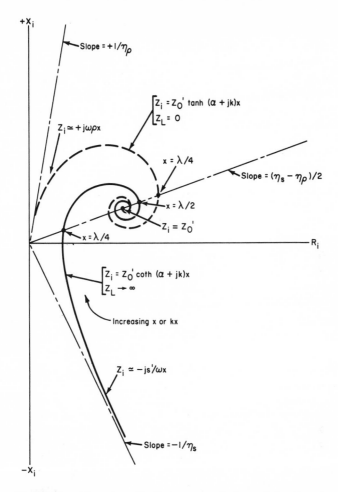

Fig. 6.8. Input impedance $Z_i$ of a lossy acoustic transmission line as a function of the radian length $kx$.

If $\eta_\rho \eta_s \ll 1$, it can be neglected, and $(\eta_s - \eta_\rho)$ is so small that only the first two terms in the series expansion for the square root of a binomial need be used. Then,

$$Z_0{}' \simeq Z_0 \left| 1 + \frac{j}{2} \left( \eta_s - \eta_\rho \right) \right|, \tag{6.45}$$

or, when $\eta_s = \eta_\rho$, then $Z_0{}' = Z_0$. If the complex compliance is used instead of complex stiffness, the qualification $\eta_\rho \eta_c \ll 1$ is not needed to conclude that $Z_0{}' = Z_0$ when $\eta_c = \eta_\rho$.

Equation (6.45) shows that if $\eta_s > \eta_\rho$, $Z_0{}'$ will be in the $+X_i$ quadrant. If $\eta_s < \eta_\rho$, $Z_0{}'$ will be in the $-X_i$ quadrant. If $\eta_s = \eta_\rho$, then $Z_0{}'$ will be on the $R_i$

axis. These three conditions are shown in Fig. 6.9. Note that the real component of $Z_0'$ always is $Z_0$. The convergence point for the spiral is determined by $\eta_s - \eta_\rho$. The other ends of the spirals are determined by $\eta_s$ and $\eta_\rho$. Thus, even if $\eta_\rho$ cannot be measured at the $Z_i = j\omega\rho x$ end of the spiral, it still can be found from a knowledge of $\eta_s - \eta_\rho$ and $\eta_\rho$. The loss parameter $r$ then is given by Eq. (6.30) from $r = (\eta_s + \eta_\rho)/2$, and $a$ from $a = r\omega/c'$. The complex velocity comes from the frequency and from the $x = \lambda/4$ or $x = \lambda/2$ points identified in Fig. 6.8.

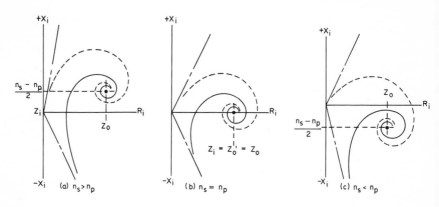

Fig. 6.9. The value of $Z_0'$ for relative values of $\eta_s$ and $\eta_\rho$.

### 6.4.6 Magnitudes of $a$ and $\eta$

The attenuation constant $a$ usually is a small fraction of one neper/cm like 0.1 or less. If $a$ were large—for example, if $a = 1$ neper/cm—this could mean that the sound pressure amplitude would decrease 8.7 dB for every centimeter of material through which the sound wave traveled. After traveling only 3 cm, the wave would be attenuated 3 nepers or 26 dB. Its magnitude then would be only 5% of the original magnitude, and the wave would contain only 0.25% of its original energy. Consequently, it would make little difference whether the absorber were 3 cm thick or infinitely thick. Even if it were physically possible to make an absorbing material with an attenuation constant as large as 1 neper/cm, it would not necessarily be useful in underwater sound. A good absorber should possess two key characteristics. First, the sound should enter the absorbing material rather than be reflected away. Second, after the sound gets into the absorber, it should be completely absorbed. If the absorber has very high absorption, so that a negligible amount of the sound reflected at the back boundary returns to the front boundary, then $x$ appears infinite and $Z_i \rightarrow Z_0'$. The reflection coefficient then is

$$A = \frac{Z_0' - Z_w}{Z_0' + Z_w}. \qquad (6.46)$$

The characteristic impedance $Z_w$ of water is a real number. Consequently, the reflection can become zero only if $Z_0'$ also is a real number; but $Z_0'$ is wholly a real number only if the absorbing material does not absorb, or if the unique condition $\eta_e = \eta_\rho$ exists.

As shown in Eq. (6.45), the greater the elastic or viscous absorption (but not both), the larger the imaginary part of $Z_0'$ becomes, which is contrary to the usual notion that energy absorption is associated with real, rather than imaginary, numbers. Consequently, a good absorber usually will be a good reflector when it is thick enough to appear infinitely thick.

There are four ways of combining high absorption with low reflection. First, the absorption $a$ per unit thickness can be kept low, but the thickness $x$ can be made high. Second, a high $a$ together with a gradual transition boundary, such as would be provided by wedges or intermediate layers, can be used. Equation (6.46) applies only to plane boundaries. Third, "tuned" or "resonant" thickness dimensions, which correspond to the points on the spiral curves of Fig. 6.9 that lie on or near the $R_i$ axis, can be used. Fourth, the ideal material, as yet undiscovered, in which $\eta_\rho = \eta_e$ can be used.

Whereas $a$ is made small intentionally for the thick layer or "effectively infinite $x$" case, the opposite holds for the case of a thin layer where the impedance $Z_i$ ideally should be wholly resistive and equal to $Z_w$. The latter is the acoustical analogy of the electrical case in which a cable having the characteristic impedance $R_0$ ohms is simply terminated with a resistor of $R_0$ ohms that dissipates all energy fed into the cable. Unlike the electric resistor, the acoustic resistor is extremely difficult to create in the form of a thin layer.

Ideally, thick layers should have low absorption per unit distance but thin layers should have high absorption. For intermediate thicknesses ($\lambda/10 < x < \lambda$), the analysis is complicated. Standing waves are present. For some thicknesses, the layer acts like a "tuned" or "resonant" absorber and the absorption is unusually high in a narrow frequency band. Such layers are analyzed by using the general formula for $Z_i$, Eq. (6.12), or its special cases, like Eq. (6.41) and the general reflection formula,

$$A = \frac{Z_i - Z_w}{Z_i + Z_w} . \tag{6.47}$$

## 6.5 Elastic Moduli and Stiffness

The subject of acoustic materials would not be complete without some discussion of elastic moduli. In Section 6.4, stiffness and plate elastic modulus were taken as synonymous. Such a definition is necessary for a plane-wave one-dimensional analysis. In more general cases, the modulus or stiffness is the quotient stress/strain from Hooke's Law.

In a solid, there are several ways that stresses can be applied and strains allowed, and each combination has its own elastic modulus or stiffness (or compliance). Figure 6.10 illustrates the various moduli.

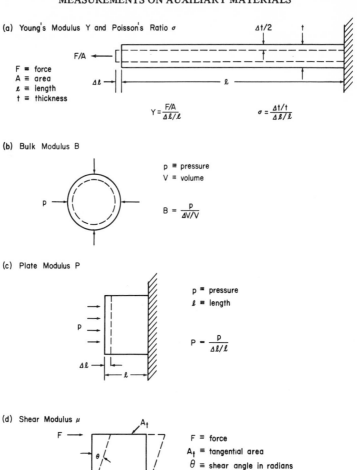

Fig. 6.10. Elastic moduli.

Young's modulus $Y$ probably is the most familiar and the easiest to measure. It applies to a long, thin solid (wire, bar, etc.), where, in an acoustic measurement or application, "thin" would mean a small fraction of a wavelength. In this case, stress exists in only one direction—the direction of the long dimension—and is given in force per unit area or in pressure. The strain is in three dimensions but measured only in the long dimension. Both the volume and shape of the material change under stress.

The bulk modulus $B$ is a measure of the ratio between three-dimensional stress and three-dimensional strain. The volume changes, but the shape does not—as, for example, a rubber ball when squeezed uniformly in all directions becomes smaller but still is spherical. The stress is given in pressure and strain in fractional volume change.

The plate modulus $P$ is the modulus effective in impedance tube measurements, or whenever plane-wave conditions exist. The stress or pressure is in one direction—the direction of wave motion. The strain or particle motion also is one-dimensional and in the same direction as the stress. More so than the other moduli, the plate modulus applies to dynamic cases. As with Young's modulus, both volume and shape change with stress.

The shear, torsion, or rigidity modulus $\mu$ involves rotational motion. The volume remains constant, but the shape changes. The stress is given as the tangential force per unit area of the tangential surface. The strain is the angular displacement is radians of planes originally perpendicular. The shear modulus is important in absorbers because rubbers often have low loss components in the "plate" stiffness but high loss components in the "shear" stiffness.

In practice, the measurement conditions or material sample size or shape may lead to stresses and strains that involve some combination of the four moduli. Care must be exercised, therefore, in extrapolating measured results to apply to samples of other sizes and shapes.

In addition to the moduli, the parameter "Poisson's Ratio" frequently is used to characterize an elastic material. As shown by Fig. 6.10a, this is the ratio of transverse strain resulting from an applied longitudinal strain.

The bulk, plate, and shear moduli are related to Young's modulus and Poisson's ratio $\sigma$ as follows:

$$B = \frac{Y}{3(1 - 2\sigma)}, \tag{6.48}$$

$$P = \frac{\dfrac{Y}{(1 - \sigma)}}{(1 + \sigma)(1 - 2\sigma)}, \tag{6.49}$$

$$\mu = \frac{Y}{2(1 + \sigma)}. \tag{6.50}$$

# REFERENCES

1. K. Tamm, "Broad-Band Absorbers for Water-Borne Sound," in *Technical Aspects of Sound,* E. G. Richardson, ed. (Elsevier Publishing Co., Inc., New York, 1957), Vol. II, Chap. 6.

2. W. S. Cramer and K. S. Bonwit, "Pulse Tube for Acoustic Measurements," U.S. Naval Ordnance Laboratory Report NAVORD 2257, 30 Apr 1952.

3. L. L. Beranek, *Acoustic Measurements* (John Wiley and Sons, Inc., New York, 1949), Chap. 7.

4. C. Zwicker and C. W. Kosten, *Sound Absorbing Materials* (Elsevier Publishing Co., Inc., New York, 1949), Chap. V.

5. E. Meyer *et al.,* "Sound Absorption and Sound Absorbers in Water," NAVSHIPS 900,166, U.S. Department of the Navy, Washington, D.C., 1950.

6. G. A. Sabin, "Analysis of Acoustic Impedance Data," Navy Underwater Sound Reference Laboratory Research Report No. 81, 5 May 1966 [AD-632 075].

7. G. A. Sabin, "Acoustic Impedance Measurements at High Hydrostatic Pressures," J. Acoust. Soc. Am. 40, 1345 (1966).

8. J. L. Lastinger and G. A. Sabin, "A PDP-8 FORTRAN Program for Reduction of Acoustic Impedance Data," Naval Research Laboratory Report No. 6906, 28 Mar 1969 [AD-686 663].

# Appendix A1

# CAPITAL LETTER SYMBOLS AND ABBREVIATIONS

| | |
|---|---|
| $A$ | area, proportionality constant, complex reflection coefficient, ratio of radii |
| $B$ | susceptance, magnetic flux density, bulk modulus |
| C, $C$ | compliance, capacitance, coulomb |
| $CL$ | coupling loss in decibels |
| $D$ | diffraction constant, diameter, maximum dimension |
| $D_i$ | directivity index |
| $E$ | energy density |
| EBW | essential bandwidth |
| $F$ | force |
| $G$ | conductance, amplifier gain in decibels |
| H | hydrophone |
| Hz | hertz (cycles per second) |
| $I$ | intensity |
| $J$ | reciprocity parameter, Bessel function |
| $K$ | a constant |
| $L$ | length |
| M, $M$ | free-field voltage sensitivity, prefix "mega" |
| N, $N$ | any integral number, newton |
| P, $P$ | projector, power, plate modulus, point in space |
| PSL | pressure spectrum level |
| $Q$ | electric charge, point on a surface $S$, quality factor |
| $R$ | resistance |
| $R_\theta$ | directivity factor |
| $S$ | transmitting current response, surface area |
| $S'$ | transmitting voltage response |
| T, $T$ | reciprocal transducer, absolute temperature, period of a periodic function |
| $U$ | volume velocity |
| $V$ | volume |
| $W$ | width |
| $X$ | volume displacement, reactance, coordinate axis |
| $Y$ | admittance, Young's modulus, coordinate axis |
| $Z$ | impedance, coordinate axis |

315

# Appendix A2

# LOWER-CASE LETTER SYMBOLS AND ABBREVIATIONS

| | |
|---|---|
| $a$ | radius, term in a binomial |
| $b$ | term in a binomial |
| $c$ | speed of sound |
| cm | centimeter |
| c-w | continuous-wave |
| $d$ | distance, depth |
| dB | decibel |
| $e$ | voltage |
| $e', e''$ | same as $e$ under certain conditions |
| $f$ | frequency |
| $g$, g | acceleration due to gravity, gram |
| $h$ | depth or height |
| $i$ | current |
| $j$ | $\sqrt{-1}$ |
| $k$, k | wave number, spring constant, Boltman gas constant, prefix "kilo" |
| kg | kilogram |
| $m$, m | mass, ratio of characteristic impedance of a material to the characteristic impedance of water, meter, prefix "milli" |
| $n$ | normal unit vector, power of a binomial, number |
| $p$ | pressure |
| $p(\theta)$ | pressure as a function of $\theta$, directivity |
| $\bar{p}$ | average pressure |
| $r$ | radius, radial distance, loss parameter $(a/k)$ |
| rms | root mean square |
| $s$ | stiffness |
| $t$ | time, thickness |
| $u$ | particle or linear velocity |
| $x$ | distance, thickness |
| $y$ | distance |

# Appendix A3

## GREEK LETTER SYMBOLS

| | |
|---|---|
| $\alpha$ | attenuation constant |
| $\beta$ | adiabatic compressibility |
| $\gamma$ | ratio of specific heats of gases, complex propagation constant, ratio of hydrophone-to-projector width |
| $\delta$ | loss angle |
| $\Delta$ | change in, maximum error |
| $\epsilon$ | dielectric constant |
| $\eta$ | efficiency, loss factor |
| $\theta$ | angle |
| $\lambda$ | wavelength |
| $\mu$ | shear modulus, prefix "micro" |
| $\xi$ | linear displacement |
| $\sigma$ | Poisson's ratio |
| $\rho$ | density (of water, unless otherwise stated) |
| $\Sigma$ | sum |
| $\tau$ | pulse duration |
| $\phi$ | electromechanical voltage/force factor, angle |
| $\psi$ | electromechanical voltage/current factor |
| $\omega$ | angular frequency in radians per second |

# Appendix A4

## SYMBOLS USED AS SUBSCRIPTS

| | |
|---|---|
| $a$ | applied, air, acoustical |
| $A$ | array |
| $b$ | blocked |
| $c$ | cylindrical wave, compliance |
| $d$ | particular depth |
| $d\text{-}c$ | direct-current or static pressure |
| $df$ | diffuse field |
| $e$ | electrical, at the "end," elastic |
| $em$ | electromechanical |
| $f$ | free field |
| $ff$ | far field |
| $g$ | generator |
| $H$ | hydrophone |
| $i$ | index, input, integer, instantaneous |
| $j$ | integer |
| $L$ | length, distance, load |
| $m$ | receiving, mechanical, magnetic, in the medium |
| $nf$ | near field |
| $M$ | motional |
| $NP$ | null projector |
| $o$ | output |
| $0$ | center value, key value, axial value, reference value, characteristic value, fundamental |
| $oc$ | open-circuit |
| $ocm$ | open-circuit mechanical |
| $p$ | plane wave, parallel |
| $P$ | projector |
| $r$ | radiation, reradiation |
| $\rho$ | density |
| $s$ | standard, spherical wave, source, series, stiffness |
| $ssm$ | short-circuit mechanical |
| $T$ | reciprocal transducer |
| $w$ | wall, water |
| $x$ | unknown |

# APPENDIX B1

## DECIBELS vs. VOLTAGE AND POWER

The decibel chart below indicates dB for any ratio of voltage or power up to 120 dB. For values over 20 dB subtract 20, 30, or 40 dB, etc. from the total until the remainder will fall in the first part of the chart. Then add the corresponding values in the early part of the chart and in the second part of the chart. For example, for a voltage ratio of 400, the corresponding dB for 100 is 40. This leaves a balance voltage ratio of 4 which is approximately 12 dB. The resultant total is 40 plus 12 or 52 dB.

| Voltage Ratio | Power Ratio | −dB+ | Voltage Ratio | Power Ratio |
|---|---|---|---|---|
| **1.0000** | **1.0000** | **0** | **1.000** | **1.000** |
| .9886 | .9772 | .1 | 1.012 | 1.023 |
| .9772 | .9550 | .2 | 1.023 | 1.047 |
| .9661 | .9333 | .3 | 1.035 | 1.072 |
| .9550 | .9120 | .4 | 1.047 | 1.096 |
| .9441 | .8913 | .5 | 1.059 | 1.122 |
| .9333 | .8710 | .6 | 1.072 | 1.148 |
| .9226 | .8511 | .7 | 1.084 | 1.175 |
| .9120 | .8318 | .8 | 1.096 | 1.202 |
| .9016 | .8128 | .9 | 1.109 | 1.230 |
| **.8913** | **.7943** | **1.0** | **1.122** | **1.259** |
| .8810 | .7762 | 1.1 | 1.135 | 1.288 |
| .8710 | .7586 | 1.2 | 1.148 | 1.318 |
| .8610 | .7413 | 1.3 | 1.161 | 1.349 |
| .8511 | .7244 | 1.4 | 1.175 | 1.380 |
| .8414 | .7079 | 1.5 | 1.189 | 1.413 |
| .8318 | .6918 | 1.6 | 1.202 | 1.445 |
| .8222 | .6761 | 1.7 | 1.217 | 1.479 |
| .8128 | .6607 | 1.8 | 1.230 | 1.514 |
| .8035 | .6457 | 1.9 | 1.245 | 1.549 |

319

| Voltage Ratio | Power Ratio | −dB+ | Voltage Ratio | Power Ratio |
|---|---|---|---|---|
| .7943 | .6310 | 2.0 | 1.259 | 1.585 |
| .7852 | .6166 | 2.1 | 1.274 | 1.622 |
| .7762 | .6026 | 2.2 | 1.288 | 1.660 |
| .7674 | .5288 | 2.3 | 1.303 | 1.698 |
| .7586 | .5754 | 2.4 | 1.318 | 1.738 |
| .7499 | .5623 | 2.5 | 1.334 | 1.778 |
| .7413 | .5495 | 2.6 | 1.349 | 1.820 |
| .7328 | .5370 | 2.7 | 1.365 | 1.862 |
| .7244 | .5248 | 2.8 | 1.380 | 1.905 |
| .7161 | .5129 | 2.9 | 1.396 | 1.950 |
| .7079 | .5012 | 3.0 | 1.413 | 1.995 |
| .6998 | .4898 | 3.1 | 1.429 | 2.042 |
| .6918 | .4786 | 3.2 | 1.445 | 2.089 |
| .6839 | .4677 | 3.3 | 1.462 | 2.138 |
| .6761 | .4571 | 3.4 | 1.479 | 2.188 |
| .6683 | .4467 | 3.5 | 1.496 | 2.239 |
| .6607 | .4365 | 3.6 | 1.514 | 2.291 |
| .6531 | .4266 | 3.7 | 1.531 | 2.344 |
| .6457 | .4169 | 3.8 | 1.549 | 2.399 |
| .6383 | .4074 | 3.9 | 1.567 | 2.455 |
| .6310 | .3981 | 4.0 | 1.585 | 2.512 |
| .6237 | .3890 | 4.1 | 1.603 | 2.570 |
| .6166 | .3802 | 4.2 | 1.622 | 2.630 |
| .6095 | .3715 | 4.3 | 1.641 | 2.692 |
| .6026 | .3631 | 4.4 | 1.660 | 2.754 |
| .5957 | .3548 | 4.5 | 1.679 | 2.818 |
| .5888 | .3467 | 4.6 | 1.698 | 2.884 |
| .5821 | .3388 | 4.7 | 1.718 | 2.951 |
| .5754 | .3311 | 4.8 | 1.738 | 3.020 |
| .5689 | .3236 | 4.9 | 1.758 | 3.090 |
| .5623 | .3162 | 5.0 | 1.778 | 3.162 |
| .5559 | .3090 | 5.1 | 1.799 | 3.236 |
| .5495 | .3020 | 5.2 | 1.820 | 3.311 |
| .5433 | .2951 | 5.3 | 1.841 | 3.388 |
| .5370 | .2884 | 5.4 | 1.862 | 3.467 |

| Voltage Ratio | Power Ratio | −dB+ | Voltage Ratio | Power Ratio |
|---|---|---|---|---|
| .5309 | .2818 | 5.5 | 1.884 | 3.548 |
| .5248 | .2754 | 5.6 | 1.905 | 3.631 |
| .5188 | .2692 | 5.7 | 1.928 | 3.715 |
| .5129 | .2630 | 5.8 | 1.950 | 3.802 |
| .5070 | .2570 | 5.9 | 1.972 | 3.890 |
| **.5012** | **.2512** | **6.0** | **1.995** | **3.981** |
| .4955 | .2455 | 6.1 | 2.018 | 4.074 |
| .4898 | .2399 | 6.2 | 2.042 | 4.169 |
| .4842 | .2344 | 6.3 | 2.065 | 4.266 |
| .4786 | .2291 | 6.4 | 2.089 | 4.365 |
| .4732 | .2339 | 6.5 | 2.113 | 4.467 |
| .4677 | .2188 | 6.6 | 2.138 | 4.571 |
| .4624 | .2138 | 6.7 | 2.163 | 4.677 |
| .4571 | .2089 | 6.8 | 2.188 | 4.786 |
| .4519 | .2042 | 6.9 | 2.213 | 4.898 |
| **.4467** | **.1995** | **7.0** | **2.239** | **5.012** |
| .4416 | .1950 | 7.1 | 2.265 | 5.129 |
| .4365 | .1905 | 7.2 | 2.291 | 5.248 |
| .4315 | .1862 | 7.3 | 2.317 | 5.370 |
| .4266 | .1820 | 7.4 | 2.344 | 5.495 |
| .4217 | .1778 | 7.5 | 2.371 | 5.623 |
| .4169 | .1738 | 7.6 | 2.399 | 5.754 |
| .4121 | .1698 | 7.7 | 2.427 | 5.888 |
| .4074 | .1660 | 7.8 | 2.455 | 6.026 |
| .4027 | .1622 | 7.9 | 2.483 | 6.166 |
| **.3981** | **.1585** | **8.0** | **2.512** | **6.310** |
| .3936 | .1549 | 8.1 | 2.541 | 6.457 |
| .3890 | .1514 | 8.2 | 2.570 | 6.607 |
| .3846 | .1479 | 8.3 | 2.600 | 6.761 |
| .3802 | .1445 | 8.4 | 2.630 | 6.918 |
| .3758 | .1413 | 8.5 | 2.661 | 7.079 |
| .3715 | .1380 | 8.6 | 2.692 | 7.244 |
| .3673 | .1349 | 8.7 | 2.723 | 7.413 |
| .3631 | .1318 | 8.8 | 2.754 | 7.586 |
| .3589 | .1288 | 8.9 | 2.786 | 7.762 |

| Voltage Ratio | Power Ratio | −dB+ | Voltage Ratio | Power Ratio |
|---|---|---|---|---|
| .3548 | .1259 | 9.0 | 2.818 | 7.943 |
| .3508 | .1230 | 9.1 | 2.851 | 8.128 |
| .3467 | .1202 | 9.2 | 2.884 | 8.318 |
| .3428 | .1175 | 9.3 | 2.917 | 8.511 |
| .3388 | .1148 | 9.4 | 2.951 | 8.710 |
| .3350 | .1122 | 9.5 | 2.985 | 8.913 |
| .3311 | .1096 | 9.6 | 3.020 | 9.120 |
| .3273 | .1072 | 9.7 | 3.055 | 9.333 |
| .3236 | .1047 | 9.8 | 3.090 | 9.550 |
| .3199 | .1023 | 9.9 | 3.126 | 9.772 |
| .3162 | .1000 | 10.0 | 3.162 | 10.000 |
| .3126 | .09772 | 10.1 | 3.199 | 10.23 |
| .3090 | .09550 | 10.2 | 3.236 | 10.47 |
| .3055 | .09333 | 10.3 | 3.273 | 10.72 |
| .3020 | .09120 | 10.4 | 3.311 | 10.96 |
| .2985 | .08913 | 10.5 | 3.350 | 11.22 |
| .2951 | .08710 | 10.6 | 3.388 | 11.48 |
| .2917 | .08511 | 10.7 | 3.428 | 11.75 |
| .2884 | .08318 | 10.8 | 3.467 | 12.02 |
| .2851 | .08128 | 10.9 | 3.508 | 12.30 |
| .2818 | .07943 | 11.0 | 3.548 | 12.59 |
| .2786 | .07762 | 11.1 | 3.589 | 12.88 |
| .2754 | .07586 | 11.2 | 3.631 | 13.18 |
| .2723 | .07413 | 11.3 | 3.673 | 13.49 |
| .2692 | .07244 | 11.4 | 3.715 | 13.80 |
| .2661 | .07079 | 11.5 | 3.758 | 14.13 |
| .2630 | .06918 | 11.6 | 3.802 | 14.45 |
| .2600 | .06761 | 11.7 | 3.846 | 14.79 |
| .2570 | .06607 | 11.8 | 3.890 | 15.14 |
| .2541 | .06457 | 11.9 | 3.936 | 15.49 |
| .2512 | .06310 | 12.0 | 3.981 | 15.85 |
| .2483 | .06166 | 12.1 | 4.027 | 16.22 |
| .2455 | .06026 | 12.2 | 4.074 | 16.60 |
| .2427 | .05888 | 12.3 | 4.121 | 16.98 |
| .2399 | .05754 | 12.4 | 4.169 | 17.38 |

| Voltage Ratio | Power Ratio | −dB+ | Voltage Ratio | Power Ratio |
|---|---|---|---|---|
| .2371 | .05623 | 12.5 | 4.217 | 17.78 |
| .2344 | .05495 | 12.6 | 4.266 | 18.20 |
| .2317 | .05370 | 12.7 | 4.315 | 18.62 |
| .2291 | .05248 | 12.8 | 4.365 | 19.05 |
| .2265 | .05129 | 12.9 | 4.416 | 19.50 |
| **.2239** | **.05012** | **13.0** | **4.467** | **19.95** |
| .2213 | .04898 | 13.1 | 4.519 | 20.42 |
| .2188 | .04786 | 13.2 | 4.571 | 20.89 |
| .2163 | .04677 | 13.3 | 4.624 | 21.38 |
| .2138 | .04571 | 13.4 | 4.677 | 21.88 |
| .2113 | .04467 | 13.5 | 4.732 | 22.39 |
| .2089 | .04365 | 13.6 | 4.786 | 22.91 |
| .2065 | .04266 | 13.7 | 4.842 | 23.44 |
| .2042 | .04169 | 13.8 | 4.898 | 23.99 |
| .2018 | .04074 | 13.9 | 4.955 | 24.55 |
| **.1995** | **.03981** | **14.0** | **5.012** | **25.12** |
| .1972 | .03890 | 14.1 | 5.070 | 25.70 |
| .1950 | .03802 | 14.2 | 5.129 | 26.30 |
| .1928 | .03715 | 14.3 | 5.188 | 26.92 |
| .1905 | .03631 | 14.4 | 5.248 | 27.54 |
| .1884 | .03548 | 14.5 | 5.309 | 28.18 |
| .1862 | .03467 | 14.6 | 5.370 | 28.84 |
| .1841 | .03388 | 14.7 | 5.433 | 29.51 |
| .1820 | .03311 | 14.8 | 5.495 | 30.20 |
| .1799 | .03236 | 14.9 | 5.559 | 30.90 |
| **.1778** | **.03162** | **15.0** | **5.623** | **31.62** |
| .1758 | .03090 | 15.1 | 5.689 | 32.36 |
| .1738 | .03020 | 15.2 | 5.754 | 33.11 |
| .1718 | .02951 | 15.3 | 5.821 | 33.88 |
| .1698 | .02884 | 15.4 | 5.888 | 34.67 |
| .1679 | .02818 | 15.5 | 5.957 | 35.48 |
| .1660 | .02754 | 15.6 | 6.026 | 36.31 |
| .1641 | .02692 | 15.7 | 6.095 | 37.15 |
| .1622 | .02630 | 15.8 | 6.166 | 38.02 |
| .1603 | .02570 | 15.9 | 6.237 | 38.90 |

| Voltage Ratio | Power Ratio | −dB+ | Voltage Ratio | Power Ratio |
|---|---|---|---|---|
| **.1585** | **.02512** | **16.0** | **6.310** | **39.81** |
| .1567 | .02455 | 16.1 | 6.383 | 40.74 |
| .1549 | .02399 | 16.2 | 6.457 | 41.69 |
| .1531 | .02344 | 16.3 | 6.531 | 42.66 |
| .1514 | .02291 | 16.4 | 6.607 | 43.65 |
| .1496 | .02239 | 16.5 | 6.683 | 44.67 |
| .1479 | .02188 | 16.6 | 6.761 | 45.71 |
| .1462 | .02138 | 16.7 | 6.839 | 46.77 |
| .1445 | .02089 | 16.8 | 6.918 | 47.86 |
| .1429 | .02042 | 16.9 | 6.998 | 48.98 |
| **.1413** | **.01995** | **17.0** | **7.079** | **50.12** |
| .1396 | .01950 | 17.1 | 7.161 | 51.29 |
| .1380 | .01905 | 17.2 | 7.244 | 52.48 |
| .1365 | .01862 | 17.3 | 7.328 | 53.70 |
| .1349 | .01820 | 17.4 | 7.413 | 54.95 |
| .1334 | .01778 | 17.5 | 7.499 | 56.23 |
| .1318 | .01738 | 17.6 | 7.586 | 57.54 |
| .1303 | .01698 | 17.7 | 7.674 | 58.88 |
| .1288 | .01660 | 17.8 | 7.762 | 60.26 |
| .1274 | .01622 | 17.9 | 7.852 | 61.66 |
| **.1259** | **.01585** | **18.0** | **7.943** | **63.10** |
| .1245 | .01549 | 18.1 | 8.035 | 64.57 |
| .1230 | .01514 | 18.2 | 8.128 | 66.07 |
| .1216 | .01479 | 18.3 | 8.222 | 67.61 |
| .1202 | .01445 | 18.4 | 8.318 | 69.18 |
| .1189 | .01413 | 18.5 | 8.414 | 70.79 |
| .1175 | .01380 | 18.6 | 8.511 | 72.44 |
| .1161 | .01349 | 18.7 | 8.610 | 74.13 |
| .1148 | .01318 | 18.8 | 8.710 | 75.86 |
| .1135 | .01288 | 18.9 | 8.811 | 77.62 |
| **.1122** | **.01259** | **19.0** | **8.913** | **79.43** |
| .1109 | .01230 | 19.1 | 9.016 | 81.28 |
| .1096 | .01202 | 19.2 | 9.120 | 83.18 |
| .1084 | .01175 | 19.3 | 9.226 | 85.11 |
| .1072 | .01148 | 19.4 | 9.333 | 87.10 |

| Voltage Ratio | Power Ratio | −dB+ | Voltage Ratio | Power Ratio |
|---|---|---|---|---|
| .1059 | .01122 | 19.5 | 9.441 | 89.13 |
| .1047 | .01096 | 19.6 | 9.550 | 91.20 |
| .1035 | .01072 | 19.7 | 9.661 | 93.33 |
| .1023 | .01047 | 19.8 | 9.772 | 95.50 |
| .1012 | .01023 | 19.9 | 9.886 | 97.72 |
| **.1000** | **.01000** | **20.0** | **10.000** | **100.00** |
|  | $10^{-3}$ | 30 |  | $10^3$ |
| $10^{-2}$ | $10^{-4}$ | 40 | $10^2$ | $10^4$ |
|  | $10^{-5}$ | 50 |  | $10^5$ |
| $10^{-3}$ | $10^{-6}$ | 60 | $10^3$ | $10^6$ |
|  | $10^{-7}$ | 70 |  | $10^7$ |
| $10^{-4}$ | $10^{-8}$ | 80 | $10^4$ | $10^8$ |
|  | $10^{-9}$ | 90 |  | $10^9$ |
| $10^{-5}$ | $10^{-10}$ | 100 | $10^5$ | $10^{10}$ |

# INDEX